THE INFIDEL EMPEROR

FREDERICK II WITH THE FALCON

THE
INFIDEL EMPEROR
AND HIS STRUGGLES AGAINST THE POPE

A Chronicle of the Thirteenth Century by
PAUL WIEGLER

LONDON
GEORGE ROUTLEDGE & SONS, LTD.
BROADWAY HOUSE: 68-74, CARTER LANE, E.C.
1930

Translated by
BRIAN W. DOWNS

PRINTED IN GREAT BRITAIN BY HEADLEY BROTHERS,
18, DEVONSHIRE STREET, E.C.2 ; AND ASHFORD, KENT.

LIST OF ILLUSTRATIONS

PAGE

FREDERICK II WITH THE FALCON. Miniature of Frederick II, from his own *Tractatus de arte venandi cum avibus*. Vatican MS   [*front*.

HENRY VI. From the Manesse Song-Book   10

FREDERICK BARBAROSSA. Portrait-bust of Frederick Barbarossa in the Kappenberg reliquary. According to the extant deed of gift, " formed from the Emperor's face." Originally surmounted by a silver crown. Lower Rhenish work. *ca.* 1150   36

HENRY THE LION. Statue in the choir of Brunswick Cathedral. (According to Dehio, Henry the Fat, died 1318)   58

KING ROGER II crowned by Christ. Mosaic in the Martorana, founded as S. Maria dell' Ammiraglio by Georgios Antiochenos, King Roger's Admiral. Dedicated 1143   72

POPE INNOCENT III. Fresco in the *Sacro Speco*, the monastery of St. Benedict in Subiaco   90

LIST OF ILLUSTRATIONS

PAGE

FREDERICK II. Portrait of the Emperor, from an
impression of the (renovated) seal of the town
of Oppenheim. The seal was made at the close
of 1225, after Frederick, during his stay in
Germany, had granted the town the right to hold
a fair. Old impression in the Hessian state-
archives at Darmstadt. The reproduction is
natural size   90

GREGORY IX's DREAM. In a dream the Pope sees the
stigmata of St. Francis. Fresco by Giotto in the
Upper Church of San Francesco in Assisi.
After 1300   126

KNIGHTS ON GUARD IN THE PALACE. Figures of
two knights from the reliefs on the west rood-
loft, Naumburg Cathedral. Guard outside the
house of Caiaphas. *ca.* 1250   136

KNIGHT AND BENEFACTOR. Figure from the west
choir of Naumburg Cathedral. Sizzo of Käfern-
burg, one of the earlier figures. *ca.* 1250   146

ST. ELISABETH. Statue in the Church of St.
Elisabeth, Marburg. Work of the early fif-
teenth century   158

PETER OF VINEA. Marble bust from the triumphal
arch in the citadel of Capua, completed 1240.
Contemporary work, presumably from a
classical model   184

GREGORY IX. Fresco in the *Sacro speco*, the
monastery of St. Benedict in Subiaco   210

LIST OF ILLUSTRATIONS

PAGE

SIGFRID OF EPSTEIN with the Anti--Kings. Tomb-
stone of the Archbishop of Mainz, Sigfrid of
Epstein (died 1249). He crowned the two
Anti-Kings, Henry Raspe of Thuringia (1246—
under his right hand) and William of Holland
(1248). Mainz Cathedral. *ca.* 1250   246

CONRAD OF HOCHSTADEN. Tomb-stone of Conrad
of Hochstaden, Archbishop of Cologne (died
1261). Cologne Cathedral. Second half of the
fourteenth centruy   268

CONRADIN hawking. " König chuonrat der junge,"
from the Manesse Song-Book   276

DEATH OF ST. LEWIS. Death of Lewis IX, the Saint.
From a MS of the beginning of the fourteenth
century (*Life of St. Dionysius*). Rylands Library,
Manchester   318

The selection of the illustrations was made by
Otto Grossmann, Berlin.

Permission for reproduction was given by :
Dr. W. Stödtner, for the pictures of Peter
of Vinea and of Frederick II with the falcon.

THE INFIDEL EMPEROR

HENRY, Roman Emperor and German King, had left Trifels. Over the Splügen pass, in cerise and gold and a cornflower-blue cloak, he journeyed towards Milan. Here the brown, velvet-bearded emissaries of the King of Armenia did him homage. He invested him with the Syrian lands whose name is The Leaden Tower. The Emperor celebrated Pentecost. But Constance did not remain with him, the woman of forty who had already rested at the convent of Meda near Monza, her body heavy and her face swelled and blotchy with pregnancy. In a litter they carried her to Jesi in Ancona, in the territory of the Imperial High Steward Markward of Anweiler, who lay before Messina on the wooden ships.

The Emperor manned galleys in Genoa and Pisa. He rode with the Swabians in the heat of the dog-days, about him the confused noises of the army proceeding in three divisions, close beside him Philip in his slender youthfulness, Henry of Brunswick with the furrowed brow and broad neck of his father the Lion, and Roffrid, the Abbot of Monte Cassino, accoutred like a man of war. The Emperor was nine-and-twenty years of age. Auburn locks and a sparse growth of beard surrounded his haggard face. Tense, as if he thought too much or in the distance beheld death, were his lineaments. Restlessness erred in his glance, the restlessness of Antony and Augustus. Everlastingly he lashed, urged, consumed himself, as if still shaken by the Neapolitan fever-venom, of which in days gone by the herbs of Berard, Archdeacon of Ascoli, had cured him. The horses bit one another, there was disorder in the baggage-train, goats with flaccid, dirty yellow udders, bounded too late through the fading broom. Flames blazed above a place which had refused the army's levy : that was Babuco. And those were the ruins of Tusculum, which three years before Henry had sacrificed to the Romans and the Pope for the Imperial diadem. Three years before at Sancta Maria Transportana there had received him and Constance the Prefect of Rome, the Count of the Lateran Palace, the Imperial Justiciary and the Treasurer of the Realm, and, swinging their clanking censers, the clergy had brought him to St. Peter's. Thrice in that progress the Senators had administered the oath to him. On the topmost step he kissed the feet of Celestine, who gave him the kiss of peace in the form of the cross, kissed too, when he loosed his raiment, the Pope's breast rising and falling under the grey hairs which left the nipples bare. Then the entrance through the main portal of silver, the trial of faith at the red porphyry stone, the procession from St. Gregory's altar to the tomb of St. Peter, the *Kyrie eleison*, the Archdeacon's Litany, the anointing by the Cardinal-Bishop of Ostia under the right arm and in the armpit, ring, sword, crown and sceptre conferred upon him at the altar of St. Maurice, bread, candles and gold, a gift of the Emperor's to the Pope, the High Mass, the exchanging of the spiritual shoes and sandals for the greaves and spears of St. Maurice, the Emperor holding the Pope's stirrup at the bottom of the steps outside and in front of the Lateran, the booming of all the bells, songs of praise, flags and flowers. But now Celestine was at enmity with the Emperor, his foe. Hesitating and weak, he had protected Tancred of Lecce, upon whose head Walter Ofamila, the long-headed Englishman, had had to place the crown of Sicily and Apulia and against whose widow and son the Hohenstaufen was on the march, to wrest Constance's heritage into his hands.

The army reached the Pontine marshland, through which afar off the buffaloes stampeded, and the plain of Fondi. September, wrapping damp vapour about poplars and willows in the lowland and pale olives on the mountain slopes, shortened the marching days. The Emperor nodded ; there were the consuls of Gaeta and of Naples, who had joined the Lord High Steward and the fleet. To Naples went Dipold of Vohburg. Rare was the fighting, in Atina or Rocca Guglielma; rapine humbled their resistance. Capua and Aversa had sent no envoys; the Emperor made no enquiries about them. Vesuvius's column of fire mounted into the clouds; blue lay the far-flung bay. With hatred the Emperor looked upon it, and he commanded that Nocera be stormed. It was destroyed, destroyed too its ancient round baptistry. And Henry himself raised the standard of the eagle, when Conrad of Lüzelinhard's Swabians mounted the walls of Salerno after but one day's siege. He avenged upon its citizens Constance's captivity. They had begged him, three years back, to have the woman, ailing in her marriage to him, healed by the celebrated physicians of the Salernian school. But when the plague of Naples covered the fields with dead, when the rumour went that the Emperor had been snatched away from her, the partisans of Tancred, sallying forth from the brigands' eyrie Giffone, had authority in the white town with its flat roofs. The Archbishop of Salerno was the instigator, Nicholas, the son of the Sicilian Vice-Chancellor Matthew Ajello; Elia de Gisualdo seized the Empress and surrendered her to the Admiral Margarito. For a year she was in Tancred's custody; then, set free, she followed the Cardinal Aegidius of Anagni; but unslaked till that day was the Emperor's wrath against them of Salerno. Their blood overflowed the bronze portal of the cathedral, the town was laid waste, and laid waste the school with its dissecting-room, into which the doctors fled, Latins and Saracens with their eyes of moonshine. Salerno was reduced to ashes. The booty amounted to 200,000 ounces of gold.

THE fleet lay at anchor near Messina, gazed at in stupent fear by the Griffons, the Greeks of a bastard blood, out in the roadstead where the braggart Richard Cœur de Lion had built the frowning tower Mategriffun.

They saw that the Pisans and Genoese, instead of riveting fast the slackened chains of the galley-slaves, began to quarrel among themselves and to take sides against one another. The Genoese forced their way on to thirteen Pisan galleys, laid low the crew and flung them into the harbour gleaming with sea-nettle. The Pisans took the mart of St. John, in which the Genoese had their quarters, and led prisoners into Margarito's palace. They prevailed. The Imperial High Steward separated the brawlers; either party was to have its goods restored. The Genoese paid a thousand marks of silver. The Pisans mocked them with a shield, a tar-kettle, ten bundles of flax, a basket of cinnamon and a galingale root, withholding valuable scarves, cuirasses and ornaments from the Genoese, who vainly complained to the High Steward. The Pisans chased a Genoese merchantman, who with ochre yellow-sails was proceeding from Ceuta to Alexandria. The *Podestà* of Genoa died of grief. While the chiefs were at his funeral, the Pisans were minded to make themselves lords of the city. The High Steward strengthened the guards and while the ceremony proceeded remained within the walls. In front of Catania, thus the rumours ran, there had been a battle between the Normans and the Emperor's army. He crossed the Faro from Reggio.

From his barque gay with bunting the Emperor stepped on to the stony beach of the shore; the Germans shouted; it was suddenly still on board the Genoese fleet. The Emperor resided at the Palazzata, which, a thin sickle, surrounded the roadstead beyond the rocky coast. He exiled Margarito and twenty-eight more of Messina and gave their property to the corporation. Those taken at Catania were dragged before him. He punished them cruelly. Sundry were flayed alive, and their bestial yells rent the night through which the snowy top of Etna glowed. The Count of Valva, a riddled trunk, was sunk into the sea. The army departed for Palermo. Henry heard that Tancred's widow, Queen Sibyl, with William, her son, and her daughters Alberia,

Medania and Constance, Archbishop Nicholas and his brothers Constantine, Abbot of Venosa, and Count Richard of Ajello, had fled to Calatabellota : Kallath-al-Bellut, the Palace of the Oaks, the Saracens had called it. The Admiral surrendered into the Emperor's hands the rocky castle of Palermo. He went to the little, auburn Teuton, the herculean corsair with pearls in the lobes of his ears, the swart Neptune born of a cobbler's wife in Brindisi, now Count of Malta. This was the hero who had seduced the Grecian Isles from their allegiance to the Emperor of Byzantium and had driven a channel to Palestine for the Crusaders, a terror to pirates and a pirate himself. He snorted like a bull through violent nostrils ; and Henry dismissed him graciously, Duke of Durazzo and Prince of the Sea.

The Emperor stood beneath Monte Pellegrino and smiled : " Palermo is mine." The promontory gleamed silver-grey with its limestone, against the deep azure of the sea and the golden light, the blue shadows of the Conca d'Oro, its fruitfulness but barely rifled by November. From the Gennolard, from tropical garden foliage shone out the villa of Roger II, La Favara—Spring in the Arabs' tongue. Brooks were there and the pond Al Behira, palms, orange-trees and thickets of lemons. Boats adorned with gold and silver swam about in the water, for the King and his women, the harem. The arcades of the one-storeyed building lay round a splashing fountain. There was a smell of drowning flowers, a sweet rottenness. The Emperor hastened into the middle court. On their knees the citizens of Palermo handed him the keys of the city.

The streets were festal—from the Sakaliba, where the money-changers were, the spice-merchants, the tailors, the armourers, the coppersmiths, the speculators in corn, to the Halisa or Hlessa, with the new residence of the Kelvids, the arsenal, the gaol, the baths, a Friday mosque. But the Emperor rode beneath the circlet of his crown, greeted by the elders of the city on their steeds and by Saracen trumpeters. With him Philip

5

his brother, his father's brother the Palsgrave of the Rhine, the Duke of Bavaria, the Marquis of Montferrat, the Archbishop of Capua, to the Kassr, the old town. The people bowed before him, waving palm branches down to the ground and the worn stone steps. Gaping boys of Jews, Griffons, Saracens hung like grapes about the capitals of the ancient temples. The inner town had nine gates : Bab-el-Bahr, the Gate of the Sea, Ain Shaa, the Gate of the Spring, the Gates of St. Agatha and of the River Rutuh, which worked mills, Ar Riadh, the Gate of the Gardens, the Gate of Ibn Korheb, that was often inundated by waters from the hills, El Ebna, the oldest, Bab-as-Sudan, the Gate of the Negroes, and Al Hadid, near the Ghettos. The Emperor guided his piebald grey to the Mansuriya.

He went across courtyards and terraces, through porticoes, saw the Greek and the Pisan tower, the golden Yoharia ; and he waved his followers away to stand by the hour with flickering gaze in King Roger's room. In this palace the great had fallen, outcries stifled between blood-stained carpets ; Queen Margaret, the daughter of Garcia of Navarre, had been unfaithful to the bed of William the Bad with Majo, the Chancellor, the grocer's son of Bari, whom the dagger of Bonellus smote— Bonellus the notary, who had conspired with Simon of Taranto and Tancred, the royal bastard, and the Count of Avellino ; William surprised, barely rescued from the strokes of the sword, stripped and trembling in this white marble room with the marvels of its mosaics— lions, leopards, centaurs, stags, herons, peacocks drinking from goblets, hounds and boars ; and like one of these bow-bending hunters William, whom the people of Palermo desired, had despatched against his nine-year old son the lethal arrow. Then had come Margaret's illegitimate brother, a whore's bastard, Monte Caveoso, the debauchee and blackmailer, Gaytus Petrus, the fat eunuch who got away to Africa with royal treasures, and, until Tancred's election, the governance of Matthew. Now Matthew, Henry's adversary, was no more, nor

6

Walter of the Mills, Ofamila, through whose quarrel with the former Constance, William's sister, had become German Queen; and death had overcome on a sick bed Tancred of Lecce, the chivalrous, who as a present from Cœur de Lion wore Arthur's sword Excalibur and who read in the stars, very soon after young Roger, whom hopefully he loved.

The Count of Calvi craved audience. He had a commission from Sibyl, the widow. The Emperor had no time for him. He was for the cathedral, the king's vault, to remove as usurpers Tancred and Roger of Lecce from its silent dark.

FOR seven days the Emperor went to mass in the Palatine chapel, on his head already the Normans' crown, which the Countess Sibyl, Lady of Lecce and mother of William (now Prince of Taranto), had surrendered to him. He took the insignia, hot with impatience. There was no retinue about him, for him alone the priests had to celebrate. He sat upon the royal throne, between presbytery and altar :—in twilight the basilica, in bright light, streaming in through eight windows, the Byzantine sanctuary. He deciphered the Greek letters under the dome : " I, King Roger, wielder of the sceptre ". Absentmindedly he contemplated the picture above : Christ as *Pantocrator*, adored by the four archangels, in the niches the kings and prophets, round the gallery the life of the Redeemer ; or, maybe, St. Peter up there, waking Tabitha, or the serpent in the tree, Adam and Eve with the lines of their muscles and long-drawn shanks. On the roofs were painted figures : a king, who, crossing his legs, held a cup and a flower, women of the harem with fans, Saracens at the chess-board or playing the lute at a spring, Saracens with the wine goblet of Mahomet's paradise in their hand, dancing-girls, warriors, hawking, gazelle-hunting, parrot-hunting, Samson fighting the Lion, George and the Dragon, Anti-Christ. The stars of the shell-formed rosettes twinkled. During the ceremonies the Emperor

7

felt a stirring in the heart, which admonished him. He thought of Constance, unloved, and the child she was to bear him. He awaited the news from Jesi.

On the eighth day, the birthday of the Saviour, he strode stiff with gold in his red silk royal cloak, embroidered by the Arabs for Roger, with its Kufic benedictions, through the portico to the cathedral, on the left of Bartholomew, the Archbishop. Battlements hedged the misty skies, the belfry rocked. The Germans and the Barons of the land were assembled. But the organ was still pealing when to the Emperor in the sacristy there stepped the monk Ubaldo, a spy with intercepted letters ; they furnished proof that many of the nobility had conspired against the Germans and of their plan that very night to murder them as they slept, with Henry himself.

Mad, the Emperor broke through the Church procession. The organ stopped. The Emperor called up Walter of Paleario, the Bishop of Troia, a spare man and an ambitious, and Count Piero de Celano. " This is how I am betrayed ! " he shouted. " Off to the palace with the Barons." The Germans—at their head Conrad of Urslingen, Duke of Spoleto, and, overtopping them all, Henry of Kalindin, the Marshal and Barbarossa's general even on the last crusade,—seized their blades. Amidst tumult the Emperor pronounced judgment in the freestone hall. The Count of Celano spoke as accuser and called for punishment. The Emperor required no verdict. He delivered it and had Conrad of Lüzelinhard carry it out.

A woman in violet veils, with grey locks among her raven hair and the Counts of Acerra's forehead, was led before Henry in the Yoharia, the widow Sibyl. He turned away ; for her silence put him beside himself. " Away with her, her and her daughters," he ordered, " to Apulia, to Germany." Archbishop Nicholas of Salerno, Archbishop Peter of Acerenza, the Counts of Ajello, Marsico and Avellino were for Trifels, for the mountain gorge where Richard Cœur de Lion had

8

cursed the Austrian and the Hohenstaufen; with triple bonds of iron they were tied one to the other. But Duke Margarito the Emperor had blinded with sharp spikes in front of the Greek Tower; with bloody eye-sockets the admiral groped in the direction of the sea dully splashing against the Molo. Blinded too was William, Tancred's and Sibyl's son, seized as he writhed insensible; pincers crushed his testicles.

But there was a young woman whom the palace servants enveloped in soft raiment. She had been the bride of William's brother Roger. She was Irene, the daughter of the Emperor Isaac of Byzantium, and timorous in her hardly touched beauty. Henry chose her as the spouse of Philip, his fair-haired brother.

A swift ship entered the harbour. That was the news from Naples, from Jesi. In the Norman kings' chamber Count Albert of Bogen bowed before his lord. On the second day of Christmas—by now he was six days old—the Empress had borne the Emperor a son; and it was her will to call him Constantine.

HENRY held Diet at Gelnhausen, in Barbarossa's Palace. October air hung about the Rhön and Spessart, and in the plain of the Main the vintagers' song, the smell of the wine-press, of fermenting must. The Palace lay above the Kinzig, the gate-tower with the dragon devouring King Ortnit in his sleep, the keep, the castellan's house, the dwellings of the grooms and ass-drivers, the chapel and, in the Palace itself, the gallery, the great hall with the oriental fireplace and embrasures of rough, green grass in the thick masonry. The officials of the household stood there: the Chamberlain, the Cup-bearer, the Marshal and the Chaplain, the schoolman of Minden. They looked out towards St. Mary's Church, whose west tower was building; there was the sound of stamping as the earth-covered beams were pressed down, and the singing of the chisel. They tarried until, within, the Emperor should arise, whom after Italy his disease shook once more. He had

9

wakened in the bower, which, darkened by curtains, even by day lights burnt in; but he did not call for Berard of Ascoli. He was a prey to his shadowy vagrant thoughts: of St. John's Eve fires, which burnt in June, when he came down from the Alps into Swabia; of the weary Lion, who had died at Brunswick with the prayer " Lord have mercy upon me, a sinner "; of the straits over against Africa and the tribute of Almansur, who had sent gold and silver, a freightage of twenty-five mule-loads; of the Genoese and how he had demanded of them that they should conquer Aragon for him, they whom before he had fooled with the joint government of Sicily and humbled in the tempest of his whim; of the homage of Cœur de Lion and the English hostages; of the King of France, who should become his vassal, yes vassal; of Byzantium, whose throne he demanded for himself as the heritage of Irene after Isaac and against Alexios Angelos, who had put out his brother's eyes and clapped him into a dungeon—all Greece as far as Thessalonica the Emperor had already craved of Isaac. And he thought of ancient Celestine, that apostolic letter of his full of pacific indignation at unbridled deeds, violation of the Church and her rights; " Naught profits it a man even if he gain the whole world and yet do violence to his soul; therefore strive thou so to exercise the power of the Kingdom upon earth that thou lose not the Eternal." To shut this lamenting Pope's mouth he had at Bari bidden the Bishop of Sutri fasten upon him the cross as a sign that he would set out for the Holy Sepulchre like his father; it meant but the taking of Palestine into his unbounded empire.

He reared himself up, and with quavering voice to the obsequiously hastening chamberlain: " Is the Chancellor not come ? " Thus he enquired for Conrad of Querfurt, Bishop of Lübeck, his tutor, who was expected from Italy, and with him Philip, now Duke of Tuscany, and the Lord High Steward Markward of Anweiler, Count of Abruzzo. Henry sank back into his feverish stupor. He had left Constance in Palermo

HENRY VI

yonder as regent, with Walter of Paleario as Chancellor of the Sicilian territories and the Duke of Spoleto as Governor. And in Foligno, with the Duchess of Spoleto was Constantine, his little son. He was to be christened Frederick, after Barbarossa. Compulsion was to be put upon the German princes by Henry to recognise the crown as hereditary. That would be his triumph. But a doubt troubled him as he reflected, a distrust of that Norman stranger and of the blessing upon her womb after nine years' barrenness. Had her frigid face ever opened to him? Was it his blood, the child, to secure three thrones to whom he had spurred on his convulsive, deadly lust for dominion? He stared into the candles, he gnashed his teeth; and he felt the impotence of his limbs.

Trumpets blared. Carriages rolled into the palace yard. The palace resounded with the thud of hooves. Horsemen dismounted. They were Philip, the High Steward and their retainers, who yesterday had gone across the red Main-bridge at Frankfort; the Emperor leaping up in his delirium, with eyes still bleared, beheld them from the window-ledge. Why did not they announce their arrival? "The Chancellor!" he commanded.

Conrad of Querfurt entered, a white surplice beneath his brown cloak, but under that again a garment of white silk, resplendent with chains of gold, worldly pleasure in his face, which, as he spoke, changed like water in the wind. He had been a student at Paris with Thomas à Becket, the courtly English Chancellor, the son of the Saracen, whom as Bishop of Canterbury the four knights slew in the side-aisle of his cathedral, the saint whose penitent hair-shirt swarmed with lice, and with Count Lothair of Segni, the Cardinal of Sergius and Bacchus, who already surpassed ancient Celestine in power. Bishop-elect of Lübeck, Conrad had also been chosen by the chapter of Hildesheim.

He greeted his master, now breathing more deeply in exhaustion and returning lucidity: "Praise be to

God, whose mighty hand has so far extended the bounds of your dominions, that we may now behold face to face what at school we but apprehended in abstruse words. What the poets have spent much time in describing, now is reality." For, like the ascetic of Canterbury, this German had the eloquence of Cicero, and with rapture he had discovered in Italy Parnassus, Olympus and the Hippocrene fount. He made report to the Emperor of the stores of money, corn and wine in Apulia, the preparation of ships against the coming year; and of the universal prayers which Celestine had ordained for the recovery of him whose piety and ardour were a beacon in the service of God.

The Emperor listened to him. Then abruptly: "You have been with the Empress. Is the boy true-born? Is he a Norman bastard? I demand an answer of you!" The Chancellor, impenetrable: "It would seem that the talk of Sicilian slanderers has penetrated into the presence. You will see Joachim of Fiori. He will certify to you what is infamous lies and what pure truth." The Chancellor knew that the Emperor, who had renewed the edict against the pestilence of heresy, was in secret a devotee of superstition. He had sinned against the Church, had had Bishop Gentile of Osimo buffeted with fists, thrown into the kennel, his beard plucked, for saying his office came from the Pope alone and, as Henry Plantagenet of the assassination of Thomas à Becket, so he was guilty of the Liége murder: Albert of Brabant, Count and Bishop, cut down in Rheims by three German knights, as he was hospitably setting them on their way out of the city. But he kept to trial by the ordeals of single combat and red-hot iron; and he swore by the dark prophecies of the Calabrian anchorite.

The Emperor raised himself up and said abashed, with tormented lips: "I will see him, the abbot. Where is Philip?" Berard came up to his couch, that the sick man might strengthen himself with food. He refused it. He tore the curtains. Daylight poured into the chamber. With uncouth shouts from the drivers and

12

the cracking of whips had come into the courtyard the retinue of the Archbishops of Mainz and Magdeburg, of the Saxon bishops, of the Saxon and Swabian princes, of the Landgrave of Thuringia. The Diet of Gelnhausen began.

HENRY had set out after midsummer-day through Alsace and Burgundy, towards the Alps. A missive of Celestine had reached him with demands of expiation for the wrongs of his brother in Tuscany, for the incarceration of the Bishop of Salerno and the mutilation of the Byzantine ambassador, whom the Emperor's men had robbed of letters to the Pope. In St. Peter's, mentioning no names, Celestine excommunicated Duke Philip. Messengers came from Germany. Conrad of Rothenburg, the second among Henry's brothers, in his feud with the Duke of Zähringen had been killed, bestially fornicating. Whilst yet in Lombardy the Emperor bestowed on Philip the fief of Swabia; and they parted.

The Emperor was on his way to Rome. He journeyed towards the north-east, to Foligno, and plucked puling Constantine to his heart. As he embraced him, he muttered to himself: "My seed, my blood," and left him to the Duchess of Spoleto. For three months he had camped in towns near Rome and sent costly gifts to the Lateran. Celestine was to baptize the infant and place the crown of Germany on his head. The Pope had jibbed. But at Frankfurt the princes, annihilating the Imperator's plan, made his son King by free election.

The Emperor was in Apulia. Rebellion glowed in the Norman territories against the German masters, among whom was one of the Bishop of Liége's murderers, Otto of Barkstein, now de Laviano. The Chancellor Conrad, Imperial legate, and Roffrid of Monte Cassino had the walls of Naples destroyed, and of Capua. But the Chancellor spared in Naples the Gate of the Snake, the Gate of the magician Virgil, who for a space of eight years removed the plague of flies by means of a brazen fly and who stablished Naples upon eggs, as a residence for a daughter of the Soldan; and two great stone images also were of him, one beneficent and one that bore calamity within itself, and hard by a magical fire the statue of an archer drawing his bowstring against Vesuvius. For Conrad of Querfurt venerated antiquity. The Augustinian monk Huguccio betrayed where Richard of Acerra lay hid, Queen Sibyl's brother, and Dipold of Vohburg cast him into captivity in Capua.

The Emperor held Diet with the Barons about Christmas at Capua. He pointed to Acerra. A horse dragged him through the streets. He was hanged, head downwards. Rupert, the Emperor's motley fool with the fiddle, tied a stone to the Count's tongue. In this wise he rotted on the gallows, torn by vultures. Through Calabria the Emperor rode towards the Faro.

Near Cosenza, there where, in the mud of the Busento, Alaric the King of the Goths lay buried, he sent for the recluse, the Cistercian abbot. Joachim of Fiori had his cell in a mountain gorge of the Sila, the black virgin forest, near the rivulets Arvo and Neto. He came, his skin swallowed by his whitish-grey beard right up to the inflamed eyes, and stared brutishly at the Emperor. He came, the new Jeremiah, who preached against the avarice of the Church and to whom it was itself the Beast, Anti-Christ. "I see," he barked and chanted, "a seething hot pot from the North. From the North approaches destruction to all who dwell in the land. For behold, I will call all princes in the kingdom towards the North, saith the Lord, that they set up their thrones before the gates of Jerusalem and before the cities of Judah. It will come to pass, that Peter must flee un-clothed and with his loins girt, the high priest in the oppression of the times. All lands have I given into the hands of my servant Nebuchadnezzar, the king of Babylon. All nations shall bow their necks beneath his yoke. And not thy doing is it, O Emperor, that thou scourgest them away with the rod of thy wrath, but the Lord's. Through the will of the Lord art thou become the hammer of the earth."

Henry had been minded to enquire about his son. But he dared not. He charged the anchorite to interpret to him the prophecies of Merlin and of the Erythræan sibyl. And, tugging him by the jewelled girdle, the demoniac who had warned Barbarossa that he would drown in the waters whispered in Henry's ear: " The end of the world is at hand, and the Emperor will drain the cup of death."

THE Emperor was hunting near Messina. His falcons were soaring, when Markward of Anweiler, Duke of Romagnola and of Ravenna, covered with sweat, rode up. He brought news of a fresh conspiracy of the Sicilian nobles ; and he whispered, lust in his eyes, that Constance herself was implicated. The Emperor spoke not a word; but he changed colour even to the bluish lips.

The falcons, with bells on their claws, stooped, the sport was over. The Emperor galloped into fortified Messina ; for his army was small. For extravagant pay soldiers were enlisted ; and now the Crusaders made their appearance also, round whom the mob slunk in awe. The Barons' army again stood near Catania. Henry of Kalindin overcame them, the Marshal who with seven thousand pounds of gold and silver from the treasures of St. Sophia was back from Byzantium, from the presence-chamber of the Emperor Alexios Angelos. The Count of Spanheim pressed into the streets, through the lower city fertilized by the lava from Etna, the ruins of the Roman theatre and of the aqueduct. St. Agatha's church burst into flames and became the grave of the women and children who sought refuge at the high altar. The Germans took the castles of the Barons by storm. But invincible was Bohemund of San Giovanni, the first of the conspirators. He it was, they said, that Constance had wished to marry.

The Emperor rode into Palermo, now without resistance. The Empress awaited him amid twinkling hanging lamps in the Cuba, the little palace in the park Gennolard, which a dome surmounted in the shape of a beehive. She sat before him, with flabby, waxen cheeks, her agate-brown eyes (whose lids were too short) half open, an old woman before her husband of thirty-two, an enemy and a harbourer of enemies. When she raised herself up she grew a head higher than he. He did not touch her, he did not rave. He merely spoke : " None shall escape ". And he noted the trembling of her shoulders. She replied : " You German, I hate you ".

Some of the Barons were plunged into the sea, where the sharks swam amid the dolphins, others cut up by saws, others scalded with boiling pitch, others impaled on the ground. Then Bohemund had to surrender in San Giovanni. The Castro, on a steep rock, near the swollen Fiume Salso and the settlement Caltascibetta—in the skies, grey and white with clouds, loomed one of Etna's peaks—was taken. In the middle of the market-place at Palermo the hangman nailed a red-hot crown fast to the Norman's skull and, as he reared, the circle of flames wound about him, discharging girandoles. The Empress had her seat next the Emperor. With the wheeled spur on his heel he pressed on her toes. She smiled.

TWO of the Crusaders' thirty vessels were wrecked in the storm. Then, in August, the great ships came to land in Messina harbour. Henry, recovered from a new attack of fever, received them. He himself stayed there, lord of lords from the villages of the Slavs on the Baltic to as far as Cyprus. But the Chancellor Conrad embarked, with golden vessels, with cups and dishes of gold and silver. To Nicosia on Cyprus he was conveying the sceptre for the Emperor's vassal, Amalric of Lusignan.

It was a year of famine, after a bad harvest. In Germany and the Alps of Lombardy the lower sort had since autumn fed on roots and the flesh of fallen animals. Now all roads were encumbered with starving beggars and dead men who had come to the monasteries' hospitable gates. Many had died through their own hand, many through robber bands. Packs of wolves trotted from the Ardennes down to the Moselle. There people saw King Dietrich of Bern on a black nag. There was famine in Rome. And over Sicily swept parching the breath of the African desert.

The Emperor, who already after the day of blood once more let Constance sign the Sicilian government's parchments, sent messengers to Swabia, to Philip, who at Easter had been married on the Günzenlech near Augsburg to the Greek Irene: he was to fetch the Imperial boy, henceforward christened not Constantine, but Roger Frederick, and take him to Germany, that he might wear the royal crown. In August Henry was hunting at the Niso.

Icy cold by night were the forests so oppressive during the daytime. The fowling dogs scared up the grey herons, the white eagrets, the greeny yellow night-herons with their tattered, tender plumage, the rosy-red flamingoes stretching their necks. Henry took off the hood of the gerfalcon on his glove and sent it off with a toss of the hand. At a boggy tarn giddiness overtook him. He turned aside, surrounded by flapping black scythrops. In the thicket of olive trees a spring bubbled. With it he assuaged his thirst.

Shambling, a claw at his heart, he was brought to Messina. Weakened by a bloody flux he called for Constance. A week later she arrived from Palermo. He no longer knew her, nor Markward who stood at his bed's head, gigantic, like a dark ferryman. Berard his physician, now Archbishop of Messina, pronounced the form of confession and gave him the last sacrament. He died on a September evening, as the sun threw a coppery sheen over the pillars.

Young Philip with three hundred men-at-arms had passed over the Brenner road and reached Tuscany. In Montefiascone a horseman flew up to him panting: " The Emperor is dead! The Emperor is dead!" In a trice the men-at-arms put about their horses caparisoned down to the ground. Constance banished the Germans from the Norman kingdom.

17

THE city on the Tiber was loud in the rainy wet
light of February. It was celebrating carnival
and the coronation of Lothair, who, the son of
Count Trasmund of Segni and the Roman Claricia
Scotta, as Pope of Christendom called himself Innocent.
Three doves had flitted about during the conclave in
St. Gregory's Monastery, and one, quite white, had
settled at Lothair's right hand.

He sat on high on the steps of St. Peter, in front of
the Emperor Constantine's basilica with its portico of
forty temple-columns. He was thirty-seven years of
age, small, forced severity in his handsome face. The
Archdeacon took from his head the mitre and, while
the populace roared applause, gave him the tiara, surrounded by three crowns and o'ershone by a carbuncle.
" And know ", he said as he did so, " that thou art the
father of kings and princes, the regent of the world, the
vicegerent on earth of our Saviour Jesus Christ, whose
name shall endure to all eternity ". With masterful
mien Innocent mounted a white palfrey, over which was
spread a scarlet cloth. Great was the procession which
the Senators as his acting equerries let pass before them :
the cross-bearer, knights with red banners, horsemen
with lances of gold, prefects, priests, bishops, archbishops
cardinals, all of them—even they who resembled parched
mummies—on horseback. Behind the Pope were ranged
the knights and nobles with the escutcheons of their
houses ; but absent were the Orsini, mourning Celestine,
one of their kin, and at enmity with the Scotta.

The procession advanced at a trot through the
triumphal arches of Gratian, Theodosius and Valen-
tinian to the tower of Stephen Petri. There, in the
Pariono quarter, stood the Jews of Rome : at their head

the Rabbi of the Synagogue, laden with the veiled scroll of the Torah. The Rabbi Akabaia ben Mahabel, blinded by cataract, handed the new Pope the law of Moses, that graciously he might acknowledge it. Innocent merely cast one glance over the Torah and said offhand : " We condemn the opinions of Jewry ; for the law has already been fulfilled in Christ, whom the people of Judah in their folly still await as the Messiah ". The Jews disappeared amidst the yells of the mob. But inside the synagogue the Rabbi prayed : " Of those who have spat upon me may my soul keep silence. The counsel of them who devise mischief against me defeat thou, O Lord, and set at naught their designs ".

The procession advanced through the triumphal arches of Septimius Severus and of Titus, past the Colosseum to the Lateran. Innocent sat down on the *Sella stercoraria*, the marble commode, the seat of unseemliness ; it was the custom of centuries. But two cardinals helped him to his feet again with the traditional words of the Scriptures : " He raiseth the needy up out of the dust and the poor out of the mire ". The Pope scattered money among the multitude and said : " Gold and silver is not for me, but what I have that I give to thee ". In the chapel of St. Sylvester Innocent laid himself on the antique couch of porphyry. From the Prior of the Lateran he received the pastoral staff and the keys of the church and palace. He was girt with a red silk girdle, from which hung a purple purse with musk and twelve seals of costly stone. People crowded up to the foot-kissing. Innocent prayed before the relics in the chapel Sancta Sanctorum. Softly the emasculated sopranos sang the " Ave mundi spes, Maria ", which he had composed.

Afterwards he dined alone at a table with golden vessels ; at other tables the clergy and the magnates. He put the wine away from him, even that from Vesuvius, the Lacrimæ Christi. Then he conferred with the prefect Petrus de Vico about the oath of allegiance and the purchase-price due to the Romans and about the avarice of Richard of Segni, his brother. In the streets the carnival whooped, lads in petticoats with puffed-out bellies, women dressed like men, children playing Chiesa, the hue and cry after a murderer before the asylum of the church steps, crude masks, blaring brass, conjurers. Wakeful, on hard pillows, Innocent read until very late in what he had written touching mortal men, their engendering between dung and urine and about the contemning of the world.

BEFORE the castle of Boron, in his tent of check silk, the news of the Emperor's death reached the Chancellor Conrad. Navigation had been impossible for four months. The Chancellor was working on an epistle about Scylla and Charybdis, about the house in which Thetis, the silver-footed sea-goddess, hid Achilles and the power of the Saracens to kill otters with their spittle, as the apostle Paul did, when a secret messenger was brought to him, a cleric of Walter of Paleario's, the bishop's of Troia. The Chancellor did not show himself in the camp of the Crusaders, who shunned him in the belief that he was bribed by the Templars and the Templars' order by the infidels. The assault was appointed for the next day, prisoners in blood-stained turbans had given away how one might creep up to the walls without exposure to the oblique torrent of the defenders' arrows. Breastplates sparkled, crest nodded by crest. Beneath the bluish moon the Chancellor had his tent and baggage conveyed to the coast of Tyre. On the morrow the princes followed his example ; and all, sacrificing the sick and wounded, pressed towards Tyre and Acre.

There they hesitated until into March. They swore faith to the infant Frederick, Henry's son, and fortified the places. There remained the young Duke of Austria and Bishop Wolfger of Passau, who soon after spoke the last prayers for the Babenberger and who was minded to go to the Pope at Rome with the Master of the German Knights-Hospitaller. There remained Archbishop Conrad of Mainz and the Bishop of Verdun. The others sailed, landed in Apulia and were set upon by the vengeance of those whom they had enthralled. They were forced to embark on their ships again, were driven towards the east, stripped by the Dalmatians in their forests. Some returned home by way of Marseilles or Genoa or Venice. The Chancellor Conrad and Walram of Limburg were, in June, the first to reach Worms. The sandy dust of the roads still in his cloak, the Chancellor with unmoved mien did homage to fair-haired King Philip.

Even after he had spoken with him for an hour in the wooden palace his countenance was impenetrable. In this city the youth of eighteen who, reported dead like Henry, had ridden home to masterless Germany, instead of being Frederick's guardian, had uttered the wish to be king himself and, after the election at Mulhouse, had adorned his head with the crown whose name is The Orphan. But an Anti-King had arisen in Otto of Poitou, Henry the Lion's second son, Earl of York and March, Cœur de Lion's hostage, the foreigner, the half-Englishman, who from the banks of the Garonne appeared in Liége and now in Cologne, welcomed by the jubilations of the priests and proclaimed by Archbishop Adolphus. A meteor flamed in the sky at Cologne, a happy omen for the people. Surrendering himself care-free to the charm of his youth, Philip smiled at his Greek wife, who had been named Mary after the Blessed One; and he led the Chancellor up to her, where she sat pale among her women, embroidering upon a veil a snow-white unicorn with purple-coloured hooves. " Speak ", Frederick besought the Chancellor, "with the Bishop of Sutri, speak with the Frenchmen's agents."

The Chancellor saw the envoys from Innocent, the prelate of Sutri and the Abbot of San Anastasio. They had been commissioned to release Philip from the interdict so soon as the Sicilians still chained to the wall in Trifels should be set free. And Philip had commended Wezel of Berg to send home Nicholas of Salerno, his brothers, the Archbishop of Acerenza and the Barons. But William, Tancred's violated brother, had died at Hohenems in Rhætia before the Pope's intercession could save him, and fled from Hohenburg, the Alsatian nunnery, was Sibyl with her daughters. Now the Barons journeyed through the Cisalpine territories, and, full of horror and hatred against the Germans, the Lombards accompanied the carts of the blinded. The Bishop of Sutri knew that the Chancellor had been a friend of the Holy Father's; and he exceeded his office by staying so long with Philip, who would not be without him at his court. He felt himself in danger and sought the other's confidence, a sign of his real views. The Chancellor Conrad, elected Bishop of Würzburg, purposed to unite it to the see of Hildesheim; a breach threatened with Innocent, whom, since he had Celestine's leave, he did not consult. The Chancellor Conrad was playing for high stakes. With fraternal kiss he counselled the Bishop of Sutri not to depart before his eyes had beheld Philip's coronation. "Report then in Rome that all Princes assent to the Swabian's title. The Duke of Zähringen even, the usurer, whom Cologne and Treves have bought for six thousand marks of silver, the oppressor of the Church and the laity, for whom the hell of Etna is made hot, has gained Schaffhausen and Breisach as a reward for going over to the enemy. The harvest is ripening in fields cultivated afresh, the trampled provinces sigh for rest."

He stood in the central hall facing the Bishops Nevelo of Soissons and Bertram of Metz, who had come on behalf of Philip Augustus to make a league with the Duke of Swabia against Cœur de Lion, Otto of Poitou, the Count of Flanders and Adolphus of Cologne. Then the Hohenstaufen entered with rapid gait, youthful and radiant. He gave solemn assent to the drawn-up pact by shake of hand, and resonant was his voice, schooled in the singing of hours and antiphons which he had learnt as provost of Aix-la-Chapelle. Music flooded the cathedral, to which Philip, Mary, the Chancellor, the Counts and the imperial vassals betook themselves. The Bishop of Sutri lighted the candles which had lain in pieces since the launching of the interdict.

When two weeks later Nevelo and Bertram took their leave in the palace, Conrad did not conceal from them that Otto of Poitou had taken Aix-la-Chapelle and, by the side of his seven-year-old bride, Mary of Brabant, had been anointed and crowned in Charlemagne's city. Philip took the field in Alsace, against the Bishop of Strasburg and the Count of Dagsburg. His warriors destroyed the castle of Haldenburg, burned Molsheim, tore down the ramparts round Epsich graveyard on the road to Schlettstadt, rooted up the graves.

THE palace in Foligno was empty of Germans. Conrad of Urslingen, Duke of Spoleto, expelled from Sicily by the Empress Constance, surrendered at Narni to the power of Innocent in the persons of Cardinals Octavian of Ostia and Gerard of San Adriano. He released his vassals from their allegiance and gave up the Rocca di Cesi and the Rocca di Gualdo. The townsfolk took and demolished the castle of Assisi. The Duke left in Foligno the foster-mother of the three-year-old child Federigo, his Italian consort. One gentle April day two Apulian counts, Piero de Celano and Berard de Loritello, plucked him out of her arms and, though he screamed and bit, hurried him to the sea near by. The child had scant, sandy fair hair, was blue-eyed, small, as if two years old, and puny. He was the son of Constance, and in their dens oneiromancers told how she, the barren woman, had had intercourse with a demon.

The child awoke in Messina harbour. It was frightened of a woman with short eyelids and faded skin who stared at him uncertainly, consumed by evil memories. Then he blinked at the glare of Palermo and the splendour of the Mansuriya. He was in the cathedral when his father was stretched out in the porphyry tomb from Cefalù which King Roger had had fashioned by

23

Greek artists. At Henry's shoes, sewn with pearls and having cork discs for soles, lay a yellow silk crown, a sword gleamed, laurel leaves and curls were strewn about the stiff face of the departed, on which a whitish crust adhered and whose tangled growth of hair seemed still to live. At Whitsun they waited upon Federigo with the royal vestments, Archbishop Bartolomeo pressed a diadem upon his head, the boy started, Bartolomeo cried through the cathedral : " *Christus vincit, Christus regnat, Christus imperat !* " The multitude made uproar, the bells of Palermo swayed, the boy slid in terror from the golden seat and cried.

Constance, for all her decaying body, wished to rule. But she trembled before Markward, who still made head against his foes in Molise and was now arming up yonder, in order by force of arms to seize the guardianship of Federigo, the son (as he said) of a Neapolitan butcher. With her were Gentile and Manerio of Paleario, the brothers of the Bishop of Troia, whom Constance had offended by taking away the seal and who might rise against her tomorrow. And suspect became Raniero de Sarteano, Count of Manente, Philip's friend from Tuscany. In Calabria Dipold of Vohburg offered resistance and mocked that land for engendering many folk, yet naught but womanish men, and there offered resistance Conrad of Marlenheim and Otto of Barkstein, the murderer. No one was the protector of the widow but Innocent, who disdained her pride. She sent to Rome, craving for herself and her son investment with the kingdom, Archbishop Anselm of Naples, Archdeacon Aimericus of Syracuse, Magister Thomas of Gaeta, Judge Nicholas of Bisceglia. He refused to grant her a voice in ecclesiastical elections, he rejected her gifts and he recommended her to bestow the royal seal on Walter of Paleario again. When in extreme humility she had obeyed, he sent the Cardinal of Ostia to her.

In the presence of the latter she swore the oath of allegiance in the Palatine Chapel, which lay underground, approached from the courtyard above by marble stairs. She held Federigo to her knee and testified that he was true-born. The boy listened to the riddling words. The Cardinal laid his hand upon the crown of his head. But he tore himself away and ran up the steps into the shafts of the midday sun, to Roger's clock with the Arabic, Greek and Latin inscription, on which he gazed full of insatiable curiosity. Drugged by the sun he fell asleep. Pigeons wheeled round the dried-up Fount of the Lion and the battlements of the Yoharia.

A year after the Emperor's death Constance tottered through the palace, an empty shadow. She fell and whimpered with the pain that was devouring her kidneys. They couched her in a dark, vaulted chamber. Her maids scattered; only Ibn Omar, a Saracen physician, endured in the smell emanating from her. She saw Federigo no more. One night torches wandered through the pointed arches, eunuchs clattered in their pointed shoes, a tumult began on the terraces. In the drowsy dawn the magnates assembled.

Magister Thomas, the Justiciary, opened the will of the departed. It appointed the Pope guardian to Federigo and granted him annually ten thousand *tari*. It appointed a College of Familiars, over which Walter of Paleario was to preside. Archbishop Bartolomeo and he of Monreale, the cathedral of the Benedictine monastery against the cypress-covered hills, were here among the Counts. Archbishops William of Reggio and Matthew of Capua were sent for. They kissed the black velvet coat of the little King, who turned away with a curl of the lips.

In place of Innocent, whose journey to his ward's dominions the Cardinals John of San Stefano and Gerard of San Adriano had already announced, there arrived Cardinal Gregory of Santa Maria. He left with Federigo a letter from the Pope. " What does he say ? " the King, fingering the scroll, asked Walter of Paleario. The Bishop of Troia, with the thin face and the mouth of the disappointed, read : " The father of mercy hath bestowed upon thee wholesome consolation and turned into a blessing upon thee what for a space seemed affliction. For did he not hang a rod over thee, it might seem as if he despised thee, like Solomon aforetime. Did he not chastize thee in thy childhood, thou wert manifestly set apart from his love, since, according to the Scriptures, the Lord chastiseth those whom he loveth. Therefore he afflicted thee in earliest infancy as a testimony that from a child he admitteth thee to be his son. And as a sign thereof he hath delivered thee up under the protection of his deputy, hath in the greatness of his mercies given thee in place of thy departed father one more worthy and of thy mother a better, of whom it is written : Her left hand lieth beneath my heart and her right hand caresseth me. According to the office of our pastoral duty which maketh us the refuge of the fatherless all together, we admonish thee : Throw off thy heaviness, drive out the darkness of thy affliction, and rejoice rather in the Lord who for a carnal father gave thee a spiritual and at the death of thy mother assigned to thee the Church to be the mother of thy childhood, to the end that thou, grown a man, still honour her who, as thou wilt recognize, hath exalted thee ". " And who is God ? " the boy Federigo, lisping and shy, enquired of the Bishop of Troia.

THE noble Henry of Aue, who came from Swabia, a Crusader not yet forty, had brought oversea from Aleppo a slave, Motarrif, the son of Chezzar the executioner, and lost him at a round watch-tower near Genoa, from which the infidel swam through the tepid tide. After six days he found him again in a black blind-alley near the harbour, among trampled pumpkins. With wasted hands Motarrif fastened upon his master, whose sword was already bare to score his brow and who took fright at the dying slave's eyes that glittered devilish in his extremity. His hands were covered with scabs and with boils the skin of his legs through his tatters. The knight, whom lust had driven into that purlieu of promiscuity, to the red curtains and painted wenches, fled; and only when, accompanied by his German squires, he saw the snow of the high mountains gleaming could he forget that haunting night.

In Biella he recognized that he was smitten with leprosy. For he had brownish scars in mouth and nose, and on his hands and the soles of his feet. His throat was bursting with terror. He decided after many prayers to journey to the physicians in Montpellier, who were famed in Christendom. Beneath the glaciers of the Grand Paradis and over the col of the Mont Cenis, through rocky gorges, black forests which spread out their withering roots from abyss to abyss and through the valley of the Arc he wandered like a blind man towards the Rhone; and only frightful wilderness answered the rattling of his wooden lazar's clapper. In the spring he had been in Avrieux, where the Emperor Charles the Bald died, poisoned by Sedecias, and at the waterfalls of St. Benedict. Amid winter frosts he reached Maguelone and Montpellier; but now he concealed his illness by a cowl, as if he had no face left, and mewed out his request for food and drink to the monks in whose stables be burrowed out a bed of straw. By night he knocked at the door of a Spanish Jew, Magister Abon, who was an ornament of the school, of the *Fons Physicæ*. The Magister bade him sit down by the darkly glowing coals on his hearth and held a seven-branched candlestick before his bony face. He had no consolation of leechcraft for the knight, however, except, as Marcellus Burdigalensis recommended, to conjure the distemper to stint in the name of the God of Jacob and Sabaoth.

The knight washed in the waves of the Lez and wandered to his castle in the Rauhe Alb, to await his evil death in his Swabian homeland. Before faring oversea he had buried his wife. Now he divided his goods among his relatives, the Church and his tenants. A farmer looked after him, who had many children. The oldest was a maid of fourteen called Gotelind. She

27

carried to her sick lord his food, and every time he cast away on to the unfruitful sod any dish and cup which he had set to his lips. For money (which he did not touch) he bought her looking-glasses, snoods, girdles and rings, perchance called her his little wife and was honest and respectful to her as if she were not of peasant stock. Sleepless he cursed the Almighty like Job who scratched his scabs with a potsherd. A carpet over stinking dung, so he screamed in his loneliness, was this lying world, all life miasma and dust. But when sleepless he ran about in the fir-wood till yellow dawn or listened to the howling of the ravening beasts or broke down in his cell, a wolfish thought came over him. He had read of Amelius, who stabbed his boys and spattered and healed with their blood leprous Amicus his friend, or of the leprous king of England, who bathed in the blood of a virgin. He saw the girlish limbs of the maid before him and lusted after her leaping heart's juice as the source of his re-birth in purity. She heard his sighs and in the strange madness of love offered herself as a sacrifice for him.

Her father and mother beat her, then with boorish obedience they parted from her amid weeping and lamenting. In her woollen village-gown she travelled with her lord by way of Ulm and the Swabian highlands into the plain of Lombardy. Again, cowled, he swung the clapper; and leaning in a tilt-cart she cowered, her fair plaits about her forehead, her suffering, glassy gaze upon his lank form, ten paces behind him. He avoided the cities, he avoided even Naples, and through the hills of Campania they reached the gulf of Salerno. Newly built up was the school of Elinus, of Pontus and of Abdallah which the dead Emperor's army had burnt down. Gifted with great learning were its doctors. They had explored fevers, the convulsions of cramp, against which they employed human blood and the eggs of ravens, ulceration of the lungs which is to be noted by the smell of the breath, the cardiac passion and sweats, verdigris as a remedy for shanker, lead for dysentery,

Spanish flies for hydrophobia, Jews' pitch for hardening of the glands, the ashes of crayfish for rabies, *kahraba* (which is amber) for bleeding, the virtue of cinnabar, of mercury, of oils, of aloes, of myrrh and of camphor. The German lord asked for Ser Oseibia from Damascus and disclosed to him his murderous aim. The Saracen anointed his ulcers with the drug *al kali*. However, the leper required of him yet again, with trembling body, the slaughter of the maid, and she averred that it was her own free will. Oseibia shut him into a room and bolted the door. The leper spied through a crack in the wall, as the Saracen strapped the innocent child stark naked to a bench and with the surgeon's knife sought for the region of the heart upon her pallid breast.

The story goes that the knight heard the ring of steel on the grindstone, burst open the door and told Oseibia he must unbind the maid. Lamenting that a heavenly crown would now be her part no more, she had torn her hair and waxed so frantic that she had come near to the death which she lamented. Then the mercy of the mother of God had of a sudden made the knight whole, and he had returned to Germany, had clothed young Gotelind solemnly in ermine, velvet and sables and espoused her. But it seems that she gave up the ghost in Salerno under the Saracen's knife, that an angel carried her soul like a poppet, a swaddled doll, up to the flaming clouds and that the sick knight, bereft of peace, who weened he had been healed and in whom the horror of annihilation raged on with cunning certainty, infected many another woman in Italy and Swabia, until Satan smote him.

PHILIP, crowned at Mainz by the Burgundian Archbishop Aimo of Tarentaise with the crown that is called Orphan, waged war against Otto in the dried-up bed of the Moselle. His troops threw fire into Bonn and Remagen. They attacked the citizens, a nunnery. They dipped one of the women into boiling pitch and feathered her. Philip punished the malefactors with death.   He stood already before Cologne, when the news that Herman of Thuringia was fighting on Otto's side forced him to turn back.

He rode into winter-bound Goslar and, when the snow thawed, into Treves.   He was on the middle Rhine in the same week of April in which, in front of Chalus-Chabrol near Limoges, Richard Cœur de Lion, wounded in the neck by a longbowman, went the way of all flesh.   In July his wandering companies camped before Strasburg.   In Rome the Pope pronounced the greater excommunication against the Chancellor Conrad, the elect of Würzburg, as well as banished to an island of the Tyrrhenian sea the Bishop of Sutri for bestowing his presence on Philip's coronation.   Of a certainty Innocent had declared that the Hohenstaufen might not keep the German crown, even should it cost him the papacy.   On that account he did not spare even his disloyal friend.

Christmas of this year, the second since the Emperor was dead, Philip celebrated in Magdeburg.   The Chancellor Conrad, master of his mien, arranged the ceremonial procession to the cathedral.   Bernard of Saxony bore the sword of state.   Philip was adorned with crown and sceptre, surrounded by the Archbishop of Magdeburg, Bishop Gardolf of Halberstadt (the Chancellor's cousin), and Hartwig of Bremen, the Crusader.   There followed Mary, the pale madonna from Byzantium, Judith of Saxony, the Abbess of Quedlinburg, more bishops.   Then the Counts, even he of Holstein, of Meissen, the Landgrave of Thuringia, who now for ready money adherred to the Swabian. Through Brunswick Philip proceeded, separating from Mary, to Hildesheim.   Bishop Harbert fled, whom only Otto's hand had defended ; and once again the Chancellor Conrad assumed the seat behind St. Bernard's bronze gates from which Innocent, angered at the arbitrary assumption of double office, had thrust him.

From Hildesheim he turned with the Hohenstaufen to Thuringia.   In the rime of the Unstrut valley, in

Mühlhausen, he and the King met with Conrad of Wittelsbach, Archbishop of Mainz, Cardinal-Bishop of Sabina, who had been in Germany since December. Pitch fires flared round the lodgings of the Wittelsbach, he dragged about with him the incurable fever of the East. His retinue was as splendid as that of any mighty one in the realm. In the name of Innocent he had published the excommunication against Conrad at the high altar of Mainz. He was wishful, against a new expedition to the Holy Land, to compose the dispute of the kings by an armistice. Eight princes of either side should then elect. He himself inclined to Frederick, Federigo, the child from Apulia. The Chancellor Conrad was with him under the cloak of night. He learnt from the Archbishop that the Pope would pardon him if he submitted. From thenceforward the Chancellor was lost to Philip's cause; but he kept silence.

Philip held Diet at Nürnberg with the Bishops of Bamberg, Passau, Freising and Constance, the Dukes of Bavaria, Austria and Meran. The Chancellor Conrad journeyed thence to Rome. He stood in the Lateran before Innocent. A letter of Otto's, transmitted by the Marquis of Montferrat, warned Innocent against the caitiff. With naked feet, a rope round his neck, the hands raised up imploring in the shape of the cross, Innocent let him kneel before him. Then sadly he embraced his friend and released him from his penalties. Conrad avoided a meeting with Philip's delegates, the Prior of St. Thomas at Strasburg, who had been with him already at Henry's court, and the Sub-Deacon John. The Pope, to whom the German Princes in Spires had announced that they would march with the Hohenstaufen, lawfully by them elected, to Rome, in order to get for him the Imperial crown as well, replied in the presence of the scarlet cardinals to Philip's missive. " Through God ", he exclaimed, " the Church is at one with herself, the Empire however sunk into discord through its sins." He would pray God for counsel and help. The

Chancellor Conrad, as the cool of the May evening breathed about him on the Aventine, was absorbed in the legends of the Minotaur and limping Vulcan.

He travelled back northward to Germany, back to Philip. He was in his camp with the Archbishop of Magdeburg, Gandolf of Halberstadt, John of Treves, Bernard of Saxony, Dietrich of Meissen, Otto of Brandenburg, Adolphus of Holstein, when the Hohenstaufen penetrated into Brunswick. Plunderers however poured into the convent of St. Aegidius, the Guelph troops at the Oker bridge beat the enemy out, the arms, clothes and utensils which he threw away covered the road under water from the raging tempest. King Philip no longer trusted the Chancellor. Henry of Glinden, Dean of Magdeburg Cathedral, hoped for promotion by his fall. The Chancellor bestowed upon him a ring, whose stone was said to possess magical powers against the disease of disloyalty. The Dean thought: "Why do you part from the ring since you stand in so great need of such a specific yourself?" Gerard of Querfurt, Conrad's brother, surprised the mocker near the Castle of Haldensleben and put out his eyes. The temporal Courts sentenced him of Querfurt to a big fine and the infamy of carrying a dog on his shoulders. The Pope in Rome released him from his excommunication.

The Archbishop of Mainz had prayed at the tomb of St. Erminolt, in the monastery of Prüfling near Ratisbon, for cure or speedy death. He died at Reitfeld on the road from Nürnberg to Würzburg, his head leaning against the motherly body of a peasant woman. Lewis of Bavaria, his nephew, seized upon the gorgeous pallia he had left behind. Wolfger of Passau proceeded with the corpse to Mainz. With King Philip the Chancellor Conrad made his appearance for the funeral by the rushing, emerald-green Rhine, and even when Philip, to annoy the Pope, conferred the archbishopric on Lupold, who was already Bishop of Worms, he remained impassible and mute.

32

MARKWARD of Anweiler, who aspired to the Sicilian crown and called himself the Emperor's deputy, had besieged the castle of Monte Cassino with Dipold and Conrad of Marlenheim and had been unable to make a breach. He begged to be loosed from the Church's ban.

The Pope caused three cardinals to go to Veroli— Octavian of Ostia, the Priest Guido of Santa Maria in Trastevere and the Deacon Ugolino of St. Eustace, who was sixty years old and a Segni like himself, endowed with enduring pride, unshakable. Markward rode into Veroli almost unarmed. Black pigs ran squealing round the chapel in which sat the cardinals and against the windows of which the June sun beat. Markward bent, swore obedience to the Pope and was freed from excommunication. Afterwards he demanded that the cardinals should come to him at Casamari, so that his followers might know he had been absolved. Ugolino was taken aback, the Bishop of Ostia nodded assent. Markward received the three, lapped in steel ; a hundred men-at-arms surrounded the house. A banquet was prepared within, and Markward drank purple wine, showing hospitable courtesy to the cardinals, who scarce ate at all. But Ugolino saw the veins of his eyes swell and whispered with the cardinal-priest. With strong foot Markward spurned the table, so that the golden cups rang : " You are prisoners ". Unperturbed amid the turmoil, Ugolino read out the conditions for a settlement with Markward : that he must remove, make good all damage, hand over the castles still in his keeping. " Such is the Pope's command ; we have none other for you." The Lord High Steward gave an ugly smile ; he was as little to be put out as the other. He pushed back his men-at-arms, eager to squeeze the Roman's wind-pipe, and asked for leave to negotiate with Innocent himself. He had secrets to tell him. His guests he conducted to Veroli.

He lied everywhere about his reconciliation with the Holy Father : that the latter had sent him two cardinals in order to ordain him regent of Sicily. And when they gave him the lie, he bellowed that he would heed the Pope for neither God nor man. The excommunication against him was renewed, an interdict darkened every spot in which he rested. Suddenly, one October day, under a leaden sky, his ships put out to sea from Salerno and steered for Trapani. There, in the mountains of Giato, lived the tribes of the Saracens and among them those Moslems who had left Palermo when Constance died or had decamped from the estates of the clergy. They rode, twirling lances or beating them against their bossed metal shields, to meet Markward's floating banner. He advanced, Sicily seemed his prey. But he still did not attack Palermo. Federigo shivered in the Favara and its faded gardens.

Innocent stretched himself out, but found no rest; for nights on end he watched till cockcrow. The Bishops of Taranto and Naples were to whet the courage of the faithful against the brazen fellow who had allied himself with heathens. He bade Berard de Loritello, the Grand Justiciary of Apulia, await the Cardinal Cinthius, who was coming with two hundred mounted mercenaries under Odo de Palombara, a cousin of the Segni, and straddled-legged James Consiliari, the papal marshal. James drove German Frederick from Malveto and made a way to Messina for the cardinal. Thither, to Archbishop Berard, went Walter of Paleario and the Familiars other than themselves, John of Cefalù, Roger of Catania, Bartholomew of Lucy. But, occupying the hills about Monreale, Markward lay down before Palermo with his Germans, Emir Magded's Saracens and five hundred Pisans under the Imperial eagle. He encircled the walls. He cut off the city's supplies, the carts with living and plucked fowls, with lambs, artichokes, herbs, onions and garlic. The people starved. The crowned child starved. Then James's forces came sailing up. They pitched camp outside the gate, in the park of Gennolard, near the pond of the Cuba.

James wanted battle, Markward delay. Through Raniero di Manente he asked whether the Familiars would grant him this. The Chancellor decided in favour; for he knew the Pope had received Walter of Brienne, whom Sibyl had married to her daughter Alberia, that the Frenchman demanded Lecce and Taranto as his inheritance and was collecting the chivalry of Burgundy for a campaign into Sicily. Nothing smouldered in the Bishop of Troia like his hatred against the Norman dynasty. He feared their vengeance, since he had fallen away to Henry. A few months before he had had himself elected Archbishop of Palermo and had had Cinthius confer that title upon him in Messina. Innocent withheld it. "If we loved thee not so much", stood written in the letter which the Pope's scribe Bartholomew handed the Chancellor, "thou wouldst recognize by the measure of thy punishment how much thou hadst offended against us." Innocent had compensated the Bishop of Troia with the procuratorship over Palermo. But he, full of bitterness and resentment against Brienne, too proud to be content with that, meditated changes. The Familiars had concluded peace with Markward, without popular excitement and without the scribe Bartholomew. The battle proved unfavourable to the Sicilians, until Gentile and Manerio of Paleario, Counts of Manupello, now opponents to the High Lord Steward, stormed the heights before Monreale. Picked up dead under a eucalyptus-bush was the brown Emir Magded in the splendour of silver crescents and horses' tails. Captured was Raniero di Manente. The Cardinal Cinthius nominated James, as victor, Count of Andria. The brothers Paleario remained unrewarded.

Again at Randazzo fortune frowned upon Markward, the defeated. But distempers diminished James's forces, he ran short of pay and turned about to the mainland. The Bishop of Troia summoned Gentile among the Familiars; and in December he went over to Markward. Markward himself became a Familiar and Lord of the island, Walter of Paleario Lord of Apulia. But he left a pledge behind in Gentile's charge, the seven-year-old Federigo, forgotten in the Favara.

The citizens of Palermo had sent him baskets with food for a week apiece. The boy wore poor, faded clothes. He was fractious and moody. The Count of Manupello showed him how to aim at song-birds with the bow. The art of dissimulation the Bishop of Troia, who came to him for an hour every third day, had taught him.

KING PHILIP was deserted by the Bishops and Counts on the Moselle and the Rhine and excommunicated by the Pope at Rome, together with those who still followed him. The Cardinal-Legate Guido of Praeneste appeared with the Guelph in Cologne, handed Innocent's letter to him and the princes, blessed him, and with extinguished candles banned all who still might oppose him.

Philip proceeded through autumnal Franconia to Bamberg. High above the Regnitz rose the city with its towers, within which lay his castle and from which one looked upon the convent on the Michaelsberg and to the Babenbergers' Altenburg. Philip and Mary knelt with Bishop Thiemo and the princes before the tomb of the Emperor Henry, the Second, the Saxon, and his consort, Cunigund, canonized for her womanly piety; upon stone pillows lay their stone heads, little dogs pressed against their shoes. The cool vaults breathed transience.

Philip held Diet. The Dukes of Saxony and Meran were there, the Landgrave of Thuringia, the Marquis of Meissen and he of Moravia, the Bohemian Ottakar's brother; also the Archbishop of Bremen and, despite Innocent's request, Everard of Salzburg. The King bestowed upon the Chancellor Conrad the spiritual fiefs in the Hohenstaufen's gift and the castle of Steineck. Two weeks before, Conrad's cousin, Gardolf of Halberstadt, had died of a high fever and utterly tormented by divided allegiance to the Pope and the young Swabian, prepared for the last journey to Rome. Easily did the Chancellor Conrad overcome the distresses of conscience.

There were traitors around Philip at Bamberg, the Bishop of Würzburg and the Landgrave of Thuringia,

FREDERICK BARBAROSSA

[face p. 36

traitors at Hagenau in December, the Bishops of Strasburg and Basel. There departed Henry of Kalindin, Barbarossa's general, in disgust at the Chancellor's duplicity, there departed the latter himself—with Magister Philip, the papal notary, who reported on him to Innocent—into the dark. The Staufic princes made officious protestations at Rome through Everard of Salzburg, the Marquis of the Ostmark and the Abbot of Salem jointly. " We desire not the lowering of the Imperial power, as some lying lips feign, but its exalting ", Innocent answered. The Chancellor Conrad had not subscribed.

Philip advanced against Treves, whose archbishop John was vacillating. He assaulted the church of St. Goar. A missile struck a crucifix which began to bleed there where Jesus Christ was pierced by the centurion's spear. Terror seized upon the army. Philip deprived the Bishop of Würzburg of his chancellorship. In November, when Otto fell back to Spires, Conrad revolted. Henry of Kalindin returned to Barbarossa's son. The royal youth hurried to Ulm and moved with his Swabians towards Würzburg. Bishop Conrad had fortified the Marienberg. He called for help upon the Guelphs, across the Alps upon Innocent. As he was going to evening service on St. Nicholas's day, Kalindin's nephews, Bodo and Henry of Ravensburg, with their followers stepped in his path amid scattering choir-boys. They shouted : " A Ravensburg ". With the same cut of the sword the elder struck off the elegant hand with which he covered his head and smashed his brain-pan. They riddled, stripped, dishonoured the body and fled.

When Philip made his entry into Würzburg, when the clergy showed him the dead man's hand and the garments stiff with blood, the Hohenstaufen wept tears. There where the murder had taken place he put up a cross, whose inscription was in the Chancellor's praise. But he did not punish the murderers. Harried by their guilt, they fled to Italy. The Pope laid upon them the tenfold death of a cruel, life-long penance. Secretly Philip sent to him Otto, a poor monk of Salem monastery.

THE Count of Brienne, with whom were French crusaders, his uncle the Count of Montbéliard, Eustache de Conflans, Robert de Joinville and gay knights from Champagne, passed over the eternal snow of the Mont Cenis to Rome and pressed forward to the south. In Naples, Capua and Salerno priests who pronounced excommunication when a town did not join his cause were threatened and turned out. Teano surrendered to him. Capua barred the gates. But he prevailed over the Germans at the rotten footbridge of the Agnella. Venafro he set in flames. He captured the castle and town of Aquino. Robert of Aquila took a life-pension in payment for Pontecorvo, Castelnuovo and Fratte. Dipold got away to the east coast. But Walter of Paleario, excommunicated by Innocent and deprived of the bishopric of Troia, went into his camp, pawned royal estates, laid sacrilegious hands on church-plate, borrowed from religious foundations great sums that he applied to continue the war against the Pope. Already he had meant to make his peace with him, already Peter Galoze, Cardinal-Bishop of Porto, had loosed him from the ban, but he refused a peace with the Count of Brienne. "If Peter", he cried, "had been sent by Christ himself to enjoin that upon me, I would not obey him, even if I should be damned to hell." He inveighed against Innocent. With him his brother Manerio and Piero de Celano went over to Dipold. The Count of Brienne took Brindisi, Taranto, the castle of Lecce. He beat the Germans a second time at the Lake of Salpi and almost annihilated them. Dipold escaped into the mountains to Rocca Santa Agata. Walter of Paleario and Manerio fled to Salpi, Otto of Barkstein and Piero de Celano became prisoners ; wheel and rope put an end to Barkstein.

The majority of the Familiars were papal, the Archbishop of Monreale, Peter of Mazzara, by the grace of Innocent Archbishop of Palermo, and Berard of Messina. But after the battle of Salpi Gentile delivered Federigo, who hid with his tutor Franciscus in the Favara, into the

power of Markward. Myrmidons plucked forth the eight-year-old child from beneath a protuberant curtain. He thought they meant to bind him. He sprang like a leopard against them, tried to crack their knuckles, tore his coat to shreds, scratched his soft chest all over. They brought him before the stranger, who had mocked him as the Neapolitan butcher's bastard and to whom Federigo was merely a precious pawn for preventing the hereditary kingship of Walter of Brienne. The twinkling, starry eyes of the impotent boy pierced scorching into the adventurer's pupils.

To set him free Innocent negotiated with Pedro of Aragon : two to five hundred Aragonese knights against the betrothal of Federigo with Pedro's youngest sister Sancha. There died in Patti, of a stone in the bladder, which the surgeons cut out of his abdomen, Markward of Anweiler, Duke of Romagnola and of Ravenna, as he was journeying to submissive Messina. In a corner of the royal castle, his fingers clutching Franciscus's gown, Federigo gaped at the departed as he lay on the bier ; and Franciscus murmured : " I have seen how the ungodly rose up above the cedars of Lebanon. I went past, lo, he was departed ; I asked after him, they knew his place no more ". From prison emerged William Grasso, the Genoese, Count of Malta and Admiral of the kingdom, whom Markward even at the last had bound with fetters. There died in Tuscany, sent by King Philip, Conrad of Spoleto. But a German became Lord of the Palace, Federigo's keeper and Grand Captain of Sicily, a hoarse-voiced man with scarred visage and crooked shoulder, the adventurer William Capparone.

IN May the monk Otto returned to Germany, with a Camaldulian, the Prior Martin. Scarce perceptibly and without committing himself, Innocent negotiated with him. Philip was in Swabia, before taking the field against the Landgrave of Thuringia. In the presence of the Bishop of Constance, the Abbot of

Salem, Henry of Kalindin and the High Steward of
Waldburg, he repeated and formally sealed under a
golden bull : for all wrongs, even the ancient wrongs
done in Tuscany, he would give satisfaction, be faithful
to the Church, sail to the Holy Land and, if he or his
brother-in-law Alexios through God should become
Emperor in Byzantium, make the Hagia Sophia subser-
vient to St. Peter's chair. He would moreover betroth
his fourth daughter Beatrice to one of the Pope's
nephews, the son of Richard of Segni.

Rumours reported that Innocent had been driven
out by the Romans. The Odolina, his cousins, had
assassinated an Orsini in the open street ; the Orsini
destroyed houses and towers of the Odolina. The Poli,
robbed of their possessions by Richard of Segni, marched
half naked, with crosses like beggars, through the
Suburra, brawled in St. Peter's, struck the Pope as he was
walking with the tiara in the Easter Procession, besieged
the Senator Pandolfo on the Capitol, reduced his square
tower and Richard of Segni's to ashes, drove even
Innocent to flight. He fell ill in Anagni, and it was said
that he was dead and one Clement his successor. But
by a miracle he recovered. He wrote to King Otto that
from day to day his love for him increased in warmth.
He exhorted the princes of the Hohenstaufen party not
to delay until the twelfth hour, lest it should befall them
as the foolish virgins of the gospel. He denied that
Prior Martin had been his agent. He confirmed Egbert,
the Duke of Meran's son, as Bishop of Bamberg, whom
Philip had had elected by the chapter, and excommunicated him. He persuaded to disloyalty towards the
Hohenstaufen, or at least to circumspection, Wolfger
of Passau, now Patriarch of Aquileia, the Bishop of
Constance and the Archbishop of Salzburg.

Philip waged war upon Thuringia and Bohemia.
The Landgrave, the Palsgrave Henry, Otto's brother,
Ottakar and Vladislav of Moravia invested him in
Erfurt ; the bird flew away. The Bohemians and
Emerich of Hungaria's wild Polovtsi plundered convents

and parsonages, caparisoned their horses with altar-cloths, dragged girls and women with them. But then, between Goslar and Wolfenbüttel, the Palsgrave seceded from Otto for refusing him Brunswick and the Lichten-burg. He fought on Philip's side at Weissensee. The Bohemians under Ottakar himself advanced as far as Arnstadt. They declined battle with Henry of Kalindin's army and marched off, deceiving him by their nocturnal camp-fires. Even at the Fichtelgebirge Otto had not overtaken them. The Landgrave Herman made his submission in the monastery of Ichtershausen. The fair-haired Hohenstaufen gave him the kiss of peace.

In Coblenz he took the oath of Adolphus, Archbishop of Cologne and Duke of Westphalia. In vain had Innocent dispatched John of Béthune, Bishop of Cambrai, in vain did he utter passionate warning to the Rhenish citizens : " Can even a mother be unmindful of her child ? In such wise too may ye not desert this king, who in respect of his kingdom is as it were your son. Ye have planted him, now approve ye careful gardeners ". There was peace between Philip and the Duke of Brabant. In the January of the eighth year since the Emperor's death, Archbishop Adolphus crowned in the cathedral of Aix-la-Chapelle Philip and Mary with the same right hand that had crowned Otto. Icy winter-blasts blew, the Rhine froze to the bottom and cracked thunderously, like the bursting of a mountain.

THE French Barons, to whom the priest Fulke of Neuilly had preached a crusade, and Peter of Capua, the Pope's Legate, rode through Burgundy, over the Mont Cenis and through Lombardy to Venice. They quartered themselves on one of the islands, San Nicolo di Lido. Their envoys had concluded a treaty with the Doge Enrico Dandolo. He promised transports for four thousand five hundred chargers and nine thousand squires, galleys for four thousand five hundred knights and twenty thousand foot-soldiers. Of every prize in land or money Venice was to receive the half.

But the passage-money was charged against the French. Many a keg of gold and silver had Count Baldwin of Flanders, Count Lewis of Blois and Chartres, the Marquis Boniface of Montferrat, Count Hugh of St. Pol carried into the Doge's palace. But they were still far short, and so Dandolo demanded that the Crusaders should win back for the Venetian Republic a stronghold in Dalmatia, Iadera or Zara, which the King of Hungary had torn from her. They assembled in the green and gold Church of St. Mark. Aged Dandolo, whose fine eyes saw nothing more, as the result of a blow on the head, mounted into the pulpit and declared that he was old and sick, yet that none could lead them like himself. He was resolved to go and live or die with them. So he fastened the cross upon himself.

The fleet sailed—Enrico Dandolo in a purple-red galley with a tent of purple silk. The sea seemed aflame with the ship's flags and banners. They came before the high walls and towers of Iadera, broke the harbour-chain and encamped. The Abbot of the Cistercian monastery of Vaux told them that the Pope forbade an assault upon that Christian town. But the Barons blustered that they would be dishonoured unless they kept their compact and assailed walls and towers with their stone slings. They of Iadera surrendered to the Doge at discretion. The Crusaders chose lodgings in the houses ; but on the third day it came to a battle between Venetians and Frenchmen, with swords, lances, cross-bows and daggers, and they were not parted till night-fall. The army of the cross remained there until well into winter. Many removed for their vows' sake, also a rude man of war with the fangs of a wolf, the Count Simon of Montfort. Young Alexios, the son of the Emperor Isaac of Constantinople, besought the Barons to reinstate him in his empire. And they made a compact with him and sailed, disunited as they were, by way of Corfu, to the promontory of Malea, to Negroponte and up to Abydos.

They entered the violet-blue Propontis and sailed to

Peræa, between gardens of cypresses, roses, heliotropes and mallows. They landed at the road of Georgios. As they were foraging about the country-side, the knights Eude of Champlitte in Champagne, Oger of St. Chéron and Manasse de l'Isle and the Count Gerard saw the tents of the Grand Duke Michael Stryphnos, who was the Emperor of Constantinople's Admiral. They put the Greeks to flight and captured tents, stallions, mules and treasure besides. For the Greeks, more cowardly than fawns, complained that the French men-at-arms were soul-destroying angels and brazen images. The Emperor Alexios Angelos sent the Lombard Nicholas Rous to the Crusaders. He would gladly give them of his victuals and goods, if they, the best of uncrowned men, would depart : they were Christians, a Christian too was he. The Barons went aboard the galleys, sailed close under the walls of Constantinople from Bukoleon and Hippodrome up to the Palace of Blachernae, before the golden church of the Panhagia Periblepta and the swarming domes, and exhibited to the people Alexios swaggering against a mast. " Behold here," they shouted, " your lawful ruler." They returned to camp, each man to his tent. In the morning trumpets were blown, and, their helmets on their heads, their lances in their hands, they leaped on to the shore.

They encamped before the tower of Galata and in the ghetto, the Stenon. They broke the iron chain ; into the waters of the Chrysokeras the garrison tumbled, screaming. The Crusaders rode as far as the spot where the Palace of Blachernae rose up yonder, threw bridges across to it and built ramparts, ditches and palisades by the convent of Kosmidion. The Venetians were on their ships and prepared for the assault. The Greeks made sorties. Walter of Neuilly tied Constantine Laskaris to his horse. Then, near the sea, the Crusaders set ladders against an avant-mure, a barbican, manned by Englishmen and Danish Varangians. They fought hand to hand with battle-axes and swords. The baggage-boys and cooks had staves, clubs, choppers and copper kettles. The blind Doge Enrico Dandolo stood, fully armed, in the bows of his galley, the flag of St. Mark over him. The Venetians ran the galley aground and bore the gonfalon with the winged lion before them. Those within fled from the walls. Six-and-twenty towers were in the Crusaders' possession. They cast fire into the city and the flames licked up to the Deuteron and beyond.

The Emperor Alexios Angelos advanced into the plain traversed by a canal and put his army in battle-array. But he turned about, without permitting Theodore Laskaris, his son-in-law, to attack. He escaped into the palace and, round about the first night-watch, fled to Debeltos with one of his daughters, a handful of chamberlains, ten hundredweight of gold and the pearls and precious stones of the Imperial insignia. In the Palace of Blachernae, the eunuch Constantine summoned the halberdiers and arrested the Empress Euphrosyne. The mob went to the prison where the Emperor Isaac languished with blinded eyes, raised him to the throne and did homage to him as *Basileus*. With his wife Margaret, the King of Hungary's sister, he received the Crusaders' four envoys. He agreed to subject the whole realm of Byzantium to Rome, to give the army two thousand marks of silver and victuals for two years and to send ten thousand men and five hundred knights against the Saracens. Icons of the *Chreistos* were melted down, altars stripped. On St. Peter's Day young Alexios was crowned Emperor. At his court was seen the King of Nubia, whose skin was quite black; a crucifix was burned with a hot iron into his forehead. He had vowed to make a pilgrimage to Rome and Santiago in Spain and to die in Jerusalem.

The young Emperor Alexios was anxious lest, when the Crusaders were there no more, the Greeks (who hated him) might kill him; and he moved them to stay till March. Discord rent their host; then they agreed. While Alexios set out with a part of the Barons to pacify Thrace, a crowd of Franks, Pisans and Venetians sacked

the Mosque Mitat, the Saracens' synagogue, and set fire
to it. In the torrent of flame aisles and pillars turned to
ashes, fiery particles, torn away, flew through the air and,
with the holocaust fanned by the north wind, destroyed
distant houses. The Emperor Isaac bore his son a
grudge ; for while the latter was welcomed in the palace
by uproarious applause from the Cubiculars, Patricians
and Senators, only a faint echo welcomed him in his
blindness. Young Alexios caroused and diced with
the Barons. They doffed from his head the *sarikion*,
with its threads of gold, stiff with rubies, sapphires,
topazes, amethysts, emeralds, sardonyxes and opals, and
themselves drunkenly swaggered in it. Over the white
skaramandion, the purple, gold-netted *sagion*, the gold,
green and violet *chlamys* they covered him with a helmet
of shaggy wool. The bearded monks flattered Isaac
that he was the *Autocrator*, regaled themselves upon his
wine and fat fishes and placed his gouty hands over the
sockets of his eyes, as if he should regain his sight by
a miracle. The Emperor had the bronze boar of Calydon,
which stood with erect bristles in the Hippodrome,
brought into the Bukoleon palace. The multitude
destroyed the statue of Pallas Athene, wearing a helmet
with horses' hairs and the aegis with the Gorgon's head ;
for they believed that the goddess was gazing towards
the west and beckoning the hordes which resembled her.
The Emperor Alexios begged for postponement of
his payment. Into the Palace of Blachernae the Barons
and Enrico Dandolo sent Conon of Béthune, the Marshal
Villehardouin, Milo of Brabant and three Venetian
senators. They declared the compact abrogated and
were almost killed in the palace itself. The French
fought many fights with the Greeks. But Alexios
Dukas alone was brave amongst the latter, whom they
called Murzuphlos because his eyebrows had grown
together. In the neighbourhood of the Pierced Stone
his horse was brought down, but with the help of young
archers he escaped captivity. The Greeks filled seventeen ships with wood, brushwood and pitch and sent

them against the Crusaders' fleet : one of the Pisans' merchantmen was consumed by fire. Then Murzuphlos won over the eunuch Constantine, surprised Alexios in his bedchamber and bound him. He put on the purple boots and was crowned with the diadem in the nine-domed Church of the Panhagia. The Emperor Isaac died ; Murzuphlos poisoned Alexios twice and strangled him. Like a shadow his father-in-law Philokalios followed the new *Basileus* about. He judged the *Angeloi*'s officials and was ardent to defend the walls towards the sea and the gates towards the land.

The Crusaders beat Murzuphlos in an ambush, from which he turned against the knights of Flanders as they passed by with droves of cattle. They prepared the assault and took counsel : when they were lords of the city, six of the French and six Venetians should elect one of the magnates Emperor. The assault lasted until midday and was unfortunate for the attackers, who lost more than the Greeks. Then they decided that two ships apiece should advance against one tower. The bishops, the abbots preached that the assault ranked among good works and absolved in the name of God and the Holy Father. The ships " Pelegrina " and " Paradiso " over-powered the first tower. Through three gates the Crusaders pressed into the city. The Emperor Murzu-phlos fled out of his purple tent through the streets to the Bukoleon and out through the Golden Gate. The gigantic knight Pierre de Braiecuel, whose helm was like an embattled town, captured his baggage and his jewels.

The Marquis of Montferrat took the Bukoleon, which had five hundred rooms, all with gold mosaic, and thirty chapels. Of silver were the hinges and brackets, the pillars of jaspar and porphyry, the floor white marble, gleaming like crystal. They found the holiest relics, the iron of the lance which tore Christ's flank, the crown of prickly furze, two bits of the shaft of the cross, the seamless coat and a phial of Christ's divine blood. Henry Count of Flanders, Baldwin's brother, took the Palace of Blachernae ; the Doge Dandolo four gilded bronze horses, which he sent home for San Marco. The Barons cheated the small fry and the poor knights, who picked up mere gold and silver, dinner services and precious stones, silk and brocade, fur of grey and ermine. But they sacked the Church of the Panhagia, its vessels and lamps, the adornments of the high altar and the rails before it, the silver of its thresholds, the clerics' golden vestments. They packed whatever they might anywhere lay hands on upon mules and, when these slipped because of the mirror-like smoothness of the marble pavement, they were pricked on with knives, so that blood and dung fouled the sanctuary. The Crusaders dragged the purple cloaks through the streets and hung their horses about with veils of fine linen. They then took oath, under pain of excommunication, to give up what they had stolen. Further four hundred thousand marks were collected. The Crusaders feasted on beef and pork with beans, they gormandized, murdered, ravished the women and virgins who, in terror of them, smeared their faces with mud.

The twelve magnates elected an Emperor. The majority of voices went, not to the Marquis of Montferrat, but by the Doge Dandolo's craft to Baldwin, Count of Flanders. He was crowned and anointed in the Minster of the Panhagia and conducted on a white charger into the Bukoleon, where he throned in Constantine's golden chair. The Marquis of Montferrat bartered the Kingdom of Thessalonica of him. They became enemies, even to armed violence ; the Doge and the Count of Blois reconciled them. The French captured blinded Murzuphlos and judged him before all the people in Constantinople. They forced him to jump down from a marble pillar in the heart of the city, so that he was dashed to pieces at the bottom.

INNOCENT was in Rome again. But the Good Men of the municipality made war upon him for forfeiting the sovereignty of the city, and the Frangipani and Pierleoni sided with John Capocci. But by sagacity and money Innocent carried off the victory, as the people of Rome grew weary. But Lupold of Worms had appeared as Imperial legate with many followers at Ancona and with him Henry of Spoleto, Duke Conrad's son. Assisi and the Lombards had welcomed him. In Fermo Cathedral at Christmas the Cardinal Cinthius fulminated excommunication against the pestilent bishop. In the spring German companies augmented Lupold's following.

Fiery-bearded Dipold of Vohburg had fought about Terracina with Walter of Brienne, who got an arrow in his eye. He was defeated and retained of Salerno only Torre maggiore. The Count of Brienne slept in an unguarded camp when, at dawn, Dipold surprised the French. Unarmed they ran, a frightened flock of sheep, to their perdition. Walter of Brienne was resting under a heavy awning. The Germans cut the cords so that it crashed down on top of him. He was taken to Sarno Castle, a bleeding prisoner. He died and was buried in Santa Maria della Foce. Dipold entered Salerno. But Innocent persuaded him to a treaty, as through the Cardinal-Deacon Allocingola he persuaded Capparone. Dipold recognized the Pope's regency over Sicily, promised in war and peace to be guided by him and never be helper to Philip. He came to Rome, to do homage to sick Innocent. And, that he should henceforward do him no hurt, Innocent sent him to Palermo.

The papal excommunication was removed from Walter of Paleario, once again Chancellor and enemy to Capparone. Outside Syracuse the Genoese had defeated the Pisans and Raniero di Manente. The corsair Alaman da Costa was a count feudatory to Genoa. Enormous, as ever, was the confusion. Dipold stood before Capparone; the latter stooped before him. Dipold took Federigo from Gregory of San Galgano, the monk who for two years had been the young King's spiritual tutor. He conducted him into the city, to the Chancellor and to Allocingola, to whom Federigo applied for information eagerly and without suspicion. He invited the Legate and the Chancellor to the palace. Fanfares blew to the gorgeous banquet. Did Dipold want to use arms? Walter of Paleario had him suddenly gagged and imprisoned, with his son.

As in years gone by, Federigo was in the Chancellor's power. Once again arms clanked, when deceived Capparone conspired with Raniero di Manente and the Pisans (who had to depart to their ships) and Walter of Paleario sought to drive Capparone out of the royal palace. Dipold got away. He sailed to Salerno and hurled himself upon the Neapolitans.

Federigo, a lamb between hot, gaping wolves, the toy of intrigue, was schooled in precocious contempt. With Gregory, Magister Nicholas and Magister John of Traetto looked after him. Even at thirteen, he lacked the stature proper to his years. His blue eyes blinked. The Saracen Ibn el Giuzi instructed him in the brooding study of dialectic. He reached manhood in a brothel of Palermo, through the hands of an ebony-black negress from Tunis.

PHILIP had made his entry into Cologne, which he had assaulted in a five days' pitched battle with Otto, whom Henry of Kalindin lifted out of his saddle and wounded. The Guelph, a lackland King, had embarked from the court of the Dane Waldemar for England and boasted in the Tower that, once he had overcome the Hohenstaufen with English money, he would win back France for John. The Plantagenet gave him six thousand marks to see him to Brunswick.

The Pope in Rome, not minded to be everlastingly reconciled with the fair-haired Swabian, chose Legates for Germany—Ugolino, now Cardinal-Bishop of Ostia, and Leo, Priest of Santa Croce, a Brancaleone, whom he had already once sent to Bulgaria. They were to go to Philip, then to Otto. Wolfger of Aquileia and Everard of Salzburg were prepared to go with them to Basel. But from here, where the magnates of the Upper Rhine and Burgundy had assembled about him, where he invested Count Thomas with Savoy, Philip departed to Strasburg. The Duke of Lorraine and Azzo d'Este, *Podestà* of Verona, did homage to him. The Patriarch of Aquileia hurried ahead of the Legates. They met with the King of Germany at Spires and appeared at the royal residence in Worms. Next his person were the Chancellor Conrad of Ratisbon, Imperial Legate in Italy in Lupold's stead, the Archbishop of Magdeburg, Egbert of Bamberg, the Palsgrave Henry, the Dukes of Bavaria and Brabant and Henry of Kalindin. Ugolino lifted the ban of excommunication from Philip. The Hohenstaufen wanted no further settlement until Otto should have renounced the crown.

The Legates journeyed to Otto, dwelling lonely in the Hartlingsburg. Princes mediated. He had the neck of an ox. Raging, he paced the scrubbed floor. Like a Gascon he reviled the Legates. Swabia was nothing to him, Burgundy nothing, to become Philip's son-in-law nothing. They had a meeting at the Finkenherd, under the rock of Quedlinburg. The Hohenstaufen stretched out his hand to the Lion's son. Otto rode away through the quaggy ground, shouting out : " Only death will deprive me of the German crown ". But they agreed to an armistice till the following August. Philip set free Bruno of Sain, Adolphus of Cologne's rival, kept a close prisoner in Rothenburg-ob-der-Tauber; he made a sacrifice of Lupold's archbishopric of Mainz to the Pope's man, Sigfrid of Epstein. At the Diet in Augsburg he decided upon envoys to Innocent.

In March, headed by Wolfger of Aquileia, they were in Rome. A new quarrel flared up, touching Waldemar the Dane, Bishop of Bremen. " Exhort thy spouse ", Innocent wrote in charity to Mary, " not to favour the Bishop, but to avoid him as one excommunicated, nor to suffer that through him scandal arise in the Church, from which grave prejudice would accrue to himself." Again the King's envoys discussed the marriage between his fourth daughter, the younger Beatrice, and the son of Richard of Segni, now Count of Sora ; also whether the Duchy of Tuscany should be bestowed as a fief upon the Pope's nephew. The Hohenstaufen might approach for his coronation with the Imperial diadem. After the Feast of the Ascension Innocent removed to his summer-residence at Anagni.

From the Whitsun court at Aix-la-Chapelle, preparing his great passage-at-arms with Otto, the King proceeded to Bamberg. He had promised his third daughter Cunigund to Ottakar of Bohemia for ten-year-old Wenceslaus, his son by Constance, the Hungarian. Bohemia and Hungary sent him auxiliaries. Mary, who followed upon the first, the elder Beatrice, was betrothed to the scarcely born son of the Duke of Brabant. Now Philip married his niece, Otto of Burgundy's daughter, to the Duke of Meran. The hymeneal pipes sounded through Bamberg. Philip accompanied the rose-decked pair towards the Cistercian monastery of Ebrach. With a small retinue he returned to Bamberg. In the low-roofed palace, overshadowed by the cathedral, he had himself let blood and, about noon, laid himself on his day-bed. With him were Conrad of Scharfenberg, Bishop of Spires, and the High Steward of Waldburg. A knight, with men-at-arms at the stair's foot, knocked —Otto of Wittelsbach, in years gone by betrothed to the younger Beatrice; he was now courting Gertrude, daughter to the Duke of Meran and St. Hedwig of Meran, and the King had opposed the marriage with him, who was choleric and dull of wit. He came in with naked sword. He twirled it, caught it, balanced it firmly on his shoulder, after the way of jugglers. Philip told him to stop such tricks. "No tricks today", he shouted. Knavishly he threw down the fair-haired King and cut his throat. The King staggered a few steps forward, a jet of blood spurted up, he broke down dead on the couch.

The Bishop of Spires hid himself behind a reliquary of gilded copper. The High Steward had his chin cleft by the murderer. No one saw him outside; only Philip's brach, lazing in the sun, snapped at him. He

51

hurled himself on his horse and vanished with his men. The story went that Bishop Egbert and the Marquis of Istria, both of the House of Andechs, both uncles to Gertrude, had known of the murderous project : that knights in the bishop's and marquis's service had been recognized among the men-at-arms. Philip was buried in the Cathedral at Bamberg. His widow Mary fled wailing to the Castle of Staufen. She gave her clothes and her royal insignia to Spires Cathedral. She died of a miscarriage. The crypt at Lorsch, a Benedictine abbey in the Swabian Alb, was her resting-place.

A comet had flamed with fiery tail. In Swabia Count Hugh of Montfort robbed travellers ; and like him acted the Count Palatine of Tübingen and the Count of Urach. Henry of Bienburg plundered the monastery of Weissenau. In Verdun Bishop Albert perished in street-fighting between people and clergy. Every man's hand was against every man.

At the Diet in Frankfort Philip's eldest daughter, a child of ten, led into the Römersaal by the Bishop of Spires, proffered her accusation against the murderers. They were outlawed. Otto of Wittelsbach lived his harassed life on the banks of the Danube, near Ratisbon. The son of a man he had done to death pointed out to Henry of Kalindin a barn near Oberndorf into which the wretch had crept. Barbarossa's general himself transfixed him. They chopped the head off the corpse, and it was thrown into the Danube. The trunk was huddled away under the clods of an unfruitful field ; ravens, avid for carrion, croaked in the trees.

MERCHANTS from Piacenza, whom Hugh of Montfort had attacked, hastened with the news to Italy. In Mantua the Cardinal-Bishop Ugolino heard them, in Milan Wolfger of Aquileia, in Monte Cassino the Pope, who was suffering from the heat. He attributed the glory to the infallible will of God. But the decree of outlawry against Bishop Egbert and the Marquis he had rescinded.

Then Innocent concluded the betrothal of Federigo to Emerich of Hungary's widow, Constance of Aragon, Sancha's elder sister. With her little son Ladislaw, now dead, she had fled from her brother-in-law Andrew of Hungary to the Duke of Austria. By ten years she was her future husband's senior, as Norman Constance had been the Hohenstaufen Emperor's. The Bishop of Mazzara journeyed across to Aragon and lauded Federigo's legitimate descent : his father and grandfather had been Emperors, his mother grand-daughter of the mighty Roger. In Zaragoza the Bishop signed the marriage-contract.

At Christmas Federigo walked about the palace at Palermo, fourteen years old and of age. He celebrated his freedom by going disguised with Amineddal, the royal master of the horse, through the byways, into the *rabats* of soldiers, vagabonds and bawds trafficking in boys and wenches. An Egyptian woman looked him up and down and told him that, sold as a slave, he would not fetch two hundred drachmas—so debile were his limbs. He knew every language spoken in the harbour-district : Italian, Greek, Arabic, as for purposes of state and his court he has learned Latin and French. Rebellion still flickered about him. The wild beast Capparone had been tamed. Robert of Aquila allied himself with Dipold against Piero de Celano and his son Reynold, the young Archbishop of Capua. As soon as the gentle breezes stirred, Federigo rode through the whole island, as far as Catania and Messina. " The rebels ", he said vain-gloriously, " bow beneath the yoke of my dominion." He, not Walter of Paleario, would rule. He wanted to cross the sea to Apulia.

Constance of Aragon landed, not with Queen Sancha, her mother, who had died, but with her brother, the Count Alphonsus of Provence, and five hundred Aragonese nobles. In the Cathedral of Palermo Frederick Roger, King of Sicily, stood with her before the high altar. She had grown fat in Hungary, the irises of her eyes were rounded, and she had the voice of a pea-hen. She loved the minstrels' canzones. Dysentery from drinking-water aboard the Spanish barks carried off Alphonsus and many of the nobles. But Federigo suppressed a revolt in the east and took from the Barons the possessions they had, to the last, withheld from the crown.

He banished three prebendaries of Palermo, for embarassing the election of an archbishop. He read a letter to himself from Innocent, the guardian of yesterday: "We are anxious lest, led astray by those about thee, thou shouldst tread in the footsteps of the cruel tyrants who, rooted out of the earth by reason of their misdeeds, now of a surety endure bitter torment. Thou shouldst have contented thyself with the temporalities thou hast of us, nor stretched out thy hand for the spiritualities which it is for us alone to dispose of. Thou shouldst have been mindful, and have taken warning thereby, that such afflictions came upon the kingdom through the trespasses of thy fathers, who likewise laid arrogant hands upon spiritualities". The letter threatened him with God's wrath upon the unrighteousness of those who presumed to give him evil counsel. Federigo put his hand up to his smooth, rounded chin and gazed into the distance, with the eyes of the short-sighted and an acrid smile.

IN the Via Mojana, at the crooked wall, where the hilly lane descended beneath the stone arch, he heard a stranger who called out on his path : " Peace and Salvation ! " The stranger had a long beard, burning eyes and a torn cowl, on which a cross was sewn. A hermit, whom the cold new snow had forced to come down from the thorny thickets of Monte Subasio into the sunlight of the streets, bleated in peevish accents, as hurried as one who does not catch the echo of his words, and disappeared behind Tommaso Cecco's pink house.

Young Bernardone felt a pricking pang in his pale bosom. His friend Bombarone da Beneviglie was gone. He had no confidant ; for he anxiously avoided those who aforetime in debauchery had formed his pleasure-seeking retinue. A sickness of which he had recovered still weakened his body. Fever and a struggle in the soul had forced him to give up the foray into Apulia, the expedition to join Walter of Brienne. He had made a pilgrimage to Rome as a penance. Startled by the avarice of those who sacrificed at the tomb of St. Peter, he, the rich young man from the cloth-merchant's house, had emptied his purse, lent his clothes to a beggar, himself put on the latter's rags and had begged and hungered for him a whole day in the portico. He strove to make himself as lowly as a brother to the leprous. Whether he was treading the heretical path of the *Cathari*, whether he was still a son of the Church, he did not know. But he served her with perplexed piety in all lonely chapels.

Francesco directed his steps to the ruins of San Damiano, a squat chapel below the town, concealed by a wall of cypresses. On a clumsy stone altar stood a Byzantine image of the Crucified in gilded tin, with the brown, gentle head of an Armenian, the figures of those mourning about him small and narrow under the gently raised arms. The image said: " Come unto me ". Young Bernardone shuddered during his love-inspired prayer. He sought the priest, who was poor and old and toothless, gave him the money he had on him for the maintenance of an oil lamp and returned to the town. Pietro his father and his mother Pica, the Domina, knew nought of it. He led his neighing horse from the stable, seized a bundle of bright-coloured stuffs, strapped it together and rode to Foligno. He sold horse and stuffs to a squint-eyed fence and carried the proceeds to the priest.

The old man was afraid to accept young Bernardone's munificence ; but he permitted him to remain in a hut near the gate. The money Francesco threw into a corner. Night fell and rose up again in the dawn ; tenderly gleamed the head of the Crucified. When, weeping over the innocence of the morning stillness, Francesco walked out on the open space in front of the chapel, he was recognized. Pietro Bernardone learned whither the thief, his misbegotten child, had escaped. Led by his neighbours, he came to fetch him. But he did not find him. Francesco trembled all over his body. The noise subsided. On his knees he implored the dusky Jesus of gilded tin.

Then he resolved to go down and declare himself to his father. He had nothing more than a smock, he was hungry and feeble, his cheeks overgrown with beard and he stared about with burning eyes. At the Piazza children greeted him: " *Pazzo! Pazzo!* A fool! A fool!" they yelled and aimed stones at him. Bernardone dashed up, hit him in the back of the neck, dragged him into the house and left him to lie in an unwindowed room. When the merchant departed on a journey, Pica, pitying Francesco with tears, put an end to his captivity.

Francesco was to justify himself before the consuls ; for his father, who had got the money back from Foligno, demanded that he should be banished. Francesco said he was amenable to ecclesiastical jurisdiction alone. The multitude poured on to the open space in front of Santa Maria Maggiore, in front of the gloomy façade pointed to a triangular pediment and built of the reddish yellow stone of Monte Subasio. In the porch with the tympanum over it appeared Bishop Guido, between woe-begone Francesco and the patricians who followed Bernardone, richly dressed and paling in his anguish. Guido advised the accused before him to renounce his patrimony. Silently Francesco withdrew into a hole behind the fountain and, naked, a bundle in his hands, his limbs covered with a cold sweat, he emerged. " Until now ", he spoke, " I have called Pietro Bernardone my father. Now I make restitution to him of all I have of his ; from now on I only wish to say : ' Our Father who art in Heaven ' ". The multitude murmured against Bernardone, who hastily took the bundle ; the bishop spread his mantle about Francesco's nakedness.

Then the *poverello* exchanged for it a cloak belonging to the Bishop's gardener. He climbed the rocky paths of the Subasio and sang into the air a *trovatore*'s worldly song. Robbers hunted him and shouted at him : " Who art thou ? " He replied : " I am the great King's herald ; what have I to do with you ? " They tore the cloak off his back and, exhausted as he was, threw him into a ditch full of snow. He clambered up the steep ravine, clad only in a torn shirt, and sang the praises of God the Almighty.

WHEN Mathilda of England, the wife of Henry the Lion, went pregnant of Otto, a blind man, Engelbert of Zülpich, prophesied that one of her sons would become Emperor. Then he stepped into Otto's presence at the time of his sore discomfiture by Philip, bare-foot, followed only by a boy dressed in green and red rags, a holy man who never ate flesh and slept on hay or straw. He was known to have many visions. Thus his disembodied soul was snatched up into a horrible cavern near Maubach ; when it returned to his body again, the Devil appeared to him and hissed: "Thy body is forfeit to me". Engelbert called on the Blessed Virgin. The Devil insisted: "Half of his head is mine; for it was being washed when the bell had already chimed the beginning of the day of rest", and poured sticky pitch over his head. To the blind man of Zülpich went out the thoughts of Otto, now sole king, when, in Frankfort, all elected him: Saxons, Thuringians, Franks, Swabians and Bavarians. The divine judgment of Bamberg had pronounced for him; he straightened his long limbs, swung himself upon his Welsh horse and laughed.

He had English money, two-and-twenty thousand marks of it, which he had distributed to the greedy princes and the greedy *minnesingers* who now in their amazement lauded the Guelphic skinflint. And already he sent Conrad of Wilre, his seneschal, and Bernard of Horstmar oversea, to fetch fresh supplies from his uncle. "Show benevolence and condescension," the Pope of Rome wrote to him, "honour and mercy to all, dearest son, and eschew hard words and deeds of violence. Be not stubborn over concessions nor sparing of promises, but keep them faithfully too. Thou must fashion thyself after the way of Kings, watch over thy manner of life, put from thee all indifference and in all things be careful and vigilant". And he pricked him with dread of Frederick, the boy in Sicily, as of a rival. Conrad, Bishop of Spires, the new Chancellor, handed over the insignia of state from Trifels to the Emperor-elect. But he had to secure the Duchy of Swabia against the last Hohenstaufen down there in Palermo. From his court in Augsburg he rode with Henry of Kalindin, the Suevi's Achilles and Hector, who had done him homage, to the Guelphs' ancestral castle of Weingarten. The King judged five who had broken the King's peace, the Count of Greifsbach among them. But the Swabians murmured against his high-handed severity; and secretly the monk of Salem monastery went over the Alps to Frederick, the true, hereditary lord.

HENRY THE LION

[face p. 58

The King applied to Innocent to crown him Emperor and grant him dispensation—likewise a notary and a chaplain—for his betrothal to Beatrice, Philip's eldest daughter and a near relation of his ; the Pope reproved him. In Nürnberg Otto did submission to Cardinal Ugolino and to Cardinal Leo, who was ready for anything Ugolino required of him ; and Conrad of Scharfenberg affixed the golden seal to the document. At Whitsuntide Otto was in Brunswick. The Archbishop of Magdeburg ordered the Marquis of Meissen out of high mass ; abashed, the King left the Church with his excommunicated friend. He summoned the Princes to Würzburg to make arrangements for the progress to Rome. " Thou hast come, the desired ", sang the choir. Ugolino and Leo welcomed the King. He sat on a throne, opposite to him the Legates, at his right hand his brother, the Count Palatine.

He asked the assembly what they thought of his union with Beatrice. " It could afford me nothing ", he said with awkward tongue, " that I have not got already, least of all riches ; for, since her father's estate falls also to her sisters, her patrimony is small indeed. It is the Princes' wish, however, that I marry her. But even if I should live six thousand years, I had rather be unwed than take a wife to my soul's peril." In Latin speech, which the Bishop of Würzburg put into German, Cardinal Ugolino declared : the alliance with Beatrice was necessary for the good of the realm and for the removal of former dissensions and not merely allowed by the Pope, but the King's very duty. The Abbot of Morimund, wearing a light grey frock and the Cistercians' brown scapulary, rose : in spite of papal dispensation that marriage was against the ordinances and only to be atoned for by the King's becoming a defender of monasteries and the Church, doing justice to widows and orphans, building a Cistercian house upon his own domain and later journeying to the Holy Land. " For the welfare of the realm be ye betrothed ", demanded Leopold of Babenberg, and the Princes assented. " I will do according to your counsel ", said Otto. Leopold and Lewis of Bavaria led eleven-year-old Beatrice into the hall. Otto put a ring upon her finger and gave her the kiss of betrothal. He placed her between the Cardinals : " Behold your mistress ", he said to the Princes and Counts, " and honour her as she deserves." Then they debated about accompanying him to Rome or, alternatively, buying themselves off with a fine.

The Gunzenlech near Augsburg, which had seen the light of Philip's countenance, was the site of the royal camp on St. James's Day. Italians knelt before Otto, Milanese and Cremonese with their keys. The army set forth : around Otto the court officials, also Henry of Kalindin, the Marshall, and Gunzelin of Wolfenbüttel, the Guelph High Steward. They surmounted the Brenner ; the Duke of Carinthia, the Bishop of Brixen joined them at the end of the pass. Chestnuts grew and vines with green grapes, still hard. The Eisak roared through its wild porphyry gorge. The Dolomites reared up their toothed pinnacles. On the hot road, where the valley narrows at Ossanigo, the King awaited Ezzelino da Romano. He was the deadly enemy of Azzo d'Este, had murderously set upon him, his brother-in-law, in St. Mark's Square at Venice, beneath the pillar of the winged lion, had previously been husband to Speronella, who ran away from him when he praised the beauty of Oldrich of Fontana (whom he had seen naked in the bath), and to Cecilia, whom Gerard of Camposan-pietro had ravished. The enemies had their teeth into one another like mad dogs. Now Torello Salinguerra had freed Ferrara town of Azzo, and Ezzelino pressed the man he hated to beneath the walls of Vicenza, when the King summoned him to the rendezvous at Ossanigo. He approached in sombre magnificence, bluish-black of chin, as vassal to the Guelph, and bestowed a splendid pavilion on the Bishop of Spires.

The Imperial Legate Wolfger of Aquileia punished Florence with a fine of ten thousand marks and read recalcitrant Siena a lesson : " We are no more what we were when two at once called themselves King; to-day there is but one King, and he is Otto, and Otto again, and Otto a third time". Innocent complained of him. Since the garrison of the fortress Hildebrand put themselves under his protection, the King punished Verona, which carried on a feud against them; and the Veronese paid him many thousand marks and built a bridge of boats. He punished Azzo, their *Podestà*, likewise for the wrong he had done Montecchi. Ezzelino wanted to avenge himself in single combat on his taciturn foeman. They fought before Otto's presence. Drawing his sword, Henry of Kalindin parted them with his Germans. The next morning the King bade them ride in his train. "Sir Ezzelino!" he called in the *lingua franca*, "give greeting to the Marquis." Ezzelino put his hand to his hat. "My Lord Marquis, God save you!" The King: "Lord Marquis, give greeting to Ezzelino". Azzo d'Este obeyed. Otto let them rein in their horses to a harmonious walking-pace, and thus they became reconciled. At his night's lodging he enquired of them what they had said. Ezzelino flattered him and his *cortezza*. From Imola the King sent off Este into the Marquisate of Ancona, and he gave up calling himself "Marquis by Papal grace".

It was September when his envoys appeared before Innocent at Viterbo, by the Tiber's stony bed:—the Bishops of Spires, Brixen, Cambrai and Mantua, Magister Henry from Cologne, the Lord High Steward, the Lord Chamberlain Kuno of Minzenberg. The Pope, when they petitioned for the coronation, did not refuse. But Otto's patience was exhausted. He hastened ahead of his army. Thus did he, aged thirty-seven, and Innocent, aged nine-and-forty, meet together on a day of sultry wind, darkening the hills. The Pope looked into the whites of the Teuton's eyes. Then, with a sick man's shiver: "This is my well beloved son, in whom I have joy". He kissed him. He sat down with him in a gallery near the hot springs, until violet shadows overran the valley; and while they ate and drank, Innocent sought to win the Guelph to a new oath, which he stubbornly avoided. Only when the Pope desired him to make peace with the French did he wax warm : " I should cast down my eyes with shame if hypocritically I were to enter upon a peace as long as France still holds an acre of my uncle's lands ". The Pope recognized that this his creature showed him no gratefulness. He parted from him with sweet words of benediction.

To make ready for the coronation ceremony, Otto dispatched the Bishop of Spires and Gunzelin to Rome with the vanguard. He himself tarried with the thousands of mailed horsemen and archers on the fortified Monte Mario. The Bishop of Augsburg with his vassals, while contemplating the attic of Santa Maria dei Martiri, uncertain whether this had not been the pagans' Pantheon, was surrounded at the bronze portal by a mob of screaming Romans ; many received wounds, others broke down dead in the stinking chasms of the streets, among the painted ox-carts. The whole vanguard fled back over the Ponte Molle. The King held the Leonina round about St. Peter's and occupied its approaches, the bridge near Hadrian's Castle and the gate towards Trastevere. But there was no room even for the coronation procession. In vain did the Guelph hurl silver coins among the seething mob, did his myrmidons lay about them with staves and lance-shafts. On the steps of St. Peter's the Pope stood waiting for Otto, whom Ugolino and the Cardinals of Porto and Albano advanced to meet. During the supramundane supplications the tumult of fighting resounded, howled the wounded and dying. There was fighting too at the Gate of the Holy Ghost. There was no getting through to the Lateran. Instead of being his guest, the Emperor Otto invited the Pope, who was helping him into the stirrups of his charger, to banquet with him outside the city, in Isola Farnese, by the ruins of Veii. They dined in silence ; then they parted.

Sobered after excess of wine, Otto received the cross from the Bishop of Cambrai. He wrote to Innocent for a further interview with him. The Papacy was the sun, the wearer of the tiara had said to him, the Empire the moon. Otto laughed over his waxen Imperial seal, which to the right of his head showed the sun and to the left the sickle of the moon. And, since no answer came from Innocent, as a signal for proceeding to Monfiascone and Siena he brandished his massy shield with the three demi-lions gules and the demi-eagle sable, the Imperial scutcheon.

WHEN at the ford of the rushing Rhone one of Raymond of Toulouse's nobles killed the Legate Pier of Castelnau, when the dark, olive-skinned Spaniards had preached against the Albigenses—on foot, without adornment of gold and silver, Bishop Diego of Osma, who called down the hand of God upon the heretics, and Dominic of Calahorra, his companion—when the Abbot of Cîteaux proclaimed a Crusade, the Viscount of Béziers made ready to save his country. For he, the Count of Toulouse's nephew, was not minded, like the latter, to surrender his strongest castles to the Church, as the Pope desired; and in their castles and keeps his vassals afforded the *Cathari* protection. And he begged the inhabitants of Béziers to hold out until help came; for he himself was expected in Carcassonne. The Jews with yellow rings on their gabardines, followed after.

High above the blue-green Orb and the arched bridge, above the walls and the town, lay the cathedral. Thither went Reynold, its Bishop, and required the citizens' submission; otherwise, the army of the Cross would cut them down with the edge of the sword. The citizens refused, from obstinacy and trust in their lord. The Bishop mounted his mule and rode to meet the French, Norman and Burgundian Barons. They camped about Béziers, between the woods of cork-oak and the aloe-bushes. Their tents gleamed white and vermilion.

Those in the town sallied before day-break, yelled,

waved linen rags, as crows are scared from a field of oats, and threw one of the Frenchmen down from the earth-works. But the king of the beggars collected his ragged crew about him, the murderers and swindlers, the counterfeit cripples, who now stretched their sound limbs, the church-robbers and foot-pads, the blind who could see and the Egyptian vagabonds, and armed them with clubs; and they pounded to pieces the earthen sides of the moat and smashed up the planks. The citizens fled into the minster. The priests tolled the bells as a requiem. The beggars plundered house after house. The Crusaders pressed in and put men, women and children to the sword. "Kill all," said the Abbot of Cîteaux, "God will recognize his own." The beggars wielded torches, and the town was consumed in flames, consumed the brocades and carpets from Chartres, Blaye and Edessa and the accumulated valuables. The fire split the minster which Master Gervaise had builded; the corner-walls crashed to earth, blazing.

The Crusaders rested for three days in gardens whose little song-birds had perished, beneath the agaves' flowery candelabra. Then they departed for Carcassonne. The Viscount of Béziers beheld them—the Counts of Nevers, Auxerre and Geneva, the Bishops of Rheims, Sens, Rouens and Autun, Lothringians and Germans, endless ranks of cuirasses; and he advised that four hundred Barons should sally out on the swiftest steeds and, even before sunset, disconcert the foe by engaging them. But Pier Roger of Cabaret, who stood beside him on the ramparts of the Cité, proof in his scale-armour, was for surprising them in the morning by the waters of the Aude. There were many dead, many wounded in the dawn. The Crusaders reduced the lower town to ashes and cut the besieged off from access to the river. In front of the walls they set up catapults and mortars with stone bullets. Meanwhile, the crossbowmen's bolts glided from the towers into the trenches.

Pallid Pedro of Aragon, Federigo of Sicily's and the Count of Toulouse's brother-in-law, who loved the troubadours, advanced with a hundred knights, and the Crusaders saluted him. On his long-maned bay stone-horse he rode with three of his men-at-arms into Carcassonne. He bade the Viscount for leave to negotiate with the Crusaders. The Viscount assented. Pedro rode back and interrogated the Barons. They replied that the Viscount should depart with eleven others and what the twelve might have on their persons ; everything else to be unconditionally forfeit to the army. The King said between his teeth : " That will befall on the day an ass flies up to Heaven ". The Viscount would rather have been flayed alive. So Pedro turned back over the Pyrenees.

The Viscount and his men discharged a hail of feathered missiles. But they did not succeed in winning back the river. The wells dried up. The flies swarmed like a grey haze ; women and children lamented. So great was the suffering that the Viscount lost heart, went into the Count of Nevers's tent and surrendered. In their shirts knights and citizens, women and virgins came out of the gates and wandered to Toulouse and over the rugged mountains into Aragon and Spain. So many horses and mules were captured that they could scarcely be distributed.

Domineering beneath a mitre like a bishop's, the Abbot of Cîteaux took up his stand on the marble steps of St. Nazaire and said that the land must become the portion of a Baron who would hold it to the glory of God in such wise that the heretics should never get it again. The Count of Nevers refused it, and so did the Count of St. Pol, having land enough and living in France where their fathers had been born. The Abbot caused the combined votes to fall on the Count Simon of Montfort, the bearded Châtelain in still blood-spotted armour. He had accompanied the Franks on their expedition to Iadera and had a mad hatred of the heretics. he was gloomy and cold, with the teeth of a wolf. He remained in Carcassonne, while the Crusaders, whose vows were limited to four weeks, kept changing. For

65

fresh champions were perpetually arriving. The Viscount of Béziers, treacherously captured by Montfort, died in prison.

FRANCESCO and his band left the little chapel of Portiuncula, their home, their native soil, and wandered to the Pope at Rome. At the *poverello's* request he did not lead them. They chose therefore Bernardo de Quintevalle, who had been a rich man, had often lodged and fed Francesco and talked with him during sleepless nights and whom, because of an evil thought against him, Francesco had commanded to walk over him three times, planting his foot upon his throat and mouth. Among the brethren there were also Egidio, full of fury in danger, Silvestre, a former priest, consumed by shame for having demanded, when the poor received Bernardo's possessions, the money owing him for stone towards the building of San Damiano, the monk Pietro, the shy and stubborn Rufino, of good family, Masseo from the village of Marignano, Filippo, the long fellow whose lips an angel touched with burning coal, Elia, the mattress-worker, Agnolo from Monte Casale, delicate and weak like Francesco, the stupid lout Ginepro, who had left the plough to go with Francesco and who always coughed, hawked and sighed when he did, and Giovanni della Capella, who afterwards fell away from Francesco and hanged himself.

They passed beneath the Rocca, the Teuton duke's ruined castle, which now only looked down upon them with the rubble and crumbling stone of the foundation-walls, through the countryside in which the smell of summer-flowers floated, over chalk-white slopes covered with vines and olives. They came to Foligno, Spoleto and Narni, into the valley of the Tiber, and the rumour went that the Emperor Otto's army stood at the Mont' Amiate in front of the stronghold of Radicofani. They had brown cowls, with rope and cross. Francesco preached and sang. He begged too and, as he was nothing to look at, he received less than manly Masseo.

They helped the reapers, were content with scanty food, slumbered out in the open. It chanced that drunken peasants mocked them, struck them, pulled at their cowls in order to be dragged along by them, that they put dice into their hands to tempt them to gaming, befouled them with dust and muck. But in the majority of places, many gathered round the penitents. For the air was full of a new force.

They neared Rome. They strayed into the evening hubbub of the streets round the Porto del Popolo. Put out of countenance by the idle lookers-on, Ginepro jumped into a crowd of boys who were amusing themselves with the see-sawing of wooden benches. He joined in their sport, and many laughed, many reverenced his simpleness. With the brethren Francesco sought the great steps of St. Peter's and waited till the morning; for he wished the head of Christendom to sanction the Rule he had written.

It was strange that the first cleric they saw should be Bishop Guido. He brought the humble band to Giovanni de Colonna, the Cardinal, who examined them for several days, perplexed them with questions and advised them to join one of the licensed orders. But he was moved by Francesco's gentle, tormented eyes. And, since the unarmed spirit of these penitents could be no heretical spirit, he promised to commend them to the Holy Father. He knew too that Jacopa di Settensoli, a Frangipani, was a patroness of theirs.

Timidly they penetrated into the Lateran and into the gold-panelled room where the Pope was enthroned. He wore gleaming robes, and round him sat six Cardinals (among whom was Colonna), all excited by the news that the Emperor had taken Radicofani and Aquapendente and would shortly besiege Viterbo. "Write to the consuls of Terracina", said Innocent, "to see to it that the mountain torrent, rapidly dashing by, do no harm to their city." But he wrinkled his brow when the pale-faced beggar bowed down to kiss his foot, and he drew away the hem of his garment.

He exhorted the twelve and merely gave them answer that he had confidence in their great fervour. But Francesco began : " In the wilderness there dwelt a woman, who was very poor and very beautiful. A king took her to wife and had sons by her. When they were grown to man's estate, their mother sent them to the court ; the king would give them what they needed. And the king marvelled at their beauty and their likeness to him, and when they told him who had borne them he pressed them to his heart and let them eat at his table as his true-born sons. I, Holy Father, am that woman ; for God hath vouchsafed me beauty. And how much dearer to the King of Kings are his true-born children than bastards ? " Then Innocent recognized that this man was not to be fobbed off. Hesitatingly he granted him his sanction ; and he blessed the penitents and gave Cardinal Colonna orders to mark them with the priestly tonsure. The mendicant monks stood, a sombre flock, outside the gold-panelled hall.

THE Emperor Otto had given Spoleto to Dipold, the robber, the enemy of the Curia ; and he was collecting an army to wage war for Frederick's crown. Eight knights Faenza offered him, Piacenza twenty, Siena and Milan infantry. The Pope reminded him of his coronation-oath, that he would maintain the rights of the Church. " Forget not thanks," he admonished him, " forget not Nebuchadnezzar, who presumptuously trusted in his worldly might and for that was turned from a man into an ox and ate grass like a beast. Beware then, that God destroy thee not and pluck up thy root from the land of the living." The Emperor Otto answered that other oaths also laid obligations upon him. The Pope had nothing to do with worldly things. The dispenser of the Lord's Supper should hold no criminal court. Nevertheless, in Ferrara he outlawed the devil-worshipping heretics.

He left the golden state-insignia in the care of the Milanese and made ready his attack on the Hohenstaufen.

The Pisans were to supply forty galleys ; they guaranteed the treaty and, on Otto's behalf, the Bishop of Spires and the Marquis of Montferrat, Saluzzo, Carreto and Malaspina. There were no more Germans in the Emperor's environment. The Dukes of Bavaria and Carinthia followed him only as far as Parma. The Archbishop of Salzburg he took along with him up to the pass of Pontremoli ; on the gospel the prisoner had to swear that in any dispute between the Pope and the Emperor he would hold out against the former. Only then was Everard allowed to go. By the channel of the Tiber, where, near Todi, an evergreen oak-wood comes down to it, Otto joined Duke Dipold, and with him and Piero de Celano the Emperor pressed down the fruitful valley of the Garigliano to deathly quiet, ghost-like San Germano, deserted by all its inhabitants. The gates of Capua were opened to him. Here machines of war were constructed for the spring, here the army wintered.

During the first weeks the Emperor sat beside the Volturno, under fig-trees and pomegranate-trees, his gaze upon Monte Tifata or the stones of the Roman theatre, and he threw his cloak around him against the clammy rain. His heart was sick for the mossy green boulders of the Harz. At night he was often in drink. One night he dreamed that a bear crept into bed with him. The bear, to begin with, was small, then became bigger and bigger and even pushed him out of bed, so that he knocked over the tripod with the charcoal-pan and burned the reed mat. The Emperor was frightened : was that beast Frederick ? He called the Bishops shavelings, Abbots monks, women trulls and taxed harlots and bawdy-houses. In January he retained one of the women he had slept with, black Juditta, who had worn men's clothes, the daughter of a money-changer.

Innocent pronounced the ban of excommunication against him. A notary in the Archbishop of Capua's service communicated to him what the Pope had written to Philip Augustus of France, who proposed to divorce the wife he had repudiated, Ingeborg, the Dane: "Where is truth still to be found, where loyalty, where morals, where law, where reverence, where piety, where trust, benevolence and love, where, finally, the law of nature? O that the character of Otto, who calls himself Emperor, had been so well-known to me as it was to thee, dearest son! Then he would not so cruelly have overreached me. His impious pride so far exceeds all bounds that he openly proclaims all kings of the earth will soon be subject to his dominion". And from three or four German princes there came to him the messages of Innocent to them, which had reached Germany by way of Flanders: "Unmindful of our benefits towards him and of his own promises, he persecutes the King of Sicily who, as an orphan, stands under Papal protection. Unjustly he attacks his kingdom and other territories of the Roman Church, contrary to his oaths and written pledges and contrary to our rights and deserts. How high a value he putteth upon you, ye may sufficiently recognize by this that, without seeking your counsel, he hath set in train so important and perilous a matter, merely following his own opinion. Should he carry it through, he will humble you as low as the English Barons have been humbled by his English relations; bred in England, he will strive, as far as in him lies, to introduce the customs of that country into the Empire. Be instructed by me, so that it may perchance not go with you that ye will not when ye could and cannot when ye would". Otto rushed to the wall, to his sword. He was Saul, whom God had supplanted by a younger. And for all that, the blood of the Lion and the Plantagenets, he would overcome the beardless David of Apulia.

He ceased to negotiate with the Abbot of Morimund, whom the Pope dispatched five times to Capua. Duke Dipold, Piero de Celano with Tommaso, his son, Gentile of Manupello, the brother of Walter of Paleario (who, disgraced and removed from Federigo's court, meditated revenge in Catania, his bishopric)—they all hoped for knight's fees and counties; they were all impatient for the trumpets of war. While in the north Azzo d'Este fell away, Roger, the son of Richard of Aquila, wrested Teano and Sessa and Traetto from his father and became the Emperor's man. The Pope himself on Maunday Thursday read aloud the Guelph's excommunication and placed an interdict on every city in which he tarried. But the clergy of Capua celebrated masses in Otto's presence with hundreds of fat candles. The priests in Apulia reckoned the years from Otto's kingship. The Archbishop of Acerenza and the Bishop of Melfi went out to meet him as he advanced with his army. In white Bari, clouds of dust and festal reception: Alberia, Tancred's daughter and widow of Walter of Brienne, now the consort of Count James of Tricarico, hailed the Emperor King of Sicily. The Saracens of the mountains invited him to come over the Faro and had presents for him, vessels of silver and lances and silken garments of Araby. And they reported that a galley rode in the harbour of Palermo, ready for Federigo's flight to Africa.

Otto waited for the Pisans' fleet. Then messengers came from Milan and messengers from Germany. In Nürnberg the Dukes of Bavaria and Austria, Ottakar, Herman of Thuringia and Archbishop Sigfrid of Mainz had chosen the Hohenstaufen for Emperor that should be. Two Swabians, Henry of Neifen and Anselm of Justingen, were in Italy. Cremona, Azzo d'Este, the Count of Bonifazio went over to Frederick. Mutely, after a night of debauch with Juditta, whose witchlike singing sent him to sleep, Otto ordered the retreat.

HENRY of Neifen had remained in Verona. Anselm of Justingen and Herman of Striberg came into Federigo's presence in Messina. He laboured to talk German with these Germans; but, unfamiliar with their language, he came to a stop, and a peevish smile passed over his face, lit up by the February sun. Should he hazard the throw for the foreign crown and, in doing

71

so, forfeit the other he had nearly had snatched from his head? But in Constance's chamber Henry, his son, was screaming. Ships were dipping up and down on the water; would the vessel of his fortunes founder? Through the windows he watched his Moslem bodyguard and a Greek who had hauled some catch or other from the bottom of the sea and from whose bronze limbs the water dripped. Several times he resigned himself and was about to go in to his Aragonese wife, who counselled him against hearkening to the Swabians' call. He forced himself to be hard, adult at last; for the voice of ambition was imperious, and he knew Otto to be still at Lodi and many of the great ones of Italy faithful to the Guelph. He solemnly promised the Germans he would march. Then he summoned the Pope's Legate, Gregory of Crescentio, the Cardinal Deacon of San Teodoro and confirmed his vassal's oaths. That very evening, by torchlight, Federigo proclaimed himself King of Sicily and Emperor-elect of the Romans.

He set forth, after he had had Archbishop Parisius crowned King; and he despised the courtiers' whisperings that Constance's child was supposititious, her own having died soon after birth, just as he despised the legend about his own parentage. He set forth with Anselm of Justingen, the Logothete Andrew, the Archbishops of Palermo and Bari and officials of the chancery, after a hasty farewell from his consort. They landed in Gaeta. A month elapsed before they continued their journey to Rome.

In April Innocent, weak and excited, welcomed the son of the Church, the beggar-king; and ever, till the day of his death, were those eyes to stick in the Pope's memory. He entertained his favourite in the Lateran. He paid his journey. " By the Grace of God and of the Pope "—such henceforth was Federigo's style. For twelve thousand eight hundred ounces of gold he pawned to St. Peter's see, besides the land of the monastery of Monte Cassino and the counties of Aquino, Pagano and

KING ROGER II

[face p. 72

Sora, the county of Fondi and the country as far as the Garigliano. The senate and the people of Rome did homage to him. "Rome herself", said he to the Logothete Andrew, "despatches us to Germany." But Azzo d'Este and Pietro Traversari of Ravenna appeared with the news that on Palm Sunday Otto had been in Frankfort with the insignia of state and that, among other Princes, the Duke of Bavaria had renewed his oath of vassalage. Federigo grew faint-hearted, but Innocent fortified him.

Hired Genoese sailed with him to Genoa, where he stayed in the Doria's house. He became the city's debtor and sold it privileges. Amidst enemies he stole through Lombardy. The Marquis of Montferrat guided him round Alessandria as far as Asti. They of Pavia spread a canopy over him. He had to go over the Po. They of Piacenza searched every vessel for the hedge-king. The Milanese fell upon the troops of Pavia, killing and wounding many. But in the gray dawn Federigo swam the Lambro on an unsaddled horse. "He has washed his breeches in the Lambro", the Milanese scoffed after him. On the far side Cremonese under Azzo d'Este were waiting and harboured him behind their walls.

He was in Mantua, in Verona, in the valley of the Adige, in Trent. But suddenly he vanished in the high Alps. Then he appeared with the Bishop of Trent in Rhaetia, in Chur. The Bishop of Chur joined the Hohenstaufen's party; so did the provost Henry Sax and Abbot Ulric of St. Gall. It was reported that strange things happened to Otto. "The shaveling's Emperor is coming and means to turn us out", he had scoffed to Herman of Thuringia in the camp outside Weissensee, when the message from Wolfger of Aquileia was brought that Frederick was in Genoa. Otto had assailed Weissensee with the catapult and, in Nordhausen, consummated his marriage with Beatrice, the fourteen-year-old daughter of the Hohenstaufens. In the nuptial chamber she had died under him or—so one

73

rumour went—been poisoned by his Italian concubine. The Swabians had ridden off secretly, the Bavarians too. Otto's army had melted away. Now he lay with two hundred knights, his cooks and harbingers in Ueberlingen on Lake Constance.

Conrad of Tegernfeld, the Bishop of Constance, was reluctant to admit the beggar-king. He wanted to receive the Emperor, who had already sent on his servants. The Archbishop of Bari, as Papal Legate, reminded the Bishop, however, that the Guelph was excommunicated; and Conrad of Tegernfeld barred the Rhine-bridge and opened the water-gate to the Hohenstaufen. Blue-gray were the billowing waves, the Säntis gleamed on the Rhaetian shore. Frederick, cheerful after the menaces of his adventure, spending monies that were not his, was master of Constance with three hundred men. Otto and his train were chased out of Breisach by a sudden revolt. But he still had strength for a lengthy resistance.

WHEN the Crusade was begun also against Count Raymond—although the Pope in Rome had listened to his plaints, offered him Veronica's napkin to kiss, presented him with a ring of chrysoprase and a cloak and given him letters of peace and indulgence— the Basques, the people of Béarn and Comminges, the Count of Foix, Savary of Mauléon and many more lords joyfully came to the Count's aid. For they despised the wiles of Montfort and of the Bishop of Toulouse, the troubadour Folquet of Marseilles, who forced his wife into a convent, turned Cistercian with both his sons and renounced the *gaya scienza*. And they thought on how Montfort and Folquet had perfidiously induced the Count to relinquish his possession of the castle of Narbonne. The Count of Foix beat the German mercenaries near Mont-Joyre. Thereat Montfort waxed so wrath that, after the fall of Lavaur, he gave orders for hanging Amaury, Lord of Montréal, and eighty knights besides him. However, after Amaury had been hanged, the gallows broke; and so at Montfort's bidding the

Crusaders cut up the eighty with the sword. Amaury's sister Giralda, the lady of the castle, was, as Montfort bade, thrown into a well and covered with stones. Four hundred heretics were consumed by fire. The others lay before the walls, bound, the girls and women in torn clothes, with uncovered bosom. Even here the *Perfecti* prayed and stammered out the fraternal lore of the new life. They still said that Christ had had no human body, that wine and bread in the sacrament were not flesh and blood, that men and women who had intercourse with one another could not be saved, that Christ had flatly forbidden flesh-eating and oaths, that he had not come into the world to save all, that the laying-on of the faithful's hands provided the redeeming baptism. They said it in death, from which, for them, there was no resurrection of the body. The curse of the orthodox was vomited over them.

The Count of Montfort turned against the city of Toulouse. But Count Raymond had news of it from a spy; and at the same time as himself the Counts of Foix and Comminges learned of it. Five hundred horse and foot marched with floating banners out of Toulouse against the army of the cross, attacked it and retired into the stronghold in face of superior numbers. Under their walls they captured Bernard, Montfort's son. The Crusaders took cover behind their boiled leather shields and attacked. They of Toulouse were brave with anger, killed upwards of two hundred and pursued them up to their tents. In revenge Montfort destroyed their vineyards and corn-fields, turning the fruitfulness of paradise into desert, and had the trenches filled up with the withering vines. Hugh of Alfar, Seneschal of Agénois, and his brother Pier of Arsis, with men-at-arms marching shoulder to shoulder, burst from out the city like devils; and one of Montfort's best friends, Eustace of Canits, with multitudes besides, sank beneath their blows. Then up came clanking those of Foix, of Béarn and of Navarre as well. The Lothringians shouted: " A Bar, a Bar ! " and the gay animal-ensigns of the reinforcements fluttered. But the Crusaders were discouraged; and they had nothing to eat. Montfort raised the siege and plundered in Foix till the winter, which was very severe. The brooks froze, snow iced over the rigid peaks of the Espinouse.

THEY came through the woods. They trod into the extinguished fires of the villeins who once had fled hither, in rags and pelts, the women with babes at the breast, the peasants leaning on their axes, banded together against the cruelty of their lords, or stalking with rude spears beneath the roof of gnarls and roots; and the lords had overpowered the peasants, poured red-hot lead over them, stuffed them with tow, put out their eyes, destroyed the sinews of their hands and their hams. They were still children, who here marched towards the south. They knew that, when famine raged, behind these same landmarks robbers had hid, who tempted infants with an apple or an egg and ate them up. They had heard of werewolves, of headless men who came nearer the more terrified you prayed, of the hanged, who howled as they bent down the branches of the dark firs and clattered down to earth and to squint at whom meant death. But they were not afraid, their gaze was radiant. For they followed the shepherd of Beaupuys near Vendôme, fourteen-year-old Étienne, and were going with him to Jerusalem.

His father Jacquot le Bossu, the hump-backed, half-witted village pauper had disappeared with the army of the Norman Knight Gautier Sansterre that, impatient of the nobles, had set out, barely armed and with but a handful of horses among them, and whose glory it had been to strangle the Jews, the enemies of Christ. As it waxed so greedy of loot, the Hungarians had killed most of the plunderers, and only a small troop of them reached Constantinople. Red-haired Étienne, posthumously born of his pious, deaf and dumb mother, the botcher Maheude, watched the sheep of those villages by the Loire. Often he sat with the woolly beasts and the tiny lambs who staggered about his legs on a hillock under the hazel-bush, there where on summer-nights the unmarried met for love and where there were fairies and a magic root, which made you rich; you had only to be able to scratch it up without caring whether it screamed, and blood dripped from its wrinkled gnome's limbs. Étienne's heart leaped; in an elm he heard the voice of the Saviour, who bade him free his grave from the infidels. The Saviour appeared to him as a pilgrim and vanished in the evening mists over the river. He left a letter behind for him to the King of France.

For a year the processions had already passed through the valley round Beaupuys, and, as the bells pealed, Étienne joined one of them. His scattered sheep meanwhile had ruined the ploughland. He meant to punish them with blows of his crook. They threw themselves on their knees, they begged for mercy. This miracle decided him that very night, without bidding Maheude farewell, to obey the pilgrim's voice. Glorifying Christ, he proclaimed the Children's Crusade in the market-place of Vendôme. He had a peeled staff and a cross of green leaves fastened to his smock with thorns. Small children and half-grown hurried after him; and no one hindered their afflux. After many days they were in St. Denis—Étienne, Colin, little Nicolette and the hundreds of others—and slept outside the three door-ways of the crenellated wall, the tower of the abbey-church, tattered, empty, a-thirst. The monks refreshed them. Étienne and Colin, who was the son of a farrier, looked at the relics, a splinter of Christ's Cross, the swaddling-bands of the Holy Child, the sherds of a pitcher from the wedding at Cana, a bar from the grid-iron on which St. Lawrence had been grilled, the head of St. Dionysius. And Étienne performed miracles upon lame children, who dragged themselves on crutches to him. The abbot gave him leave for this; for, according to the testimony of the Scriptures, God vouchsafed the gift of prophecy to the shepherd Amos also. But Étienne did not see the oriflamme or the King of France.

The King of France commanded him and his crew to turn back, as the School of Paris pronounced against the boys. The Vendôme shepherd disobeyed, in ecstasy " O Lord God " he sang until night-fall outside the abbey-gates, " O Lord God, give us the true Cross again ". " O Lord God, give us the true Cross again ", shrilly and softly sang the thousands.

They filled the streets, the dark forests. They brandished banners, incense-burners, wax candles and poor crucifixes. Women and greybeards mingled with them. So soon as a castle or a city hove in sight, the children : " Isn't that Jerusalem yet ? " and the answer about their goal was : " We are going to God and want to seek the Holy Cross beyond the sea."

THE shepherd Étienne and the thousands marched into Marseilles with pilgrims' staves and pilgrims' scrips, Étienne on a wagon decked with carpets. They camped in front of the cathedral, the oldest church in Gaul, which the blessed Lazarus had founded, driven out of Jerusalem with Martha and Mary, his sisters, and Marcella, their serving-maid, with Maximinus and other disciples of Christ, exposed to the fury of the winds in a bark without sail or rudder ; but the will of God had steered the boat to Marseilles. They camped in front of the Paradis monastery. They wandered starving, the girls already with crazed eyes, the boys hoarse and enfeebled, through the narrow lanes. These lanes were black and dirty, the many wells allowing of no gutter, and ran down to the harbour, which smelt of rotten tunny-fish and over which the limestone dust eddied. The children chanted : " *Crucem sanctam nobis restitue* ".

The town of Marseilles debated how they might be rid of them. Then the tale was told that they had been deluded by clerics, who had been prisoners of the Sheikh of the Assassins and had got free with the promise to deliver Christian blood into his hands. And there threatened, if they had to be fed for more than a few days, lack of victuals for the people. On that account the town agreed to the offer of two shipowners, Hugues Ferré and Guillaume le Porc, to convey without payment, for the glory of God, seven thousand of the children on their ships to Syria.

Seven vessels put out to sea, already raised by the autumn storms. On the third day, after heavy weather, two ships ran against the rocky island of San Pietro. Or perhaps the black magnet-mountain bewitched them, of which the Saracens tell. Ten pillars carry a cupola of Andalusian brass, on the tip is a brass horseman holding a leaden tablet covered with maleficent charms ; and no one knows precisely the place of it. The other ships were steered by Ferré and le Porc to Egypt, where, in Alexandria, they sold the children with devilish rapacity. A portion of the slave-boys and slave-girls was taken to the Caliph of Bagdad. Budding Nicolette, with roses in her brown pigtails and a silver-edged silk cloth, checkered like a chess-board, under her walnut-big breasts, landed in a Vizier's harem. Or they died quick, unspeakable deaths, like Colin, whose belly was trampled to jelly by a camel, or Étienne himself, baked kiln-dry by fever in the cracked desert near the Red Sea, while in his tearful dream he was meeting his flock on the shady banks of the Loire ; later he had a martyr's name.

THROUGH Germany bands of child-pilgrims made their way, singing and shouting " Nicholas, Nicholas ! " He was a boy of knightly family, who had first shown himself in Cologne and announced that God had commanded him to go to Jerusalem and save the Holy Land. He had hair fair as honey and light garments ; and he pleased the women, who vied in giving him alms, and wicked thieves, who slunk after the children to rob them. One was caught and expiated on the gallows. The young pilgrims struggled, with cockle-shells in their hats and gaily coloured crosses on their clothes, through the towns of Upper Germany towards the Alps. Their number was swelled by adults, men and women ; there was scum among them already at Augsburg, and a house of courtesans emptied itself in the stream. Many of the children lost themselves on the roads, enfeebled by the piercing heat. Many collapsed on the Alpine summits or, if they loitered behind by themselves, were devoured by bears, attacked by eagles with sweeping wings. Several tumbled into the waterfall of a ravine or bled to death, their soles torn by loose stones. It was August when the pilgrims descended into the Lombard plain. There brigands lay in wait, smote them with the sword and threw them bare and naked into the wilderness.

The remnant came to Genoa, where Federigo, the young Sicilian, had been. They put their trust in a miracle. At the harbour they stared into the hot blue, which God would dry up for them, so that they might get to Jerusalem on foot, without hindrance; and as the sun paled they dispersed into the inns. Nicholas, unclean and (since he was now not far from his fifteenth year) with a sprouting beard, slept in the arms of the harlot Isotta. The morning dawned. The little Crusaders assembled; for a second day the Genoese would not suffer the strangers. The little Crusaders wandered on through Italy. In every town, every village they diminished by sundry, who groaned and whimpered and were glad to be engaged as farm-boy or maid. Many had their hands white and scabby with leprosy. Those who persisted in their madness were broken up in Pisa, in Rome or in Brindisi. Mocked and ridiculed, without chant or cross, they trod the roads home again, barefoot beggars. Nicholas was carried off, on a truss of rotting straw in Bologna, by the poison which Isotta's kiss had instilled into him.

PEDRO of Aragon had advanced and stood with an army before Muret; and he sent a summons to Count Raymond at Toulouse to hasten to his aid. Trumpets blared; the streets were thronged with armed men. The Count had the great catapults brought too. And when with the Counts of Foix and Comminges and the Seneschal he had joined the King, they opened the attack with great fury. They battered in one of the gates and took possession of the town. Against the castle they achieved nothing as yet.

But it was reported to the King that Simon of Montfort was to be seen with countless Crusaders—far more than previously—from Lombardy, Auvergne and Germany. From their camp, into which they returned, the Barons of Toulouse observed the mailed horses, the crystal sheen of helms and swords in the trembling air that floated over the green heights by the Garonne. Thus, unhindered by their enemies, the Crusaders advanced into the town, as far as the market-place, and into the houses, in which they found superfluity of bread, meat and wine. The King and they of Toulouse had a council of war on a mead of white narcissus, and then they shouted : " To arms ! " They charged the French with such impetuosity that they compelled them to barricade themselves in. They hurled arrows and lances through one of the town-gates, which was coloured red with the blood of the others and themselves. Then Montfort had the horses bridled and with the French Barons privily rode out of the Salles gate to fall upon the enemy or hack his way through to Autoillars. Bishop Folquet blessed them, and they spurred their steeds through the swamps, the beauty of their banners unfolded.

Pedro of Aragon was the first to perceive them and galloped towards them with a small following. He called : " I am the King ". But they paid no heed to that and smote him out of the saddle ; swimming in his blood, his coronet and plume in tatters, he embraced with all his length the loamy earth. Fear that they were betrayed swooped down on the besiegers ; they fled to the Garonne. Many drowned in its swift eddies. They who reached the bank did not draw rein till they reached the bulwarks of Toulouse. The Count of Montfort remained master of the battlefield, which was strewn with booty. In Muret church dark Dominic was offering prayers of thanksgiving to his God, standing in ashes, awry, laying himself on his belly, kneeling down and getting up, his arms stretched in the shape of the cross. A rusty iron chain girded his body, disfigured by pustules.

Count Raymond, exiled and defeated, left Toulouse. The citizens, lordless, surrendered to Montfort. He jeered at the ambassadors and took from them their liberties until Lewis should be come, the King of France's son, to whom he had sent the news. Bishop Folquet said the city should be set on fire at all four corners; it must be destroyed stone by stone, and forgotten. Montfort razed the walls and himself took up residence in Toulouse as tyrant. The Dauphin of France returned to his father; endless was the train of sumpter-mules and their drivers in the sunny valley of the Tarn, hauling the sparkling treasures.

AT his court at Coblenz Frederick, elected King of the Romans at Frankfort and crowned at Mainz with counterfeit insignia, had summoned the Princes to a campaign against the Emperor, against Aix-la-Chapelle. But at Whitsun neither himself nor the army was on the spot. In vain had he invested the Haldinburg in the autumn; the scale holding the Guelph's fortunes was rising.

In Aix-la-Chapelle Otto espoused Mary of Brabant. No priest conducted the bride to him, but the Count of Holland. The Emperor, heedless of the shavelings' king, was preparing for war against Philip Augustus of France. A thrashing he wanted to give him, whom he hated since his boyhood's days with Cœur de Lion, when the King had presented him with Chartres, Orleans and Paris and afterwards had jeered that he was talking of three puppies of his. In July Otto joined forces at Nyvel with his allies. They were the Dukes of Lorraine and of Limburg, the Count of Holland, Ferrand of Flanders (the son of Sancho, King of Portugal, and son-in-law to Baldwin, the lost Emperor of Byzantium, Philip's released, perfidious prisoner) and Reynold Dammartin, Count of Boulogne, Varennes and Mortain.

William Bigot, Earl of Salisbury, the brother of the prince-murderer John, stood with the English on the right wing.

King Philip began his advance from Péronne and took Tournai and Mortagne. He wanted to force the enemy from the sea; but as the Emperor regained Mortagne he had to retrace his steps as far as Lille. To the west of Tournai was the Marque, a little river emptying itself into the Lys; and its brown water lost themselves in fen-land. Only two roads crossed it, the one to Tournai, the other near Bouvines. If Philip could not get a footing on them, he would flounder like a sturgeon in the net. The Viscount of Melun rode out to reconoitre and with him Brother Garin of the Knights Hospitaller in Jerusalem, who had been consecrated Bishop of Senlis. From a hill they saw the enemy marching up in battle-formation. And it was certain that they must now halt and fight.

The French foot, the cities' *Sergens d'Armes*, were already crossing, two by two all the time, the narrow bridge between Sainghin and Cysoing; when there came at full speed to Philip, as he was resting under an ash near a little church, messengers calling out that the enemy was already pressing the rearguard: the Viscount of Melun and the archers were only withstanding the onslaught with difficulty. The King quickly had a mass said, took bread and wine with the Barons and ate a dish of soup with them. "This day, Sire, will see that I am a traitor", said Count Gaucher of St. Pol, who came second and whom the King had once before accused. The trumpets sounded, the cry went up: "To arms!" Philip pressed into battle, without the banner of St. Denis, which Gallon of Montigny was to bear behind him. The French had the sun of that July day in their backs, so that it shone in the others' faces. Round the King were William des Barres, the flower of chivalry, Count Henry of Bar, Gerard Scropha, Peter of Mauvoisin, William of Garlande and many besides. In the midst of the enemy's host, on the Emperor's four-horse

83

chariot, rose up his banner, a dragon, and over it a gilt eagle.

The furious battle began between the Flemings and the townsfolk of Soissons, the Abbot of St. Médard's vassals, who fought on foot. The Flandrish nobles despised the commoners from Champagne. But two of the boldest among them, Walter of Ghistelle and Buridan, were overpowered in the mellay. "Death to the French", shouted Eustace of Maquilin. The citizens of Soissons lifted him out of the saddle, and one of them drove his knife between chin and breast-plate into his quivering heart. St. Pol came, Beaumont, Montmorency, Duke Eude of Burgundy, who had a charger killed under his fat, lazy body, Hugh of Malaunaye, who crashed down and leaped up again. It was a hurly-burly of smashing, bellowing and stamping.

Meanwhile, in dull grey iron helmets, the infantry of the towns pushed forward, they of Corbeille, of Amiens, of Beauvais, of Compiègne and of Arras, thither where in Montigny's grasp they saw the King's red silk oriflamme and the lilies of France. But now the Germans thrust with great might against Philip. Reynold of Boulogne had already pressed through to him; but, in awe of slaying his liege lord, he had turned against Robert of Douai. The German footmen plucked Philip with hooks and supple lances into the dust, and he would have been a dead man but for his armour, in which they could not find a crack. Peter Tristan threw himself against the halberds. Montigny waved the oriflamme as he shouted for help. So the King was saved before the German knights had yet come up. The townsfolk relieved the left wing, which turned. Count Ferrand, bleeding from many wounds, was taken prisoner. He had to surrender to Hugh of Mareuil and his brother John. Salisbury was captured. The French pressed into the centre, up to the Emperor's chariot. Otto of Teklenburg shielded him, Conrad of Dortmund, Gerard of Randerath and the gigantic Saxon Bernard of Horstmar. Mauvoisin caught the

Emperor's horse by the bridle, Scropha thrust at his breast, once and again ; but the weapon glanced off into the beast's eye, which reared in its last agony. Bernard of Horstmar gave the Emperor his. He and the three others fell into the hands of the foot-soldiers. The Imperial chariot was smashed, the dragon smashed to pieces, the gilt eagle, without its pinions, laid before the King's feet as a trophy.

The Count of Boulogne, with desperate courage, remained in the fray. He had two rows of knights round him, like a beleaguered castle, and when he was exhausted he advanced among them, to break out anew. Only six were now left with him. Then Hugh and Walter des Fontaines and John of Rouvrai mastered him. As they were squabbling about the spoils, John of Nivelles came running up with his knights, who was fair of form, but until that hour of the day had not wielded the sword. And his would have been the honour but for the Bishop of Senlis, to whom the Count of Boulogne surrendered himself, begging for his life. For an archer called Comot had already deprived him of his helmet and was drawing his dagger against his abdomen and the joints of his armour. The longest to endure were seven hundred footmen of Brabant. They were brought down by fifty knights and two thousand men on foot under Thomas of St. Valéry, fighting against superior force like lions.

Night hid the crimson field. Philip had no thought of pursuing the defeated. He proceeded towards Paris. The reapers fastened their sickles to their leather belts and taunted Count Ferrand, who was driven in bonds past their villages, that he now was *ferré*, with iron on his hooves and no more able to lash out against his master. Count Reynold, who secretly sent counsel to the Emperor Otto to muster his army at Ghent again, expiated in dragging chains, which hung from a revolving pillar in a dark tower at Péronne. Salisbury was given by the King of France to Count Dreux, that he might exchange him against Robert, his son. The remaining prisoners Philip clapped up in the bridge-towers of Paris and in sundry castles. The inhabitants of Paris celebrated Bouvines for seven days and, with crackling torch-light, for seven nights, amid carpets and garlands from the houses and singing and dancing and sweet music of flutes and shawms.

The army of the Hohenstaufen, to whom Philip Augustus sent the mutilated eagle, crossed the Moselle, to profit by the Emperor's defeat.

THE Emperor's flags still flew from the gates of Aix-la-Chapelle, which had repulsed Frederick and would not receive him to be crowned, from the Imperial castle Landskron, which the keeper Gerichwin of Sinzig did not surrender, from Trifels, from Kaiserswerth and the walls of Cologne. Crusading preachers wandered through the length and breadth of the Rhineland, cursing the excommunicated Guelph. The schoolman Oliver pronounced the anathema against him. He, the schoolman, was the most fanatical of all. In Herten the villagers had set up a ram on a tree next to a pageant, had decked him with gay ribbons and were taking their places for the dance. He threatened them: " Hearken, hearken, ye disobedient generation, this very day will God punish your idolatry with such a plague that your children's children will yet tell of it to their children ". They remained hard of heart and hearkened not to his words. As they were dancing under a clear sky to the sounds of cymbals and flutes, fiddles and tabors, lightning flashed, thunder rolled and so terrific a hail descended that the village was greatly ravaged. In Bedum in Friesland Oliver was preaching on the Friday before Whitsun. In the air were revealed three crosses, one white one to the south and another white one to the north. A third showed the cross-beam and, upon it, the figure of a man with outstretched arms, his hands and feet pierced, his head bowed. And yet more miracles stupefied the wits of men. To a nun in Aix-la-Chapelle there appeared a deceased Count of Jülich, who had been a cruel enemy of the church, with dun, sunken face and spake to her: " I am William, sometime Count of Jülich ". She asked him how he fared and he replied : " I burn utterly ". As he lifted his garment the flames of hell leaped up from under it. With a cry of pain he vanished.

The Emperor no more set foot outside his lodging in Cologne, ashamed of his defeat and because he lacked the means proper to his station. He lived upon the alms his uncle allowed him from England. He sent messengers to John, to Magister Henry, the priest of Piacenza, and Magister James. The King of England paid a debt of two hundred marks he had made with merchants in Ghent, and he bought eighty butts of wine for him in Poitou. But the Empress Mary squandered her own and borrowed money at dice. When she passed through the streets, in her cap, her ruff and the open cloak with the brooch, her throat and the apples of her bosom uncovered, her brazen maids behind her, the citizens knew she was hurrying to the gaming-house, where she sat whole nights through ; and none made way for her, so familiar to the people was the sight.

King Frederick, in the chapel of Eger castle, had once more made oath to the Pope, his master, by whose goodness, labour and care he had been bred, protected and advanced, and had promised in a golden bull that he would extirpate the heretics. He held courts in Basel, where Burgundy came over to him, and in Metz, where, in order to subdue the adversaries of his kingdom, he made over the territories beyond the Elbe and Elde and in Slavinia to Waldemar the Dane. In Andernach he agreed with the Archbishops of Mainz and Magdeburg, the Papal Legates, to a new expedition against Aix and Cologne. Kaiserswerth fell, stormed by Count Adolphus of Berg ; for the walls were sapped. The Bishop of Münster, the Count of Käfernburg and the hostages taken by Otto were set free. Aix-la-Chapelle too fell the same day. A part of the citizens gained possession of the gates, drove the Imperial bailiff into a stronghold near the palace and received the Hohenstaufen with great honours.

Archbishop Sigfrid undertook also the second coronation, not yet with the genuine insignia, but in Charlemagne's cathedral. Frederick, now one-and-twenty, strode into the Romanesque edifice, beneath the candelabrum, Barbarossa's votive offering. In the arcade between palace and minster he ascended the Frankish Emperor's six-stepped marble throne. The Archbishop handed him sword and sword-belt, cloak, sceptre and staff, he anointed and crowned him. On the third day the great Emperor's bones were laid in a precious silver shrine which the citizens of Aix had had fashioned; it had a picture of Carolus Magnus seated between two bishops, and Frederick's picture too, inserted last thing. He divested himself of his coronation robe and drove the nails into the covering of the shrine. But after mass he himself fastened the cross to his shoulders. " We offer ourselves a sacrifice to God ", he cried, " in thanks for so many benefits." His example was followed by the Archbishop, the Bishops of Liége, Bamberg, Passau and Strasburg, the Dukes of Meran, Brabant, Limburg and Lorraine, many counts, nobles and knights. The crusading sermons continued.

From Neuss Frederick advanced on Cologne. The Archbishop of Treves was in Otto's city and spread discord among the citizens. They wanted to be rid of the Emperor, cancelled his debts and paid him six hundred marks to be gone. In vain did his adherents object. Otto fled, fled to Brunswick, the Empress Mary with staff and shells in her hat, in the disguise of a pilgrim; in her pocket rattled the dice. The city was released from the interdict. Nor did Landskron hold out, or Trifels.

Frederick made his entry into Cologne, he the King now, surrounded by homage, and the other the Lackland, Herr Otto. The Hohenstaufen sent Bishop Lupold to Sicily, to his Aragonese wife and his son.

From Cologne he addressed a letter to the Cistercian abbots. "And even though we be a sinner; yet, since through God's ineffable mercy the governance of the Roman Empire has fallen to us, may He grant us through your pious mediation the spirit of judgment and of truth, so that under us the realm be directed and ordered in such wise that Holy Church, redeemed by His blood on the altar of the Cross, may rejoice in the desired tranquillity of peace; and that when this temporal kingdom shall have come to an end we may be able with you to attain the Kingdom which hath no end and see decked in His glory Him who disdained not for us to be lowly and despised; because we tremble in fear not to attain this through our merit, therefore do we hope and desire that we may attain it through your pious prayers." On the Danube the fires of the Duke of Austria, the Boiler of Heretics, were already alight.

"MULTIFARIOUS vermin", so Innocent had complained before this Council, " is busy to destroy the Lord's vineyard and to such purpose that thorns flourish already instead of the vines and, as I sigh to report, the vines themselves bear nightshade instead of grapes." Now *Orbis Terrarum* assembled round about him in Rome: seventy primates and metropolitans, four hundred bishops, eight hundred abbots and priors. The Kings of Germany, France, England, Aragon, Castile, Hungary, Cyprus and Jerusalem, the great princes and cities through their representatives paid homage to his power. So overcrowded was the Lateran that great prelates were almost squeezed to death on the stairs.

The Pope opened the Council with the saying of Jesus Christ: "Heartily have I yearned to eat this Paschal Lamb with you, before I suffer"; for his sickness did not leave him. But murmuring was mingled among the voices of humility. There was debate touching the ban upon the English barons, the rebels against the scabbed sheep King John, whom the shepherd in the Lateran had graciously admitted again to the flock of the Church. There was debate touching the dethronement of the Emperor Otto. For him here were the representatives of Milan, for Federigo of Sicily those of Cremona and the other Lombards, the Marquis of Montferrat and Archbishop Berard of Palermo, with a parchment of Frederick's in his hand, which turned the County of Sora, Richard of Segni's fief, into a Barony of the Roman Church. The Milanese said that Otto wished to submit, repentant, to the Pope's commands. If the ban of excommunication against him were not lifted, there was no foretelling what might yet happen. The Marquis of Montferrat named six reasons for continuing the excommunication: he had broken his oaths, retained lands, protected an excommunicated bishop, locked up another, to the Church's disgrace dubbed Frederick the shavelings' King, converted a nunnery into a castle. The Milanese were unworthy to be members of the Council, openly favouring heretics. Abusive speeches were exchanged, weapons waved. In white array and scarlet shoes Innocent leaped up, wearily he raised the fisherman's ring with the image of St. Peter sitting in a boat and drawing in the net. He interrupted the session. Then he delivered his judgment: Otto remained excommunicated and deposed. In the circular colonnade round the hall echoed, but slowly growing fainter, the disputants' wordy warfare.

The Lords from Provence were summoned. Count Raymond brought his son Raymondet, whom Amand Topina had fetched amid dangers from England. And he himself endured much further hardship with him at sea. Count Raymond's spirit was of sufferance, not of mutiny. For that reason he inclined to hesitant weakness; and he would have submitted to the Church, if the Council of Arles had not then demanded too much of him: to expel the heretics from Toulouse, surrender to them all whom the Legate or Montfort might name,

POPE INNOCENT III

FREDERICK II

[*face* p. 90

pull down his castles, pay all taxes and revenues to the Church, fight against the Turks in a Hospitaller's garb and not set foot on his land again unless the Legate willed it. He waited, Raymondet beside him, his greying hair over his bent brow, the golden sword-hilt in unwarlike hands. The Count of Foix strode up and down like a soldier. Innocent climbed into his chair, prepared to hear; ascetically he chewed at a lemon's bitterness.

The Count of Foix took up his position in front of the Cardinals' seats and spoke: "The Count of Toulouse, my liege lord, has submitted to thee, Holy Father, with Provence, Toulouse, Montauban. But thy Legate has delivered up the inhabitants to torture and death, to the most cruel and furious enemy, to Simon of Montfort, who claps them in chains, hangs them and roots them out without mercy. I myself, according to thy command, have left the castle of Foix and its strong ramparts. I had bread and wine, store of meat and corn, clear, good water under the rocks and brave men in shining armour. I was without fear for my castle. There is no faith in covenants more, if I do not receive it back from thee. I honour Holy Church and also my lord with his young son, who is gentle and good; and we beg thee for thy just verdict". Then Bishop Folquet leaped up, red with hatred as he was with shame when at the King of France's board some minstrel played his troubadour songs to the Lady Azalais, and spoke: "Holy Father, the Count of Foix has said that he has severed himself from the works of heresy; and yet with him it has struck its deepest roots. He has loved the Albigenses and hospitably received them. Only for them was Puy de Montségur erected. His sister is a heretic since her husband's death. She lived for three years in Pamiers, and many have fallen away through her teaching. He has killed and hacked to pieces the pilgrims, the soldiers of Christ; the field of Montgei was covered with them, to the sorrow of France and thy dishonour. Whoso did this, he should forfeit the land". "And had I known that there would be this outcry at the Court of Rome," Arnold of Villemur called out noisily, "we would have cut off their eyes and noses ! " But a sign from the Pope made him hush. " I was never a friend of the heretics," the Count of Foix retorted vehemently, " never for a day was Puy de Montségur in my possession. If my sister is a heretic, I have nothing to do with her sin. I swear by the Crucified, that no pilgrim was ever ill-treated or killed by me ; never was their path molested by any of mine. But the robbers who bore the cross against me, them I marked on eyes, feet and hands. The Bishop of Toulouse, he, I say, is a traitor to God and us. With his lies, his deceiving words which are every man's undoing, and his smooth satires he, the monk and abbot, still remains the juggler. When he was chosen bishop, such fire went over the whole world, that never will there be water enough to put it out. He seems, methinks, more like Anti-Christ than a Legate of Rome." With his slender hand, round which the white robe was folded, Innocent calmed the Bishop ; but, however much restraint he put upon himself, it was as if a fist had struck himself. All was silence.

The Pope gazed at the mosaic of the pavement, the apostles Paul and Peter, both with gospels in their hand, the straps of their sandals woven round the toes, against a dull gold ground, with golden aureoles, Peter with a jutting, bare brow. There were little stones which ought to be lifted out and replaced. Servitors stirred the braziers of glowing coals. " Count," said Innocent slowly, " thou hast well set forth thy right, but diminished ours. I will enquire whether truth is in thee. Every sinner who repents of his misdeeds will be welcome to the Church." And, to the Bishops and Abbots : " But ye all are mindful of what I enjoined upon you. Be illumined of the heavenly light. Fire bring ye and water, punishment and forgiveness. Grasp the cross and the sword, the symbol of earthly justice. Let clemency prevail and eschew what is forbidden of God ". The

Baron of Roquefeuil cried : " Holy Father, have pity on an orphaned child on whom, despite his youthful years, the ban presses, whose father, the Viscount of Béziers, Simon of Montfort has killed. Return him his land. And if thou refuse it him, I shall demand it of thee at the day of the Last Judgment, on which we shall all be judged, sheep and goats ". " I shall decide ", said Innocent. He went with the Cardinals into the garden of the Lateran. Dark clouds veiled the Celio and the Aventino ; he shivered. He, the imperturbable, wavered ; in his limbs and his soul was sadness. Then, after hours had passed, he re-entered the palace. He told Count Raymond that he could do nothing for him now. He was to go and leave him his son. Count Raymond went alone to Viterbo. To the Count of Foix the Pope gave his land and absolution ; and he pondered compensating Raimondet with the County Venaisse, which was the Emperor's.

FRANCESCO had been discouraged and worn out, ship-wrecked on the shores of Dalmatia—whence, because he begged them very earnestly, sailors took him along to Ancona—and by heavy sickness forced to a speedy return from Spain. Rolling among thorns he scourged himself. In a skiff he had himself rowed on to an island in the Lake of Perugia, crept into a close thicket of sloes, the lair of an animal or a bird-catcher's shelter, and, after Jesus's example, fasted for forty days and forty nights without eating more than half a loaf. At that time, with his favourite, Brother Leo, who was in his third year with the mendicant friars, he was passing one of the castles of the Romagna, Montefeltro near Macerata. It was gay with the splendour and sound of a knightly tournament. But Francesco walked into the courtyard with Leo and, from a low wall, sang the verses and preached upon them :—" *Tanto è il bene ch' aspetto ch'ogni pena m'è diletto* ". A part of the company listened, and Orlando dei Cattani, Count of Chiusi, was so greatly moved that he offered Francesco a mountain, where he and the members of his order might abide, the lonely Alverno. Fifty armed men were to go with them, to protect them against wild beasts.

It was a peak high above the valley of the Arno, a sheer plot with pines and beeches, round which the tempest roared. There the brethren ran up a few cells out of branches. Francesco soared in prayer to heaven. But more frequently he abode in the Carceri, the rocky caverns hewn out of Monte Subasio, fronting the deep forest. There, too, a league from the town, several brethren had settled; a rough stone bench was his bed. There were now two colonies started by the order, the Portiuncula and San Damiano, and in San Damiano was its sanctuary, the convent of the Clares. Chiara Sciffi had dedicated herself to the gospel of poverty which he proclaimed, she and Agnes, her sister. She had fled to the Portiuncula on the night of Palm Sunday, and after matins he had cut off her hair and put the veil about her. Then the Benedictines made him a present of San Damiano for her and her companions; and Chiara's friendship was the love of souls to him, sweet spiritual marriage.

He loved God's creatures, more tenderly than in the year of the eclipse. On the road, with the brethren Masseo and Agnolo, he came to Savurniano castle; and as the swallows outshrilled his sermon, he bade them, his little sisters, keep silence until he should have finished with the word of God. He was between Cannaio and Bevagno; and he preached to the birds that sat on fields and trees. "Ye birds, my dear sisters," he spake, "greatly obliged are ye to God who created you. Ye sew not and reap not, and yet he keepeth you. For that ye should ever praise and magnify him." And they opened their beaks, stretched their necks, fluttered with their wings. He made the sign of the Cross over them as over men, and they flew away with song, one flock to the east, one to the west, one to the south, one to the north, vertical and horizontal like the arms of the cross.

FREDERICK kept his court at Würzburg. By his side, brown of beard and burly as a ploughman, in the white cloak with the black cross, stood Herman of Salza, the Master of the Teutonic Order, the chief of that pious chivalry, who had come from the Holy Land and of whom the King doubtless had need, in respect of his expedition overseas. Was the quiet, loyal Master destined for the youth's adviser? Peter de Sasso, Cardinal Preacher of Santa Pudentia, was drawing near, in the capacity of Papal Legate. And Engelbert of Berg took his place amid the nobles of the realm, the new Archbishop of Cologne, who received the regalia here and was confirmed by the Legate, not the King.

Federigo was elsewhere with his thoughts. The Abbot of St. Gall was secretly negotiating on his behalf in Rome. Now the Council of the Church had pronounced for him, he wished his five-year-old son Henry to come to him in Germany. Two crowns on the boy's, on his own head; he was uncertain and calculated with the bland deliberation of cunning. "Your Eminence, grant me audience", he begged the Cardinal and went apart with him. Wrinkled Peter de Sasso had a message for him. The two crowns were to be separated. He himself might no longer be King of Sicily, was to release Henry from his paternal authority. That was the inspired will of St. Peter's successor.

News came from Apulia. With the Colonna and the Lords of Supino, Count Roger of Fondi had risen against Innocent and been overcome; over four hundred human beings of every age were burnt to death at the taking of Morolo castle. Dipold, Duke of Spoleto, sought to make inroads into the kingdom. He was recognized near the Tiber by his flame-coloured beard, the Roman Senator had him in keeping and released the Pope's enemy for ransom. Now he was fighting again on the scene of his exploits. In July King Federigo submitted to all the Pope's demands; till Henry should be of age he would hand over the regency in Sicily to an administrator of the Church. Albert of Everstein, related to his queen, Hungary's widow, departed with her, with Henry, with Berard Archbishop of Palermo and the Imperial Admiral William Porcus for Germany, by sea as far as Santa Eufemia in Calabria. Innocent was reported in Umbria, enjoining peace for the sake of the Crusade.

He was in Perugia and in San Lorenzo's consecrated the altar of St. Herculanus. A fever overtook him. Pope Innocent died. In the cathedral James de Vitry, Bishop of Acre, saw the corpse from which thieves had by night stolen the gold-worked vestments. The corpse was bare, surrounded by the breath of corruption. The Bishop of Acre reflected with awe on the vanity of this world's glory. Sixteen Cardinals were present at the funeral. A marble sarcophagus, near the window by which the altar of St. Herculanus also stood, withdrew Innocent's remains from sight.

As the Perugians were urgent, the Cardinals proceeded to the Papal election. They proclaimed Cencius Savelli, the Cardinal Priest of San Giovanni and San Paolo, under the style of the third Honorius. James de Vitry supported the decrepit old man, who was bowed with age and had made over almost all his goods to the poor. In him the College did honour to the Church's treasurer, the author of its rent roll. But it was notorious that the dominion would be exercised under him by the Cardinal Bishop Ugolino of Ostia.

Frederick wept over his guardian's passing; then he threw back his head with the reddish curls, and his short-sighted eyes gleamed. He was campaigning near Goslar and Quedlinburg. In late, dark autumn he set out for Leipzig and Nürnberg, to welcome the queen and his son. The former had come by land, Henry by ship by way of Gaeta to Genoa. From the convent of San Peregrino the *Podestà* Frogerio da Correggio brought him to the centre of the bridge over the Guiligna. Thence envoys from Reggio and Parma conducted him to his mother. December snow lay over Franconia, near the gates by the Pegnitz. Federigo showed the widow of Hungary every courtesy. As yet he had hardly touched a woman in Germany. In the darkness of the castle he tore the silk coverings of Constance's couch to ribbons. When his lust was slaked, he departed into the bath-room, where by torchlight the maids poured tepid water into the tub, where they washed him, refreshed his weariness with spiced drink and crowned him with a wreath of dried flowers. He rewarded with bracteates a minstrel singing of Tristram of Lyonesse and the swallows with Iseult's fair hair.

POPE HONORIUS had admonished the princes to stand by King Frederick and extended the term for his crusade. Frederick showed no sign of fulfilling the vow made on his coronation day. His envoys were in Rome, the Marquis of Montferrat, the Abbot of St. Gall, the Dean of Spires cathedral, the keeper of San Miniato; and Honorius replied to them, he should so demean himself that the love of the Church for him be not weakened. Without him the pilgrims departed, King Andrew of Hungary, the Dukes of Austria and Meran, the Bishops and Counts from Friesland, from the Rhine and from Westphalia. After three months they returned disheartened, the King of Hungary excommunicated by the Patriarch of Jerusalem.

The Landgrave Herman of Thuringia, who had four times broken his word between Philip and the Guelph, had, in going over to Frederick, hoped for the possession of Nordhausen. He was preparing to betray Frederick to Otto, who perhaps was stretching himself for his last leap. The Landgrave Herman died suddenly in Gotha. He was bewailed by the singers, who, allured by Herman's liberality, had competed in the Wartburg, together with Klingsor, the Hungarian magician. His first son, of the same name, was dead. Lewis, the younger, not yet seventeen, had himself invested by the Hohenstaufen. He was pious, like his bride Elisabeth, the daughter of Andrew. No singer now knocked at the Wartburg gate and was entertained in kitchen and wardrobe.

Otto crossed the Elbe and devastated the villages and towns of Archbishop Albert. The Hohenstaufen advanced through the Harz to meet him. Near Gernrode they avoided one another. Frederick gained neither the castle of Quedlinburg, occupied by the Imperial captain Cæsarius with robbers and outlaws, nor Otto's place of refuge, the stronghold Brunswick. During the winter the Marquis of Brandenburg and the Count of Anhalt notified the Guelph that they had renounced allegiance to him. In Bokel arose the peasant Obert and confounded the people with miraculous cures.

Otto burnt down Aschersleben. In May he went from the Harlingsburg to the Harzburg. With a brew of herbs he purged his entrails. A flux rent him, he felt death upon him. He heard Woden's Chase, heard horns and the barking of hounds : and again the screaming of many devils and imps, dragging his soul down into the mountain Volcano and forcing him to drink from a red-hot goblet. He summoned the Abbot of Walkenried that he might lift the ban of excommunication from him. He tottered in his terror.

The Abbot of Walkenried tarried. The Emperor sent for the Provost of the Cistercian nuns of St. Burchardi's at Halberstadt. "I will obey the Pope", he panted. The Provost gave him the host and unction. The Emperor became a wretched skeleton. Then the Abbot arrived. The Emperor commanded the doors of his apartment in the castle to be shut. Only the priests were to stay and Mary, the Empress. Dully sounded the *Media in Vita*. The Emperor stretched himself out on the floor at the Abbot's feet, confessed his sins and acknowledged that he had taken the Cross straightway upon his coronation in Rome ; but the wiles of Satan had hindered him from setting forth. From his breast, bathed in cold sweat, Mary undid the Cross. He yelled that they should chastise him with rods. The priests sang the *Miserere* and stroked him. "Scourge me to the blood", he shouted in his madness and himself seized the thorny staves. The priests whipped him till, covered with weals, he sank into a deep swoon.

He died after administration of the eucharist by the hand of Bishop Sigfrid of Hildesheim and was buried, as he had ordained the day before, with a crown which he had had made against his death, in a Saracen cloak, with orb and sword, by the choir of St. Blasius in Brunswick. A nun of St. Burchardi's had a vision: the Emperor besought that his remains might be freed from taint of sin in Rome. Mary the Empress departed, shrilly laughing.

COUNT RAYMOND was in Spain, to fetch support; and meanwhile eighteen-year-old Raimondet fought for the inheritance kept from him, and faithful to him were Guy de Cavaillon, Dragonet, Guiraud Adhemar and his son Guiraudet. They set out to besiege Beaucaire. But the citizens sent them the keys of the town gates. They of Avignon came by ship along the Rhone and they of Tarascon likewise, and they rejoiced in their beloved lord.

In the stronghold of Beaucaire sat Montfort's men, the Seneschal Lambert of Limoux, William of Lamette, and Bernard Adalbert. They made a sortie, galloped through the streets and shouted: " Montfort, Montfort ! " A tumult ensued. There was hurling of spears, lances and darts, smiting with axes, clubs and swords. Rolling stones from the attic windows, they of Beaucaire crushed the knights' shields and breastplates and compelled them to return to their keep. Raymond's army was camped behind pallisades near Ste. Paque; a fleet rode before the rocky bank. They of Beaucaire had set afire the slopes under the castle. The French, suffocated by flames and smoke, were already treating for evacuation.

The townsfolk were waiting for the surrender. Meanwhile they of Beaucaire built a rampart of bricks, with a double gallery and stairs. When the stars of night paled, in the colourless dawn, women and damsels were hauling up water, looking after the water-level and the pulleys and singing the troubadours' ballads as they worked. The camp near Ste. Paque was surrounded with defences against Montfort. The garrison of the keep could not get to the river any more, to fetch water for themselves or their mounts. But the city had oxen

and cows in abundance, pigs and sheep, geese and hens, partridges and turkeys, game and flour and the varied wine of Genestet, the wine of the perfumed country.

Simon of Montfort oppressed the citizens of Toulouse whom he knew attached to their lord. Count Raymond was on his way from Spain; and they sent messengers to him. He set forth to free them. The Count of Comminges went ahead to secure the roads and gorges. When they had come outside Toulouse they could not see, so thick was the fog. But amid prayers and tears they made out in imagination the pinnacles of the city. Jean and Raimon Bellenguyer and other citizens went forth to meet the Count. Then banners were waved and music sounded. Many kissed the Count's coat and shoes. Everyone took up arms, and so they slew them who had sworn to the French.

Simon of Montfort found the city barred. He let off a vast machine, called *Chat*, the Cat, in order to destroy the brick walls. But sickness beset him; and he was wroth with Bishop Folquet, who reproached him with ill words. On the day after John the Baptist's, his brother Guy fell down on the boards of the Cat, pierced by an arrow. Simon knew now that God cursed him, God hated him; and he yearned to get away from this war, to turn Knight Hospitaller. While Guy of Montfort was still groaning, women were winding a catapult in St. Sernin's church, under a service-tree. The stone flew through the air, dashed against Simon's helmet, crushed skull, eyes, forehead and jaws. Simon of Montfort died, bloody and black.

At the gallop, the knights Gaucelin and Rainier rode up and concealed the corpse under a great blue scarf. Fear and terror seized on the army.

FREDERICK had led the Duke of Lorraine as a captive with him for months on end, before allowing him to return home from his board. In Goslar, on St. John's day, Otto's brother delivered up the insignia of state against eleven thousand marks of silver. Now, in

September, Frederick kept his court at Hagenau. Thither, through the russet woods, came the Marquis of Montferrat, Bishop James of Turin and Honorius's envoy, the Sub-Deacon Alatrin, a Spaniard.

Frederick smiled his smile of impatience. The weasel-nosed Spaniard was, following upon the Prior of Santa Maria Nuova, the second messenger whom the Pope had sent to him. Up till Michaelmas, not far off now, Honorius had granted him fresh delay for the Crusade, and he had thanked the Holy Father—not however as he spoke to Innocent, but rather with the quick arrogance of youth. The Pope had had to move his quarters to Rieti. People molested him in Rome; in Viterbo itself he was probably safer. "The Holy Father", Frederick said to Alatrin, "does amiss if he believes them who slander me as an offender against the Roman Church, which nourished me with her milk and finally, with God's help, brought me up to more solid food. I say with clear conscience: If, according to the Princes' council, my son the Duke of Swabia is chosen King of Germany, it will be done in order that during my absence better rule be exercised to the glory of Christ. Nor have I meddled with ecclesiastical elections, laid hands on the *patrimonium Petri*. The Marquis, the Bishop of Turin are my witnesses that I demanded no oath of allegiance from them of Ferrara." "Rainer of Spoleto", maintained the Sub-Deacon, "has subscribed himself Duke of Spoleto." "That", said Frederick, with equanimity, "is the custom in Germany among the sons of Dukes. Never did I give him that title. It may be too that notaries in my chancery employ antiquated documents in treating with the cities." And he called the Capuan to his side, to whom for the first time he had just entrusted a seal, mute Peter of Vinea: "The inhabitants of Narni and Spoleto are to be informed that they must not rebel against the Holy Father; severely I enjoin it upon them".

Peter of Vinea went. Alatrin intoned: "The Christian army outside Damietta asks for speedy succour.

Delay has twice been granted you and yet you do not prepare against your crusade. Hasten, says the Holy Father through me, to conclude the mighty work commenced by your grandfather of glorious memory ". Frederick started, flattered by these words and with a sudden evil memory from earlier than his birth. Then he promised to man galleys for the crusaders whom Honorius had commanded to sail from Genoa to Egypt. Alatrin communicated the last demand: from the moment of the Imperial coronation Henry alone was to wear the crown of Sicily and, since he was not of age, a regent be appointed for him by the Pope in conjunction with Frederick. Frederick bluntly declined.

The Bishops of Faenza and Reggio announced his speedy arrival to Damietta. Count Matthew followed with eight galleys. At his court at Nürnberg Frederick committed Burgundy to his son. It was said that the Duke of Lorraine had been poisoned with a drink given him by a courtesan in the king's pay.

FREDERICK reported to the Pope that without his privity the princes of Germany at Frankfurt had elected Henry their king. "Far be it", he wrote, "that the Empire have aught in common with the Kingdom or that, by reason of this election, we unite them. Rather will we strive with all our powers against such union coming to pass in other days." Alatrin was in Frankfort, likewise Conrad of Urach, the German Cardinal Bishop of Porto, who sought to move the crusaders to fight not overseas, but against the hated Albigenses. The Court-Chancellor Conrad of Scharfenberg, Bishop of Metz and Spires, as Imperial Legate, made ready the King's way through Italy, and Alatrin went with him.

Frederick and Constance bade their nine-year-old son farewell at Augsburg. He left him in the charge of Henry of Neifen. Engelbert of Cologne he appointed his guardian and governor of Germany and Burgundy. He embraced Henry with brief, surging tenderness.

Only they who had taken the Cross departed with him, at their head the Duke of Bavaria and Anselm of Justingen, Imperial Marshall since Henry of Kalindin's death. In Bolzano the Bishops of Passau, Brixen and Trent joined the King. Into his camp near Verona, there where adventurously he had crept his way through to the north, there came to him the notary Peter of Salerno, despatched by Honorius. Frederick did church-penance, as the Pope counselled him. " I am his debtor to all eternity ", he said to vagrant Alatrin. He crossed the Po near Borgoforte. Now he was in Spilimbergo, now by the Reno. Even outlawed Milan did him homage. But the Genoese disappeared, in a passion at the privileges of which he was defrauding them and at those he was granting Pietro Ziani, the Doge of Venice. And Honorius was dissatisfied with the Imperial Legate's negligence in the restitution of papal property.

Rebellious Rome had propitiated the Holy Father. To him Frederick sent Herman of Salza, the protonotary Henry of Tann and Bishop William of Como. Once again, in the presence of Alatrin and the Cardinal Bishop of Tusculum, he confirmed the Church's feudal lordship over Sicily. Like the Guelph he camped on Monte Mario. On St. Cecilia's day he was received for the solemnity of his coronation. November veils floated about the Sabine Hills. At the Tiber bridge Frederick confirmed by oath the Roman municipality's statutes. Peter of Vico, the Prefect, marched in front with the sword. The hymns of the clergy resounded. On the steps of St. Peter's, amidst the Cardinals, the Pope enthroned ; for kissing of his feet and gifts, Christ's deputy gave his kiss ; then the coronation oath in the side-church Sancta Maria in Turri. The canons put the Imperial vestments on Frederick, the cloak with Arabic inscription from the silk weavers' in Palermo, on whose panels the lion was destroying the camel, the alb with the purple border, into which gold and silver had been broidered, the blue dalmatic with the pictures of Jesus, the disciples, the Baptist, the apostles and the

saints, with the plants and flowers of Paradise. The silver gate of St. Peter's sprang open before Frederick. At St. Mark's altar Honorius anointed him, crowning him at the high altar, gently trembling. "All hail to the illustrious Emperor of the Romans! Victory be his!" the assembly cried out. Frederick looked out over them. He saw, too, Sicilian magnates, Walter of Paleario, Bishop of Catania, the Abbot of Monte Cassino, the Counts Roger of Aquila and Richard of Celano. He was very inattentive during Constance's coronation with a crown and a mitre of the Arab Isa-Ibn-Gabir, from the pearl rings of which plaited ribbons flowed down. Stripped of his pomp, he had to be serving-priest to the Pope at the high altar. Afterwards he guided Honorius's horse as far as Sancta Maria Trans-portana. Without him he rode back to Monte Mario.

Once again he took the Cross from Ugolino's hands. He vowed he would sail oversea in August. For the honour of God and His Church he would proceed against the heretics, the *Cathari*, Patarenes, Leonists, Speronists and Arnaldists, as likewise against their harbourers and patrons. Should the temporal power fail, the faithful were authorized to extirpate them on their own account. For it was worse to offend against divine than against terrene majesty. Once again Honorius and the Emperor met; and the Pope admonished Andrew of Hungary no longer to withhold from his brother Emerich's widow her jewels and her dowry to the value of two counties. As on the road from Rome the envoys of Pisa and Florence exchanged abuse on account of the dog with which a cardinal had presented each, Pisans and Florentines gave one another bloody pates in the fortifications of Monte Mario. The Emperor set out towards Sutri. Once more he was Federigo, the Sicilian.

HE had already crossed the frontier of his adored kingdom—not with Germans, like his father Henry; for the Chancellor Conrad had already been dispatched to Tuscany. The Sicilian barons had slunk about their lord in St. Peter's church. He set free Raniero di Manente and Dipold of Vohburg, whom on this occasion his son-in-law Count James of San Severino had caught and who was now to grow grey in the Teutonic Order. But Thomas of Celano, Count of Molise, Federigo did not pardon, for all the pleas of his son Richard. In December he was in Capua. " The Emperor Henry ", he threatened those bidden to court, " often abandoned what he should have maintained. After his death many privileges were forged under his seal, the greater part of the Royal Domain is dissipated. In this wise did they who held power during my nonage carry on to the undoing of the realm." He proclaimed a law cancelling all that had been wrung from the Crown after the year that William, the last of the Normans, had died. Richard of Segni, Innocent's brother, had surrendered Sora, Roger of Aquila Sessa, Teano and Rocca Dragone. Thomas of Celano, urged to rebellion and betrayed by his vassals, remained defiant in the craggy eyrie of Rocca Mandolfi, in Celano and Ovindoli.

The Pope in Rome waited. He wrote to the Cardinal Bishop Pelagius of Albano that, if possible, he should conclude an armistice until the Emperor's arrival before Damietta and sent Ugolino as Crusade-Legate through Italy. In silk vest, uncuirassed, tense of face, Federigo drafted, with Peter of Vinea, a letter to Ugolino: " I am rejoiced that the Holy Father has sent a man of blameless life, illustrious piety, pure morals and renowned talents and experiences ". And lightly he sketched the appeal for recruits for the Crusade, which was demanded of him. " Up, ye faithful champions of the realm, arm ye with the arms of Christian knighthood ; the eagles of the Roman Empire are already advanced." He was in Naples, and to fetch the Empress, in Sessa. By way of Capua he went with her to Salerno and to Foggia. That was the neighbourhood round the Gargano, near the oak woods of Apricena, a green hunting-ground. Above the mist rose Monte Vulture with its dead crater.

March he spent in Trani, Bari and Brindisi, April in Taranto. He saw the Germans' ships sailing for Egypt. In May he sat enthroned in Messina. He promulgated laws touching blasphemers and dicers, the mountebanks who composed slanderous *sirventes*, the beards and yellow patches of the Jews ; also the harlots, forbidding them to live in the city or to bathe with honest women. When the Duke of Bavaria had gone too, the Emperor enquired through Alatrin, whether the Pope would grant him further delay until into March. And he despatched Anselm of Justingen and forty galleys under his Admiral Henry of Malta, who had fought against the corsairs under the Genoese flag. " Remember ", cried Honorius to the Emperor, wroth on account of the episcopal election, " how God checked the abuses of thy ancestors in such wise that beside thee scarce one remains of their generation." The Pope conferred on the Marquis of Montferrat, about to reach Damietta with a brave chivalry, the title of a *gonfaloniere* of the Church and authorized the Legate Pelagius, a second Joshua, to attack.

The army of the Cross besieged Damietta, a thousand nobles, five thousand horsemen besides, forty thousand men on foot. They bombarded a mighty tower which the Saracens had erected in the Nile. With beams and ropes Germans and Frisians put up a shelter on boats. The Saracens cast Greek fire into masts and ladders and, when the Christians climbed on drawbridges up to the top story, they fired it over their heads. Then the Crusaders took the tower and cut off all access to the town. Dead horses and camels floated down the Nile, skins with provisions for the besieged. One of the Templars' ships was holed and sank. Violent rain washed the tents of the Christian army away, disease fastened upon loins and feet, blackened the shins and ate away the gums. But they in Damietta likewise were in distress, corpses lay in the streets, the living wandered about exhausted, with suppurating eyes. The Sultan Malik-el-Kamil declared himself willing to return

Saladin's conquests without the castles Karak and Shau-bak. John of Brienne, the brother of Walter, King of Jerusalem, favoured the treaty with the Sultan. The Legate Pelagius rebuffed the erring knight's insistence. Damietta fell. But El-Kamil destroyed ships and bridges, pierced the dams. On one arm of the river the Christians could get no further. They were like birds entangled in the snare. They stood up to their belts in the yellow, rising tide of muddy water. They suffered hunger and shouted desperately. The chiefs of the army negotiated with the Saracens. In return for the evacuation of Damietta, the Sultan concluded an eight years' peace. Only a crowned Christian King sailing to the Holy Land might open hostilities before. John of Brienne, Pelagius, the Duke of Bavaria and eighteen Barons remained as hostages. In the lagoon of the Nile-delta Henry of Malta came into collision with Herman of Salza and the Grand Masters of the Templars and of the Knights of St. John, who were being rowed by fellahs to Damietta. Germans and Italians stormed the houses of the French and Greeks. But on the eve of the Nativity of the Virgin the Saracens won back the town without a stroke of the sword. The army of the Christians assembled in confusion by the sea.

Herman of Salza landed with the news in Palermo. The Emperor was startled. He was surprised in the mild intoxication of his pride. This Pope would put the blame on him, accuse him for his negligence. Warily he sent Bishop James of Patti to Rome with a letter for Honorius. Did the troubadours dare decry him? " The Egyptian vulture ", one of them sneered, " has chased the Imperial eagle from Damietta's white tower. Craven is the eagle who succumbs to the vulture. Shame is yours for this and honour the Sultan's." Frederick, Federigo, took revenge on Henry of Malta, took not his life, but punished him with captivity, without removing him for ever from his court. Hotter was his lust for vengeance against another who had been in the admiral's flagship, against Walter of Paleario. Of him, the spoiler of his childhood, he wished to rid himself. But the Bishop of Catania fled to Venice and died, lonely and poor like that blinded, clumsily groping Margaritone, who was murdered by his servant in one of the *truands'* dens in Paris.

ABOUT Christmas of the year following terror seized upon the nations. In Germany a cloud-burst raged through the mountains of Saxony, swept a monastery into the abyss and drowned men and cattle. It rushed along over Eisleben, and everything perished in the waters. They who, after the floods had run off, were found in churches or houses had skins of gleaming white ; black as coal were the corpses of the others, found in tents or taverns. In this wise did God mark and distinguish the good and the wicked.

From the Alps to the Apennines, from Venice to Genoa, the earth quaked. The bells of St. Mark's belfry rang of themselves. In Lombardy it rained red sand, which dyed the rivers. The Veronese were in the Arena when the walls tottered. The forts of Marano and Lazise were destroyed. In Brescia palaces, churches and houses collapsed. The quaking lasted an hour. The citizens camped outside the towns. They gathered together for intercessional processions to appease the anger of God. But the feuds went on, and many more broke out. The Bishops of Brescia and Modena perse-cuted the heretics. The sectaries in Brescia however armed themselves, tore down sanctuaries, and, excom-municated, pronounced excommunication against the orthodox.

The Pope fell ill and, half-recovered, went to Feren-tino. The Emperor, escorted by cardinals, betook himself to the frontier town of Monte San Giovanni and waited until, after two weeks' rest, Honorius could see him. With Frederick appeared the magnates of the Frankish orient, John of Brienne, King Demetrius of Thessalonica, the brother of Montferrat, the Patriarch of Jerusalem, the Bishops of Thessalonica and Bethlehem and a Templar who represented the Grand Master. There appeared Herman of Salza, Henry of Neifen and, for Engelbert (who had crowned Federigo's son at Aix-la-Chapelle), Bernard of Horstmar. In Veroli the Pope had placed the Emperor and the Empress under the special protection of the Church. But Constance had died during the summer at Catania. Federigo had had her tomb put up in Palermo. His eyes gleamed more arrogantly than ever.

With mistrust Honorius saw this impetuous man who in Veroli had wished to sever Spoleto from St. Peter's garden, the Papal State, who for an hour had forgotten his circumspect mien. But they deceived Christendom into thinking them at one. In two years the Crusade was to begin. One turoneys a month was every layman's tribute. The King of Sicily had taken from the Bishop of Cefalù the administration of his property; the Bishop complained to the Pope. Federigo agreed to reinstatement. The Patriarch of Jerusalem stepped forward and, like him, the Cardinals importuned the Emperor to contract an alliance with Yolande, John of Brienne's daughter. Honorius joined his voice to theirs. Federigo asked for time.

He was eager to get back to Apulia. His army still invested Celano. Provided he gave up his castles, he assured Count Thomas he should stay free and be enfeoffed anew. For three years he was to accompany the King of Jerusalem to the Holy Land and, till his departure, not to quit Lombardy; should he break his oath, his son and the son of Reynold of Aversa, his brother-in-law, were to become Federigo's prisoners. He swore, and he broke the covenant; for he escaped to the Tiber. The Emperor punished Celano; it ceased to be. He meant to build it up again as Cæsarea. He ordered the arrest of the barons: they were Roger of Aquila and Thomas of Caserta, James of San Severino, Dipold's son-in-law, and the grandson of King Tancred, Alberia's and the Count of Tricarico's son. Everyone who budged was crushed by Federigo's slender fist.

During the last year he had waged war against the Saracens of Sicily, against the precipitous Jato, which lay on an impregnable hill-top deprived of running water. He had taken it, torn with his spur the flank of the Emir Ibn-Abbad when he clasped his feet in the tent, and commanded to hang him and his son. Two merchants of Marseilles had been seized too, Hugues Ferré and Guillaume le Porc, they who bartered the children of the Crusade as slaves ; and they too, squirming like pigs, were strung to the gallows-tree. But later the Saracens slaughtered the garrison. The Emperor brought them low a second time. His fleet plundered the island of Gerbes and dragged off the African Muslims. He settled a portion from the Jato in the Capitanata, round Lucera. With long walls, with round and four-cornered towers, there rose up on a flat hill-top, solemn and northern, the citadel. He gave the Saracens for ploughing a thousand oxen with curled horns. They forged arms as in Damascus, they wove hinds and parrots into brownish carpets. In return for the tax of the Gesia which he put upon them, they enjoyed toleration for their faith. Monks sought to convert them ; Federigo paid no heed to that. They were their auburn Sultan's bodyguard.

Federigo called stone-masons and sculptors to Foggia. On the Tavoliere, the chess-board of Apulia, amid meadows and fruitful plough-land, Bartolomeo created a white palace for him. And he had a bow built into the gate, ornamented with foliage and his eagles, the eagles of victorious Cæsar Augustus.

FRANCESCO despaired of his work, from which he had slowly been estranged. He merely felt it and could do nothing against it : against the cleverness of the Cardinal Deacon of Ostia, robbing him of his apostolic freedom, nor against the demons of ecclesiastical statecraft and learning. It pleased the Holy Father to imitate the Order of the Minorites in the Dominicans, the preaching friars of the Spaniard Dominicus de

Calahorra, who had had himself given the rope by him. Francesco, in order entirely to be like him; and still the Spanish heretic-hunter's fiery, killing gaze lay on the walls of the Portiuncula. In purity Francesco sought martyrdom, on the Crusade to Egypt and Syria, for which a child, pointing with its finger, made the choice among the brethren; and before the Egyptian Sultan in Damietta, who enquired for him and wanted a miracle from him, he had testified to the gospel of Jesus Christ. Men thought he was dead until he landed in Venice and until, stirred up by the alteration in the statutes, he took his farewell and laid down the governance of the Order. "From now on", he had said to the brethren, "I am dead to you."

He was uncertain whether all his hardship, his self-chastisement, his misery were not a mistake. In the wintry nights he hungered for simple happiness. He threw himself naked into the snow and fashioned images, the image of a woman. And then he played with the thought and disfigured it. "That", he said to himself, "is your wife. And after her come two sons and two daughters. Those are a serving-man and serving-wench. They are carrying the baggage, the burden." In this wise in his dilirium did he wish to go on cozening himself about what feverishly he yearned for. Or bitterness and hatred came upon him, the gentle. "Ah," he cried to God, "accursed by thy celestial court and me, thy unworthy servant, be all they who overthrow and destroy what thou hast made in the beginning." This was shortly before the great earthquake which affrighted the spirits of men.

For the last time he saw in Rome the Cardinal Bishop of Ostia. Dinner was served, and he was missed. Then he came in, bread in hand, which he divided, the bread of charity, bread from the Lord's Table. Cardinal Leo asked him to live with him; and with his companions he spent one night in a tower. But demons appeared to him, as a sign of God's punishment. How could he enjoy rest here while his poor brethren were in want ? He hid himself on Monte Colombo near Rieti and celebrated Christ's nativity, the infant in the straw of the manger ; ox and ass blew their warming breath over it, the villagers hastened along with their torches and sang songs, exulting.

He withdrew into the solitude of the Alverno ; and it was summer once more. As he was unable to get on, the brethren put him upon a donkey which a peasant lent them ; and for this Francesco brought it about by his prayers that a fine spring gushed forth in the forest, whose clear water the man, tormented by thirst, lapped up. The saint's cell hung over rifts and gorges which had rent the rock asunder in the hour of Christ's passion. Francesco prayed, and it seemed to Brother Leo that from time to time he raised himself up from the earth, once even to the height of a beech-tree, and that a radiant light shone about him. Then Francesco removed from the others, to a still more hidden spot, on the far side of a chasm over which they laid a tree trunk ; here he desired to fast, distracted by no noise, and no one was to hear his calling. The devil drew nigh to throw him down. As he clasped the rock and pressed himself against it, it yielded like wax, so that Francesco's hands and face were limned upon it. A hawk waked him for Mass with a short cry and always later, as the strength ebbed from his wrecked body.

Francesco had the vision of a fiddling angel, drawing the bow over the strings. If he had made a down stroke with the bow, Francesco's soul would have flown from his body with rapture, so intolerable was the sweetness of that melody. A seraph hovered down from heaven with six fiery wings, with twain over its head, with twain spread to fly, with twain covering its shape ; and beneath them was the image of the Crucified. The Alverno was a mass of flames. So strong was that glow that the shepherds were alarmed and the muleteers, on their way to the Romagna, saddled their beasts and loaded them ; for they thought the sun had risen. Of a sudden Francesco's hands and feet were pierced by

8

black nails ; to the right on his ribs gaped, blood-red, the stab of the spear. When he descended he could not set the soles of his feet to ground. Blood trickled in his raiment. He had the mystic stigmata of the Lord.

THE Emperor Federigo was in Catania when, unmercifully and to please the Pope, he promulgated a new edict : all convicted heretics were to be apprehended by the authorities and punished by death at the stake or the loss of their tongue. But he was imperious towards Honorius : " So I am led astray by false counsel," he queried of Herman of Salza, " carried away by the ardour of youth ? Is what I have done for him not yet enough ? He says of France that it above all others has accustomed itself to fight God's battles. Does he know that at St. Denis the King of Jerusalem said not a word about the Holy Land to the eighth Lewis but merely about the rooting out of the Albigenses and that Lewis has no thought but of the war for the English crown ? Why does the Pope not grant pardons in greater abundance ? If it were our affair to vouchsafe pardons, we would not be thus niggardly. In place of the Begging Friars, why does he not send a Cardinal to France and England to pacify them ? It might yet be that the Church be charged with sloth, whereas heaven and earth are our witnesses that, as far as we and our realm are concerned, we aimed verily at carrying through the great undertaking ". The Grand Master of the Teutonic Order he sent with a letter, to Rome, Bishop Patti to Acre, to Yolande of Brienne as his betrothed.

During the autumn he fell sick at Capua—of poisoning so it was said, and ever after he was hot in hatred against the Bishop of Taranto. Round about Christmas he was in Palermo, in the spring in Foggia and in the hunting lodge of San Lorenzo in Pantano, where on a lake with artificial conduit the waders quacked. As his guest in Capua and Foggia he had John of Brienne, his father-in-law, the vagrant knight who, as a pilgrim to

Santiago of Campostella, had wooed Berengaria, the daughter of King Alphonsus of Castile. In the company of Henry, the King of Germany, and of the Cardinal Bishop of Porto he had been at Cologne with Engelbert, now sole governor since the death of Conrad of Scharfenberg. John of Brienne was a braggart, Berengaria (his third consort) affected and stiff. The Emperor was surfeited of their company. He summoned to him at Foggia the hierarchy of the Sicilian kingdom and kept them as pledges. For he wanted from the Pope fresh postponement of the Crusade until after St. John's Day. Honorius, with Ugolino, was in Rieti, because the citizens of Rome, the Conti and Richard of Segni were fomenting riots. Thither Federigo deputed his envoys. And as soon as the negotiations took a favourable turn, he set archbishops and bishops at liberty.

In San Germano he himself met the cardinals who bore the Pope's commission. They were Pelagius, the vanquished of Damietta, and Gualo, the Presbyter of St. Martin. In the Emperor's train were the Dukes of Austria, Carinthia and Spoleto, the Marquis of Andechs, Bernard of Horstmar, the Bishops of Bamberg and Merseburg, and Oliver of Paderborn, the crusading preacher and schoolman, already chosen by the Pope Cardinal Bishop of Sabina. Frederick swore that within two years he would set out on his crusade with a thousand knights, a hundred ships and fifty well equipped galleys and that he would maintain this force in the Holy Land for the space of two years; moreover, that he would furnish ships for two thousand horsemen and deposit one hundred thousand ounces of gold or their value in silver with the Grand Master of the Teutonic Order, with the King and with the Patriarch of Jerusalem. Should he die before or during the expedition the money was forfeited. He also let the Duke of Spoleto swear by his soul. And he concluded an alliance for his son, not with Isabella, the sister of Henry of England, whom the Governor had wanted to unite with him, not with Agnes of Bohemia, but with Margaret, the daughter of Leopold of Austria, who knelt before him as his vassal until he gave him his hands.

In August a fleet under Henry of Malta, the reinstated admiral, put to sea for Acre, with the Bishop of Patti, to fetch Yolande. In October Federigo awaited her at Brindisi harbour, there where a gigantic pillar of oriental marble marked the end of the Via Appia and a red fort flamed across the wanly gleaming waves. The Emperor was standing by John of Brienne's side when the line of sail emerged on the horizon. Simon de Maucastel, the Archbishop of Tyre, who had crowned the bride Queen of Jerusalem, Balian, Lord of Sidon, the Constable Eude of Montbéliard and many knights and ladies disembarked and, in the midst of them, Yolande, who propelled herself with short steps and whose eyes were drowned in wavy black curls. In the bare cathedral of Brindisi Federigo and she exchanged rings. Bright were the windows of Oria on the nuptial night.

At the wedding-board Federigo pressed his father-in-law to resign the title of King of Jerusalem, which belonged by rights to him, the Emperor. To the sound of the trump, while the cups passed round, John of Brienne obeyed. But Federigo looked full of distrust upon one of the younger knights, who sat apart, upon Walter, the King's nephew. In the first hours of the morning he travelled with Yolande to Foggia without speaking to the King. John of Brienne followed with Tancred's grandson.

They were sitting at chess, at an ivory board with pieces of ivory and ebony, great as cannon balls. Suddenly Federigo grew pale, for in a fury John of Brienne cried out : " *Fi de beccer, diabele* ". That was the old devouring affront upon the butcher's son, the demon, the devil. The Emperor put his hand to his sword. John drew Walter away by the arm, down to the gate, and they galloped along the road to Barletta, ill-girt and ungreaved. He saved Walter by his cunning. Bidden by Federigo to Melfi to hunt with him, he turned aside with his nephew outside Cannæ and crossed the Ofanto. They fled along the coast to the frontier of the kingdom and northwards to Rome through the fever-fraught Maremme.

IN Germany the spiritual court judged the Provost of the Nuns of Neuwerk near Goslar, the Premonstratensian Henry Minnike. The Bishop of Hildesheim had admonished him, the Emperor refused to hear the nuns' complaints of him. Now their Superior, flaxen-haired and dour, was the Bishop's prisoner. In Bleckede on the Elbe the Cardinal of Porto investigated the heretic's false doctrines. Minorites, begging friars crowded about his chair. Present, full of sneaking blood-lust, was the preacher Conrad of Marburg. The Cardinal questioned Henry of Minnike what he had said about the Trinity, about the Virgin Mary, Satan and sin. The Premonstratensian gave answer, lost in sadness. He refused the oath on the Gospels, refused to recant even under the screws and nails of the torture-chamber. He was condemned, the provost's habit torn from his stout peasant's shoulders. Then he was delivered over to secular justice. The council burnt him at the Lily, a tower in the town walls. With a pair of tongs the preacher Conrad of Marburg stirred the fire. The heretic in his shirt sang of the heavenly Jerusalem until his flaxen pate bowed into the crackling flames.

In Gdumunda in Swabia six school boys with a priest were holding a wake. When they had said a psalter, they went out and saw the horned moon and between its horns six crosses. A mighty dragon approached, to swallow the moon together with the crosses. In terror of the monster's gaping maw the moon gave a jump. The crosses swayed and were drawn asunder. The school boys stared as if thunderstruck. Then two candles of white wax came falling down. They handed them over to the church of St. John the Baptist. Famine and pestilence tormented men and domestic animals.

Round about Lent there came to Valenciennes a man in a hair cowl, covered with damp foliage and with eagle's claws on his gnarled fingers. He said he had been living like a beast in the forest of Vicogne; but that he was Baldwin, Count of Flanders and Hainault, the Emperor of Constantinople who had been lost to the world as a prisoner of the Bulgarian Czar Joannisha. The people thronged to him. Clerks and laymen who had known the Count examined the hermit. He was eloquent and well to see in matters of chivalry. On his body, when it had been washed and anointed, he pointed out Baldwin's skinned-over wounds. He was smaller and not over-familiar with Flanders and the places thereof: so bent had been his bones, so darkened his memory by the years of wandering and distress among Greeks and Muslims. The Countess Joan went to him, the daughter of Baldwin and the wife of Ferrand, who was still mewed up in the iron cage in Paris. William of Holland, who had fought with her for her imperial fief, was dead; and a widow also after him, that old man, was the Emperor Otto's young widow, Mary of Brabant. But hostile were the designs of all the Countess's neighbours. She saw the hermit and doubted. The Duke of Brabant decided in favour of his genuineness and supported him. With solemn pageantry the towns of Lille and Ghent did homage to him. As Emperor of Constantinople and Count of Flanders he made investitures. He conferred knighthoods, lorded it at Whitsun under a crown, had a cross borne before him. Joan fled with her sister Margaret to Paris, in order that the King of France should restore Flanders to her; Douai and Sluys and half the spoils of war should fall to him. The King invited him to Péronne and received him with the Papal Legate Romanus of San Angelo. Baldwin too brought a great train. But the repudiation of the Bishop of Liége, who called him a juggler, the repudiation of Joan and her sister perplexed him. He stammered out that he was exhausted. They despised him. Only a few lay brothers of Villers Abbey endured with the Emperor of Constantinople, as he hastened on his return journey. From the Rhine he intended to go to the Pope at Rome. Disguised as a merchant he journeyed through Champagne and French Burgundy. Sir Clarembald of Chappes seized him and delivered him up to Countess Joan. Wearing a cap of infamy he was carted round the rebellious districts, the nobility under Arnulf of Oudenarde sentenced him to death, at Lille he was hanged. Men said that on the rack he had given away his true name, Bertrand de Rais. The people in Flanders and Hainault lamented for him.

In the same October, at Frankfort, Engelbert took his leave of King Henry. The Duke of Austria had sent Agnes of Bohemia, who had been in his care, to her father. Nor did the Plantagenet princess become Queen of Germany, as the Governor wished. But he complied with the Emperor's command, promising to perform his office at the nuptials in Nürnberg. Engelbert had combated the resistance of the great and that of the guilds. None loved him; stern and wrinkled and long in the nose his head grew out of the marten-fur. A body-guard protected his carriage. He dismissed them as he was proceeding from the Diet at Soest to Schwelm to dedicate a church. Count Frederick of Isenburg, his wan-faced kinsman, whose trespasses he had suffered and who yet bore him a grudge because he deprived him of his rights, followed him without word or greeting. In the evening twilight and a high wind, when they were level with the Gevelsberg, he fell upon him with his retainers. Like madmen they struck down the Count of Dortmund and the Archbishop himself. Engelbert of Cologne bled from eight and thirty wounds. He saw the gleaming stars in strange, dull gold patterns and gave up the ghost. Under cover of night two servants brought the cold corpse to Schwelm.

The castle of Nürnberg was full of naught but joy. In the chapel Henry was married to Margaret and the Duke of Austria's son to Agnes of Thuringia, the daughter of the Landgrave Lewis and Elisabeth. The

Governor was missed. Then the news spread that he was slain. On the third day the King sat in judgment. Engelbert's bloody cloak was laid before him. He asked Gerlach of Büdingen whether even now he might pronounce outlawry against the murderer. Gerlach said Yea. Frederick of Truhendingen yelled that the Count of Isenburg must first appear in court. Swords were raised flashing, the stairs broke, burying forty men : twenty died in the inns of contusions they received in the fall. The young King outlawed Frederick of Isenburg and discharged his subjects of fealty. The corpse was kept in Frankfort, in Main, interred in St. Peter's Cathedral at Cologne by the Cardinal-Bishop of Porto, like Thomas à Becket the martyr.

Isenburg's wife ran mad, killed herself and her little son. In the habit of a citizen he escaped to Liége. Sir Baldwin of Jeneffe sold him for two thousand marks of silver to the new Archbishop of Cologne Henry of Molenark. Outside the gate of St. Severin he was bound to the wheel. While he moaned out his soul the clergy sang a jubilant Te Deum. He had, they said, repented of the murder. His brothers and accessories, the Bishop of Münster and the Bishop-elect of Osnabrück, were tried by the Pope in Rome. The Bishop of Münster died in Italy on the way home. Thereupon the miracles at Engelbert's grave ceased.

WHEN John of Brienne had fled, the Emperor sent his wife to Terracina Castle at the foot of the Torre Maggiore in Salerno, there where the Salernians had once kept her mother, the Norman, a prisoner. He beat Yolande. Anais, one of the French ladies who had come by ship with her, Tancred's grand-daughter, concealed herself from his searching gaze. He violated her timid, scarce nubile beauty. For weeks on end, he did what he would with her, who was quickly made shameless by him. A groaning spread in Terracina from Yolande's chamber. She lay on a blood-stained bed, her womb had borne a child that was dead. Federigo, greatly troubled, cast himself down before her as she lay sobbing.

The Emperor raised himself up, to prepare his campaign against the Lombards. For the Pope left it in his hands, in order to advance the Crusade. " We shall teach them ", he said to Peter of Vinea, who was as dumb as a spectre, " to insult our Majesty. Them in Milan we will persecute for what they have committed against our grandfather and our father, trample under foot the scion of infamous licence." In ill-humour he received the Cardinal Bishop Oliver at Salerno. Henry of Morra, the Grand Justiciary, took Yolande to the castle dell' Uovo on the island outside Naples. In Pescara the Emperor took the head of the Sicilian vassals. He advanced through Rimini. Bishop Bonaventura brought female heretics before him. He gave command for burning them on the wood-pile. He signed to Herman of Salza and with his seal sealed the parchment by which the Culmerland and all future conquests in heathen Prussia should belong to the Teutonic Order. In Ravenna, in the weather-worn, round-arched palace of the Byzantine Exarchs, the German magnates presented themselves : the Archbishop of Magdeburg, Count of Romagna, the Bishop of Naumburg, the Duke of Saxony, the Landgrave Lewis of Thuringia. Here he tarried ; for about Easter an army was to descend from the Brenner under Henry, his son.

He was fowling in the lagoons near Ravenna when Peter of Vinea pulled a papal letter out of its cover. It dealt with the appeal to the men of Spoleto. " What does Honorius write ? " the Emperor asked. " Does he call us a Nebuchadnezzar as he called that Otto a Pharaoh ? " and with the swiftness of rage, slinging the bound falcon to the ground, he read : " Keep well before thine eyes what in latter days befell thy ancestor Frederick, who, disregarding the faith he owed the apostolic see, set St. Peter's temple on fire and did other grievous harm to Holy Church, as a reward for which he suffered torments in his own body, which his sons

inherited, according to the words of the Scripture:
' I am the lord of heaven, who visits the sins of the children upon the third and fourth generation '. Frederick himself, as he was on his way to the Sepulchre of the Lord, was afflicted with the lot of the Israelites, who for their sins were not granted to see the promised land. For, before he set foot in Jerusalem, he died a sudden death in the waters. And after him, as the whole world knoweth, the punishment of heaven overtook his sons Henry and Philip. Therefore pay heed that God destroy thee not and root not up thy generation. But we will not refrain from chastening thee with excommunication if thou persist in thy corruption ".

The Emperor gave a hissing laugh. Without a word he rode back to Ravenna. He shut himself up with Peter of Vinea in his apartment in the central building of the palace. Already before night they had finished off the reply to Honorius. " Far beyond all expectations ", one of the sentences ran, " and against the counsel of the Princes, have we always been prepared to do you service, so that none of our predecessors ever has shown such devotion." Were the benefits of the Church so certain, had she not called his deadly enemies of Brienne to Sicily and recognized Otto, was she not the abetter of the disobedient Bishops, of the Archbishop of Taranto, the conspirator who had laid hands on royal property, of the Bishop of Catania and his maladministration? Did not the blood which the Bishop of Cefalù had shed testify, or the unavenged murder of the Castellan and several citizens? And if he did insist on the tribute from the people of Spoleto for his army, why did the Church entrench upon his rights, why did she not take pains to ease the burden of the Crusade for him? On the morrow he was hawking again, a thin smile about his lips.

In Saint Zeno's church at Mosio the Lombards had renewed their confederacy for twenty-five years. The Rectors of the towns offered the direction of their armies to John of Brienne, who came from Rome to Faenza.

He informed them that he could not contribute to depriving his daughter of her rule, her crown. The Germans from the north were already in Trent, crashing horsemen in armour and scant infantry. The Lombards closed the passes of the Alps against them. Only isolated individuals got over the Adria to the Emperor, German bishops and counts. King Henry turned back through the valley of the Adige. Trent was consumed by fire.

Frederick camped near Cosna, between Faenza and Forli, to one side of the Strata Francigena. In order to show their scorn of the Emperor they of Faenza, under the Imperial ban because of their feud with Imola, did not close their gates upon him, though they harboured John of Brienne and the Rectors of their Confederacy. They permitted the baggage and part of the army to pass through. A collision and fighting ensued. The townsfolk seized horses laden with money-bags and killed a knight whom—on account of his helmet and, when they had smashed that, on account of his auburn hair—they took for the Emperor. The *Podesta* compelled them to give up the plunder again. The Emperor kept silence about his humiliation. They were in the territory of Bologna. Frederick negotiated with the Bolognese. But he deluded them by inviting them to confer and departing from Medicina first thing in the morning. A frightful cloudburst raged, the Reno, Aposa and Savena were swollen, masses of water washed every bridge away. The Emperor, with the Landgrave of Thuringia and a small company, just succeeded in crossing the Savena by a ford. The rest, under the Archbishop of Magdeburg, the Count of Schwarzburg and Meynard of Molberg had no choice but to go into Bologna. Quarters were granted them for one night. Near the leaning towers—the Garisenda and the one next to the Asinelli's castle—the multitude collected round them as they marched off and mocked them. There were dead and wounded. In alarm the vanguard dashed along over the flooded road. Frederick had slept in a dirty village, on a rustling litter of birch-twigs. The darting ray of the sun woke him; the rain floods ran off. In San Giovanni di Persiceto they saw a cordon of armed men. They were the town-guards of Cremona, Parma, Reggio and Modena, campaigning against them of Bologna. They conducted the Emperor to Modena. There he joined the Sicilians.

In Reggio the townsfolk wished to drive the cattle following in the rear of the army off the pastures and stabbed the Duke of Saxony's baggage-boys. Then they were in Parma. The cathedral and marble baptistry opened their doors for the Whitsun celebrations. The Pope's answering letter, written by Thomas of Capua, the Cardinal Bishop of Sabina, was delivered to the Emperor. Frederick read it, with no one present. " Sith the Church ", thus did Honorius warn him, or he who spoke in the old man's name, " was urged by no necessity to take upon herself the burden of thy tutelage committed unto her by thy mother, thou shouldst in thy ingratitude not go so far as to charge her with deceitful stewardship and maintain that in the guise of defenders she sent, clothed in the pallium, enemies into the realm seeking the life, dominions and crown of her ward. Thou hast enjoyed the fruit of others' labours, reaped where thou hast not sown, garnered where thou hast not planted." The epistle was as full of the classical spirit as of the Bible; not without pleasure did the Emperor pass an expert's appraisal upon this rhetoric. " Such a proceeding thou didst not find in Julius Cæsar, who spared the life of Domitius and who forebore his vengeance against Metullus when he proffered himself to the swords. Were there not places of refuge among the people of Israel, and shall a Christian people not have such ? David was a saviour to the persecuted, and should the Pope, great David's successor, withdraw his countenance from the oppressed, who verily cannot harm thee or thine, unless perchance their mere living appear intolerable to thee ?" His glance hastened to the end : " As, however, the hand of the Lord has not waxed too weak to break the pride of the mighty and bring down them that are exalted, do not thou in the glory of success abandon the humility which thou didst display in the days of thy affliction. We hope that the past of so submissive a prince will not sink to such a degree into oblivion as to fall into the fault of ingratitude which was reprehended in his rival or place a guilt upon him which he condemns in his adversary ". It was his, the Holy Father's, good pleasure to scold ; the Emperor saw his toothless, mumbling mouth. But with acted politeness, until time had been gained, he would respond. And he called for Herman of Salza's phlegm ; him, Cardinal Conrad of Urach and the Bishop of Hildesheim he sent, together with the Patriarch Gerald of Jerusalem, the Bishop of Parma, the Abbot of Reichenau, Provost Degenhard and the Schoolman Ulric of Strasburg, to the Rectors of the Confederacy at Mantua.

The Emperor removed his court to Borgo San Donnino near Fiorenzuola, on the edge of the Apennines, and to Cremona. As the Lombards contemplated disgraceful conditions, the Duke of Saxony and the Landgrave Lewis departed in order not to go on waiting. That Alatrin and the Dominican Guala of Bergamo, the confidant of the Cardinal Bishop Ugolino of Ostia, were, to Frederick's keen-scented hatred, the authors of the obstacles. In the church of Donnino he sat in judgment upon the towns. A Papal Brief which, for the redemption of Christ's cross, placed him under the apostle Peter's protection, was published by the Bishop of Hildesheim at the altar shrine. It pronounced excommunication upon Milan, Brescia, Lodi, Piacenza, Alessandria, Vercelli, Verona, Mantua, Vicenza, Padua, Treviso, Bologna and Faenza. The Emperor declared them under the Imperial ban, their citizens and friends deprived of their rights and outlawed. But the sound of trumpets was in the air ; he had to quit Lombardy.

He proceeded through a crooked valley of the Taro, crossed Monte Bardone over the La Cisa pass and came to Pontremoli. Marquis William of Malaspina, whose brother was in Frederick's train, plotted treachery. Anxiously the Emperor waited until the Pisans came riding to meet him and conducted him to their city by the blue, curved Arno. Here he summoned Niccolò to him, the sculptor, and the mathematician Leonardo Fibonacci, who had been in Spain, Greece, Syria, Egypt and, likely too, in India. For from the Indian sages he had his art of reckoning in numbers, the ground and secret of which was the symbol Nought. Magister John of Palermo asked him difficult problems, Federigo joined in, and he marvelled at the speed and profundity with which the Pisan solved them. He thought no more on Honorius's beard.

He rested in the Imperial castle of San Miniato, until higher up on the Elsa the fighting forces of Florence and Lucca made their appearance. In Spoleto he confirmed the fiefs of Tancred of Campiglia, Viscount of Tuscany, who intercepted on Berthold of Urslingen's behalf messages between Rome and Radicofani with Papal letters and whom Honorius cursed as a son of Belial. Through the gorges of the Abruzzi Frederick set foot in his kingdom. In Ascoli, in the Capitinata, he held his court. With last warnings the Pope sent Leonard, one of the brethren of the Teutonic Order. Anew he made solemn promise of ships for the crusaders, for as many as might be ready for a pilgrimage to the Holy Land. He was at one with Honorius, through him concluded peace with the Lombard Confederacy. He went to Sicily, made as if to be reconciled with John of Brienne. In quick pangs Yolande had borne a girl.

WELL-NIGH blind, Francesco had returned to the Portiuncula. He rested in San Damiano, in the nunnery of the Clares, near Chiara, his friend. For fourteen days he could not distinguish light from darkness ; and continously he shed tears. In the convent garden the nuns built him a cell of reeds. Mice and rats scurried round his retreat. Yet it did him good to abide there ; and, a *Joculator Domini*, one of God's jugglers,

GREGORY IX's DREAM

[face p. 126

he sang in the bliss of the universe his hymn to the sun.

He went to the hermitage in the rocks of Monte Colombo. The doctors wished to heal the disease, which was worsening, by cauterising his forehead. "Brother Fire," said Francesco to the red heat of the sharp iron, "who art beautiful among all created things, be merciful to me in this hour; thou knowest that I have ever loved thee." The illness became only the more inveterate. After he had been to a doctor in Siena he burst a blood-vessel. As he begged for it, they brought him home to Umbria. His legs were swollen. The citizens of the city in which he was born sent armed men to meet him, lest Perugia should gain possession of him. He was to die among them, in the Bishop's palace. Leo, Angelo, Rufino and Masseo tended him. Once he lamented, rebellious and mournful: "Where are they, who have taken away my brethren?" Even in these latter days he forced the Bishop to make peace with the excommunicated *Podestà*. To cheer her he wrote Chiara a letter in the vulgar tongue.

In the autumn he seemed to recover from a new hæmorrhage. A physician from Arezzo sought to comfort him. "But I am no cuckoo," he cried out in a saying of Italian peasants, "to be afraid of death." And, with folded arms; "Welcome be thou, brother Death". Leo and Angelo had to sing the hymn of the sun. He sang with them day and night until, their loud persistence becoming a nuisance, they transported him through the city, past the temple of Minerva and through the olive grove to the Portiuncula. Half-way, near the lepers' lazar-house, he had the litter stopped once again. His gaze had the hopelessness of farewell. In the Portiuncula he received the visit of Jacopa di Settensoli, who had journeyed to him with her two sons, Senators of Rome, and a great train of folk on horseback. "Brother Jacopa," he called her; and, even when he knew her no more, she knelt in a noble widow's grief, with her golden frontlet, by his couch. He had the wish to die on the ground, in the embrace of his mistress Poverty. They lifted him back on to his bed. So he died. They buried him in San Giorgio. In front of San Damiano the bearers put down the *Poverello's* coffin from their shoulders. Chiara threw herself upon it.

ANCIENT Honorius had become so weak that the Romans already declared him to be dead. Famine and dearth oppressed them. Lest they should lay unlawful hands on Papal property, the Cardinals showed him at a window in the Lateran. He grieved over the Lombards' prevarications, who, pretending that the peace-protocol had fallen into the water and become illegible, demanded new copies. He sent Guala, the white Dominican, to them. He died one March day and was buried under the dome of Santa Maria Maggiore.

The Cardinals congregated for choosing a Pope in the house of Gregory *apud septem solia*. The voices in the committee of three were given to the German, Conrad of Urach. But he declined. The election went to Ugolino, the eighty-year-old Cardinal-Bishop of Ostia. He called himself Gregory the Ninth. He was consecrated in St. Peter's, crowned with the tiara in Santa Maria Maggiore. A procession of luxurious splendour passed from St. Peter's basilica over to the Lateran. The Pope rode on a magnificently harnessed steed led by the Senator, the Prefect of Rome, the higher clergy shone in purple, the streets, redolent of odours from perfume-burners, were covered with carpets, trumpets blared amid the priests' *Kyrie Eleison* and the beggars' shouts of congratulation. But immediately after the election Gregory wrote to the Emperor to prepare with strong arm for his journey oversea, to fight the fight in the Lord's behalf with pure heart and unfeigned devotion and so win the crown of unfading glory; then he would honour him, whom for long past he had reckoned among his friends, with even greater zeal. " But do thou in due piety towards him who governs the destinies of man hearken to our representations that thou bringest us not peradventure into embarrassment, from which we could not, even if we would, readily free thee."

In the park of the Cisa Federigo overcame his annoyance with the Lombards. He gave ear to the song of Sicilian troubadours, read his mute Peter of Vinea's stanzas on Cupid and the Bitterness of Death. He bent back when Yolande was carried through the shade with her child. The hot summer began. Pope Gregory removed to the Sabine hills, to his native town of Anagni. Federigo travelled up to Apulia, to Gravina. He sent the Master of the Teutonic Order and the Archbishop of Reggio to do homage to the Holy Father. He gave the inhabitants of Celano leave to build up their houses again. Thomas of Aquino, Count of Acerra, preceded him to Syria as Governor.

In August the Emperor was in Melfi. The Dominican Guala appeared, pale as wax in the heat of the day. No breath of air moved from the hills. The monk with the Lenten preacher's hollow jaws requested supplies of corn from the kingdom for the starving Romans. Federigo gave the orders to Henry of Morra, the Justiciary. But the monk also had a letter of Gregory's with him. The Emperor unrolled it, reluctant and suspicious. For it was a letter about the Crucified, about the Sacraments of the Lord. " Behold the spear ", the Pope cried out to him, " whose sharpness pierced His side, to the end that thou mayest feel violent pain and the sting of contrition. The key it is to Paradise, into whose gates no hardened soul may enter, but only one made soft in the oven of burning love." It was a letter about the triple crown. " Three-fold coronation will be thy part also, as it was the Saviour's, who gained the crown of the mother, Mercy, that of the stepmother, Justice, and that of the father, the crown of Glory. In Germany thou wert crowned by the mother whose milk nurtured thee, by thy stepmother in Lombardy, by thy father the Pope with the crown of Glory, the Imperial diadem." And further : " If now knowledge and love, these two beacons, were to be extinguished, if these victoriously advancing eagles were to fall and be caught in the net of earthly joys, how couldst thou still point the way of salvation to all posterity ? But we, who in humbler office already embraced thy eminence, will carve principles into thy heart with a style of bronze nor neglect aught that could serve thee to escape the danger of eternal death ". Inattentively Federigo picked to pieces the golden umbels climbing up, as high as a man, to the flat gallery. He sank into a weary day-dreaming when the Dominican had gone : then he asked for the King of France's messengers.

He betook himself from Melfi to Troia. The Crusaders came through Italy, men of Lorraine, four hundred from Worms, the Bishops of Augsburg, Bamberg and Ratisbon and he whom the plaints of the pious Elisabeth had accompanied and who in Schmalkalden concealed from her the hour of his setting forth, the Landgrave Lewis of Thuringia. The Emperor paid him four thousand marks ; the Counts of Wartburg, Brandenburg, Molberg and Stolberg followed him. From England thousands of pilgrims were expected under the Bishops of Winchester and Exeter. But a host of Germans remained behind in Rome. In the portico of St. Peter's was seated a Papal Vicar who, for glittering silver, sold them dispensations from their vow. The Vicar and the seal of his commission were counterfeit ; it was six weeks before, on the demand of Gregory, tarrying at Anagni, the Prefect of Rome took action against the impostor.

As far as Troia the Emperor advanced to meet the Landgrave and, with him, by way of Barletta, Bari, Monopoli to Brindisi. The harbour was full of sails ; and yet there was lack of ships. Many turned back, because they were told they would not find room enough. A pestilence stalked through the tented camp ; every food seemed poisoned, every spring dried up. The fleeing died along the northward roads. Federigo trembled with cold, and once it befell that he lost his senses. He slept with Yolande. Then he sent the Empress to Taranto. A fleet with seven hundred knights, already fed by him, went to sea under the Duke of Limburg, Henry of Neifen, Guerri de Dunes and Gobert d'Aspremont. The Bishop of Augsburg died. Federigo and the Landgrave had themselves rowed to Andrew's island, outside, by the purifying waters. They took their leave of Yolande in Taranto. With death in his bosom, the Landgrave went into his cabin. The Patriarch of Jerusalem gave him supreme unction and the viaticum. He died, quivering with fever. The Thuringians kept his cooked remains.

The Emperor was shaken by cramplike spasms. A Saracen physician put damp bandages round his bursting head. In the evening he took counsel with the Patriarch, with Herman of Salza, with James of Vitry and declared he would sail in the coming spring. The Master of the Teutonic Order parted from him. All the sails dipped under the horizon. With his servants Federigo journeyed through the mild September to Pozzuoli. Blue was the bay, steaming the Solfatara. He took the healing baths, loosened shells between the ruined pillar-shafts of the Serapeion and sat in the empty amphitheatre on the weather-eaten Imperial seat of black marble. A convalescent, he played with the world and had a woman about him, the low-born German, Adelaide, the mother of seven-year-old, silky-locked Enzio.

" WE, nevertheless, not to resemble dumb hounds " —Pope Gregory had excommunicated the prodigal son in Anagni and St. Peter's. At first Federigo thought he should be able, through the Archbishops of Reggio and Bari, to appease this raging, this unchecked hostility against him, whose reprobate heart (so the letter of excommunication said) had been enticed to perjury by the enjoyments and delights of his kingdom. In vain had he gone to Gaeta, nearer Rome. Then, from Capua, he had made his defence. Seriously he now took up what hitherto he had merely been playing with as a whim, the Crusade overseas. "We, who have received a name and a power which are a terror to the barbarians and more exalted than those of all the princes of the earth." He proposed journeying to the Holy Land in May ; that was his declared intent. But Gregory had disdained the transgressor's words and on Maundy Thursday excommunicated him for a third time, in the Lateran, also because of the complaints touching Sicily and for his having robbed Templars and Knights of St. John of their property in the Kingdom. On Easter Monday the Pope celebrated mass in St. Peter's. The people of Rome, under the families of the Frangipani and Capocci, whose towers he had torn down, and the priest Annibale Anibaldi, pressed upon him, reviling him. He had difficulty in getting away safe to the Vatican Palace. Then he departed to Rieti. On the place of the Capitol between Marius's trophies, Roffred of Benevento published the Emperor's appeal to the metropolis. Federigo bought the lands, fields and vineyards of the Frangipani, who had fortified the Coliseum, the triumphal arches of Titus and Constantine, and gave them back to them as fiefs.

He celebrated Easter in Barletta. "That is the Roman fashion ", he said to Peter of Vinea. "Behind disgusting phrases, in which honey is laid on honey and oil on oil to enhance the sweetness and charity, an insatiable blood-sucker lies concealed. That first church of Christ Jesus was founded on poverty. Now the alleged church rolls in riches, is reared up on riches, sails along upon riches. When will the world unite against this unheard-of tyranny, this universal danger ? " Archbishop Berard of Palermo had arrived from Egypt, back from the Sultan El-Kamil, with strange presents in return for the Emperor's : produce of India, Arabia and Yemen and a gigantic tame elephant who carried a litter broidered with adamant. To Barletta came Thomas of Aquino, the Imperial Governor in Acre. El-Kamil's brother, El-Muazzam, Sultan of Damascus, had replied to the

Archbishop : " Tell your lord that I have nothing for him but the sharpness of the sword ". Thomas of Aquino brought the news of El-Muazzam's death ; Ennasir-Daud, his son, was not of age. Federigo sent five hundred more knights to Acre with the Marshal Riccardo Filangieri. He was in Troia, when messengers came galloping through the April day, messengers from Andria. The Empress had been delivered of a man-child. And Frederick thought of the Hohenstaufen kings, of the slim horseman in Bamberg cathedral, as he gave the name of Conrad to his second heir. But after ten days a new messenger came in black mourning. Yolande lay dead in Andria. Federigo shut himself up with his French wife's corpse and recalled to mind the Aragonese. Here again he stood confronted with the great, ultimate rigour. He had Yolande lowered into a vault at the entrance to the cathedral.

He summoned a court at Barletta. Under the open sky he sat enthroned and addressed the Archbishops, Bishops and Counts of Sicily. He appointed Reynold of Spoleto Governor and bound him and Henry of Morra by oaths. Should the fate of Barbarossa, whom the Calycadnus swallowed up, be his, the right of succession was provided for. Two Franciscans had appeared, once again from the angry Pope. To Gregory he sent the Archbishop of Magdeburg with two justices of the Sicilian High Court to beg him, now, on his departure, not to withhold from him the blessing of the Church. The Pope wanted war. He was already enlisting mercenaries, with money levied for crusades, and already in Abruzzi the Lords of Popleto, supported by Rieti, were rebelling against the Emperor.

Federigo gave orders to build a castle in Brindisi with the stones of the old aqueducts, theatres and temples. His galleys weighed anchor. Without penance he sailed over the dancing waves and without absolution. He stood on board with Demetrius of Montferrat, the King of Thessalonica, with the Archbishops of Bari, Reggio, Palermo and Capua, with Sicilians and Swabians. Rosy red glowed the wild rocks of Epirus. The air was as transparent as crystal, the Ionian Islands reared up, gulls circled about harbour walls, the jagged coast of the Peloponnesus hove along, the mountains of Crete rose to their summits and were lost in vapour. For three weeks, incited by whips when they wearied, the convicts from the sulphur-mines panted on their benches. Then Federigo landed in Cyprus, outside the town of Limisso. In the roadstead there received him Thomas of Aquino, Riccardo Filangieri and Balian of Sidon. There was a party among the Barons, who offered the Emperor the regency, the guardianship of eleven-year-old Henry of Lusignan, Queen Alice's son. But his uncle was ruling in his name, John of Ibelin, the Constable, who was in possession of the castle of Beirut.

Federigo invited him and the young king to come from Nicosia to Limisso. A festive banquet was prepared. The Emperor's knights came in at the hall door, armed. Federigo leaned over the table to Ibelin : "Restore Beirut and what you and your brother have squandered these ten years". Ibelin gave a courteous, evasive answer. The Emperor leapt up, clasped his cranium : "By this head, which wears so many a crown, I want what I demand or you are my prisoner". Practised in the subtleties of statecraft, the Constable sought to extricate himself from this sudden arrest. The Emperor compelled him to appear before the feudal courts of Jerusalem and Cyprus, to promise two of his sons and twenty of his vassals as hostages. During the night Ibelin and his barons got up and away. Alarmed by the noise in the dark Federigo fled into the tower of the Knights of St. John, near his ships. He besieged the Constable in the impregnable castle of the God with the Quiver, the *Dieu d'Amour*. With him there advanced against the stronghold Bohemund of Antioch and Tripolis, the divorced consort of Queen Alice. Songs flew as if on golden ribbons over the battlements. John of Ibelin submitted and went with the Emperor, who put in his own castellans and bailiffs and, with a smile, borrowed thirty thousand bezants of Guy de Gibelet, to Famagusta, the home of the magician Fortunatus.

THE anchors burrowed into the mud of Acre. The Crusaders were awaiting the Emperor. The Archbishops of Narbonne, Cæsarea and Nazareth showed him honour, but they did not kiss him with the kiss of peace, as the ban of the Church was upon him. He told them that real, not feigned illness had brought him to such delay and he commissioned Henry of Malta and the Archbishop of Bari to negotiate on his behalf with the Apostolic See. He entrusted the supreme command to Herman of Salza, Filangieri, Eude of Montbéliard. Peter of Montague, the Master of the Templars, and the Lothringian Bertrand de Texis, a Knight of St. John, renounced their obedience to him. They fought, they said, for the Cross in the name of God and Christendom alone. The Emperor camped in Ricordane by the river Bel. From Nabulus came messengers of El-Kamil's, with Arabian stuffs, an elephant, racing camels and Arabian mules; also the Emirs Fakruddin and Salauddin El-Arbeli. The Emperor perceived: in his quarrel with his brother El-Asraf, the Sultan of Mesopotamia, over the booty of Damascus, El-Kamil wished to gain time. Fakruddin begged the *Emberur* to give them Thomas of Aquino and Balian again. Then El-Kamil departed as far as Tel-el-Ajul, the Hill of Calves near Gaza. In Ricordane the Assassins of the Lebanon submitted to the Emperor. Youths from the Sheikh Hassan Salah, the Old Man of the Mountain, knelt in burnooses before him, transfigured by the yearning for death and accoutred with daggers.

The Emperor went to Jaffa, a day's journey from Gaza. The sea broke against sombre basalt. The town was built on a sheer rock. It smelt of soap-boiling and the workshops of tanners; the house of one of these was pointed out to him, that of Simon, with whom Peter had lodged. Storms delayed the arrival of the ships, the army was in distress. They reached harbour with news for Federigo. The Pope had in Perugia released his subjects from their oath of allegiance. He who called himself Emperor was Frederick, a servant of Mahomet, raging against the servants of Christ. With his brother Berthold, Reynold of Spoleto had occupied Papal territory and had been excommunicated. Soldiers had mustered under the Cardinal Priest Giovanni de Colonna and that ass John of Brienne, who was accompanied by Walter. While he, the Emperor, lay in this stinking port, Gregory was planning his dethronement. Federigo concealed his grief behind a cheerful countenance ; and he was impelled to turn back.

Starving pilgrims having robbed places near Jaffa, El-Kamil, now El-Asraf's fraternal friend against Ennasir-Daud, sent Federigo arms ; of them the country had abundance. The Emperor, disarming himself, sent him his helmet, his sword, his scale armour. He conversed with Fakruddin about the sages of Araby, the poet Mutanabbi, about Islam, fiery Jennahan, spirits, djinns and, a joke for him, the blue-eyed, about the sura in which the Prophet speaks of evildoers with blue eyes. Through Fakruddin El-Kamil surrendered secret letters to him. Pagellus Guidonis, the Pope's notary, and the Dominican Walter had written to the Sultan not to restore the kingdom of Jerusalem to the Emperor and had betrayed his life to Frankish knights. Express ships from Apulia came to land outside the ring of basalt. Sicily was in danger unless help were sent for. Federigo opened himself to Fakruddin after chatting with him about the riddles of mathematics. " The Kings and the Pope ", said he to him, " know of my voyage. I would lose their esteem if I achieved nothing among you. Is not Jerusalem the cradle of the Christian religion and have not you yourselves destroyed it ? Give it to me in the condition in which it now is, in order that I may lift up my head among the Kings. I renounce all profit in advance." The Sultan ceded the Holy City to him and, to the end that henceforward the pilgrims might

KNIGHTS ON GUARD IN THE PALACE

[*face p.* 136

Palermo. Clasped in her symmetrical brown arms he fell into drunken sleep.

The glow of morning made orange-yellow the sky. Sheikh Abdelkerim clambered up the white minaret on the Caid's house and sang the sura of the Koran: "Never is the Messiah too proud to be a servant of Allah, nor are the angels who stand near him". The Caid reproved the Sheikh for disregarding the Sultan's prohibition. The Emperor woke and asked: "O Caid, who is the man who early this morning climbed the minaret and gave voice to the sura?" The Caid made excuses. Federigo spake: "It is wrong, that ye should change your law and your customs for my sake. Ye would not have to do that, even if ye were in my realm". He betook himself back to the house of the Knights of St. John. There Herman of Salza reported to him that, through the Archbishop of Cæsarea, the Patriarch had put the Church of the Holy Sepulchre under the interdict. Walter the Dominican was saying masses only in churches of no renown. The Emperor learned that the Templars plotted to murder him at the spot in the Jordan where Jesus had been baptized by the Baptist. He straightway gave orders to depart away from Jerusalem.

The pilgrims hurried after him. The Canons of the Holy Sepulchre had refused a tax towards the re-building of the fortification-walls. Now they wanted to pay. The Emperor said this was not the time for dis-cussion. Without seeing anyone more in the city he set off in angry haste on the road to Jaffa. In Acre he called the Patriarch to account, who greeted the excom-municated with impenetrable countenance. "I, not you," he shouted—because with the King of France's money Gerald was recruiting an army of knights for the Holy Land—"am King of Jerusalem." The Patriarch responded that his soul were in peril if he obeyed one under the ban of the Church. Through his heralds the Emperor summoned the Christian army, laymen, priests and monks to the open field. "I will suffer no foreign

Fakruddin, a smiling guest. He entered the Sakhra
and beheld on the cupola the golden inscription of the
great Ayyubite Saladin : " This Jerusalem Saladin has
purged of the idolaters ". " Where are the idolaters ? "
he asked, and, of the wardens : " Why are there lattices
before the gates of the Sakhra ? " They said : " So that
the sparrows cannot come in ". The Emperor smiled :
" And now Allah has brought you the pigs ". Pillars,
bases and capitals were inserted from Solomon's temple
and that of the goddess Venus. It was the time of the
mid-day prayer ; with the Muslims the Emperor obeyed
the call of the muezzims. He knocked over a Christian
priest who begged of him in the Sakhra. " You swine,
the Sultan in his clemency has allowed us to tarry in this
mosque, and you do such things here. By God, he who
does so again shall die." He looked at Mahomet's
judgment seat, the precipitous gorge over which Solomon
had spanned the steel blade, the copper horn stuck with
threads of cobweb. And he desired to know where
the horsehair was to be fixed on Doomsday, the bridge
for the souls of the dead. But Fakruddin felt that he was
a Dehri, without faith in the Last Judgment or
Eternity.

The evening was pale purple, voluptuously blue
the night. The Emperor avoided the Christian pilgrims
and, at the Caid's table, ate with the Saracens. He talked
about sun, moon and stars with Sheikh Alameddin, the
learned astronomer whom El-Kamil had sent to him.
Ibn-Sabin dedicated to him a treatise on logic, surnamed
the Imperial. Federigo clapped together his hands
bathed in oils and spices. A curtain parted, flitting
jugglers of the East displayed their arts. Dancing girls,
with silver bosses over their breasts, their stretched,
henna-red bellies bare, danced, twisting their navels.
They were the black-eyed houris of Paradise, in which
flows the fountain Salsabil. The *Emberur's* couch was
shared by a woman from Antioch, half Greek, half
Arab, the lovely Theophano whom he had brought with
him from Jaffa. She was destined to follow him to

barking as they begged for alms. Golden lamps threw quivering circles on rose-coloured limestone; the marble wall in the tomb was rasped away by filthy lips. Through yonder two windows on Easter eve the fire of Heaven came flaming in. In yonder sacristy were preserved the sword and spurs of Godfrey of Bouillon. In yonder deep crypt Helena, Constantine's spouse, had found Christ's cross. Through a crack the blood of the Saviour dripped into a hole under Golgotha, awakening Adam. The Emperor, a shiver along his spine, muttered the name of Mary's and the carpenter's son and that of Allah.

The day following was the fifth Sunday in Lent. He would hold service, despite the interdict, Frederick had told Herman of Salza. He desisted for no representations of his. No chant resounded, no priestly benediction. In the dead twilight of the Church of the Sepulchre Frederick, his blue dalmatic hung about him, took a king's crown of gold from the altar and crowned himself with it. In the House of the Knights of St. John he addressed the pilgrims in Frankish, Berard and the Archbishop of Padua present. The Pope had urged him to the voyage, had excommunicated him, written in hostile intent to Jaffa, misled by the rumour that he had proceeded not to the Holy Places, but to other regions in order to raise an army against the Church. To end the quarrel he would do anything redounding to the honour of God, Church and Empire. High as God had exalted him, he was prepared to bow before the Highest and also before him who was his vicegerent on earth. In Latin, then in German, Herman of Salza interpreted this speech.

With a small following the Emperor went across to the Saracens' quarters. The *hodjas* of the rocky cathedral had lamented the entry of the Christians with sighs and shrill chanting. At El-Kamil's command Shemseddin had driven them away, compelling them to leave in the mosque the silver lamps and vestments they had carried off. Federigo came, accompanied by the Caid and by have a free, safe road to the Sepulchre of the Lord, the districts as far as the coast and Jaffa castle, moreover Bethlehem, Nazareth, Toron, Sidon and Montfort. For their prayers the Saracens were to keep in Jerusalem the Kubbet-es-Sakhra, the Caliph Omar's rocky cathedral and the mosque El-Aksa with the space round Solomon's temple. Prisoners—those of Damietta too—were to be exchanged, a new ten years' armistice was to begin.

The Emperor summoned to him four of the Syrian barons, after them the Grand Masters of the Orders and the bald, ruddy-cheeked Bishops of Winchester and Exeter. "Within a few days", he boasted, "more has been attained by a divine miracle than by human power, that which in days gone by mighty princes have been unable to compass either with innumerable armies or by fear and other means." The Bishops were incredulous towards blasphemer's theology of this sort; they said it was for the Patriarch Gerald to decide. The Patriarch scorned the compact. The Emperor solemnly ratified it in the presence of Fakruddin and Salauddin; if he broke it, he would consume the flesh of his left hand. The Germans rejoiced. Without the Patriarch, Frederick advanced through the dusty grey plain towards Jerusalem.

THEY were in a hollow road when upon dark hills appeared a maze of stone, tower-battlements, domes and roofs, huddled together like sheep. They fell to the ground in the parched, riverless valley of Kedron. That over yonder was the crest of the Mount of Olives, where, beneath the cypresses of Gethsemane, the Saviour had suffered. At the gates the Emperor was received by Shemseddin, the Caid of Nabulus. He had his quarters in the House of the Knights of St. John. He visited Christ's sepulchre. He walked through the entrance with the red and yellow marble slab, on which Joseph of Arimathea and Nicodemus wrapped the dead Jesus in cloths; and he saw the tattered creatures knight here ", he said. " The Count of Acerra, my deputy, will chastize anyone who disobeys." Crossbowmen stamped on to the gates of Acre and put iron bars on them against the Templars. Begging friars who preached against Frederick were torn from the pulpits. They were beaten naked, with clubs, through the streets. But Templars crept in, disguised, nor did the Emperor succeed in gaining possession of their Order's fortress.

He had the cargo-ships broken up and the machines of war carried on to Henry of Malta's galleys. On the first of May, before dawn already, he went to sea behind the slaughter house. The vulgar people had lain in wait for him. With bristling lances John of Ibelin and Eude of Montbéliard pushed them back. They pelted the Emperor with camel's dung, which filthied his eyelashes, and with shrill mockery commended him to the protection of God. While the vessels were yet near the coast, swarms of locusts came humming along under the clouds. Brushing their feelers the vermin flew into the breakers and against the masts as well. They were trodden into a mash by the soldiers' feet. The Emperor squirmed with disgust and vomited.

EVEN while the Landgrave Lewis was alive, the Landgravine Elisabeth had been given to works of mercy. She had seen the Crucified in Eisenach church and was filled with such fear that she recovered her senses only after water had been sprinkled over her face. She put away crowns, clasps, ribbons, veils and buttons and wore smocks of hair and wool over her body, which she ploughed up with her scratching nails. She looked after the starving, who were feeding themselves on crab-apples, roots and sloes, and built a hospital for the sick under the Wartburg. Once, the story went, the Landgrave had met her and a maid-servant. They were carrying burdens of pitchers and of baskets with meat, eggs and bannocks for the poor of the town. " Let me have a look ", said her lord and lifted up the folds of her cloak. There were no victuals in the baskets, but heaps of red roses. The Landgravine had dealings with the emissaries of the Minorite Order, with Francesco of Assisi's barefoot brethren. Her ghostly father was the preacher Conrad, the judge of heretics.

When she became a widow, Henry Raspe, her husband's brother, drove her from the Wartburg. Bishop Egbert of Bamberg, her uncle, gave her and her household Botenstein Castle to dwell in. Her thick hair turned gray, the salt of sorrow darkened her eyes. Then she received from the Bishop the news that the train from Italy with Lewis's remains was drawing nigh through the land of Franconia. Priests, schoolboys and laymen went out to meet the hearse, amid mournful chanting. The Landgravine Elisabeth prayed in the nave of Bamberg cathedral in which, before the silver cross, they set down the bier. She opened the bier; the dead man's bones rested in it. As the candles gleamed, the priests bellowed out the vigils, here and in Reinhardsbrunn, the monastery where he was buried.

Rudolph of Vargula, the cup-bearer, reconciled Elisabeth and Raspe. But she did not desist from chastizing herself, humbling herself in lowliness. She journeyed to her confessor Conrad in Marburg. She had a peasant's cot in Wehrden, round which she planted bushes. She slept against the stairs. The smoke made her eyes water, she suffered discomfort with rain, frost and wind. Together with her maids, she built herself a little house of lath and mud next the barefoot friars. She was content with peas, beans and cabbage, wore only a coarse dress, washed trenchers and vessels and teazed wool. She undid the shoes of a leper-woman, washed the sick without repugnance at their filth and, in the moonlight, bestowed bread and flaming fire upon those who still lingered in corners and under hedges, who were crippled and could not go.

She was an idiot, a fool in God. Conrad the preacher spoke to her about the snares of the devil and about the heretics, who in their congregations fornicated with a black cat or a frog the size of an ox. He said : " Kill the sin within thyself ". He tore the garment from her white bosom, under the cowl his glance was greenish, like that of a wolf falling upon a flock. He whipped her, struck her maid-servants, struck her even over the ears, flogged her with rods. She kissed his sandals and, afterwards, the flags he had trodden. She showed her women her raw shoulders which were crusted with clots of blood. " See, such is the holy man's love for me and the love I bear to God."

THE keels of the galleys approached Brindisi harbour. Pope Gregory had declared Frederick for dead. There was no Emperor but himself, boasted John of Brienne, elected Latin Emperor of Constantinople. On the coast he distributed guards, to fasten upon his rival. if he should return. But with displeasure he and the French heard flitting about the *sirvente* of a troubadour from Toulouse, Guilhem Figeira : " Rome, it is my consolation, that soon thou wilt come to perdition, when the rightful Emperor restores his fortunes and does what he should. Verily, Rome, then wilt thou decay. O God, Saviour of the world, let me live to see that ". Of a sudden the winged rumour arose, Frederick had come. John of Brienne and the Cardinal Colonna announced it to Gregory at Perugia. In his hatred the Pope vacillated. He must be extirpated, the enemy of the Cross, damned to the pit of perdition, the contemner of morality, the anti-Christ.

The flags with the eagles waved on the Emperor's ships. The inhabitants of Brindisi hesitated till, staggering, Federigo descended from the bridge. He was at the extreme edge of his lost kingdom. But in fear of him the Cardinal Pelagius retired with the Papal army from beleagured Sulmona and joined with Brienne and Colonna against little Caiazzo. Reynold of Spoleto came to the Emperor with the bow-practised Saracens of Lucera. Barques swam through the Adriatic with German lords and knights from Acre. They had already hoisted sail before Frederick—Conrad of Hohenlohe, the Counts of Heiligenberg, Helfenstein, Leuchtenberg and Dewin in the Slavonic marches. They had had Venice for their goal and were obliged to come to land in a storm. They were ready to serve the Emperor against the Pope. He was preparing in Barletta, subduing places that had fallen away; and after two months he proceeded to the attack. He wrote to Fakruddin, his friend, with words of longing: "Cut was the cable of patience, despair in us after the enthusiasm of your converse, burst the girdle of hope". He wrote to him about the Messiah's successor and the priests of the Christian religion, about the crew of scoundrels and criminals whom their duplicity had mustered. "Now, accordingly, without wasting time, we go against the enemy."

Thomas of Aquino was in Capua, to encourage the city. The Emperor sent the Archbishops of Reggio and Bari and the Master of the Teutonic Order to Gregory. "The Pope", he mocked, "is trembling for his own skin." He knew that the Cardinal Colonna had left the Army of the Keys and was in Perugia; *denarii* for the mercenaries were lacking. On the Scoltenna the Imperially inclined towns of Cremona, Parma and Modena defeated the Bolognese. With siege-engines mounted on carts the latter smashed up the *Carroccio* of Parma. Dead was the crew, dead the team of oxen. They of Cremona won back the *Carroccio*, they of Bologna threw their own into a ditch. The fierce battle lasted throughout the moonlit September night. The Sienese beat the Florentines and harried them from hill to hill.

Near Foggia, which barred its gates against him, Templars and Knights of St. John from Jerusalem asked Frederick to receive them. They were wishful to acknowledge Conrad, Yolande's son, if he would send him across the sea. He told them he would shortly do everything necessary. He cut across the hill country on the road to Avellino. Now he made his appearance in

Capua, now he took Calvi, Mairano, Alife, Venafro. The Papal army fled over the frontier to Rome. John of Brienne, mindful of the Byzantines' crown, turned over the Alps of Savoy into *la doulce France*. Only with pains did Cardinal Pelagius prevent the garrisons of Monte Cassino, the fortress-monastery, and of Rocca Janula from dispersing.

Federigo, the new Alexander, was encamped near San Toma. Noble families of Rome did homage to him. He rewarded Suessa and reduced Sora to ashes : the plough was to tear up the stricken site. Many were flayed, many hung from the gallow's tree. In Aquino Frederick celebrated the feast of St. Martin. Herman of Salza brought the Pope's assent to a cessation of hostilities. The Emperor, the victor, desired absolution of Gregory. He was indulgent to the Cardinal Priest of Sabina, Honorius's classical letter-writer, who journeyed to him at Aquino with the Archbishop of Messina. For the Legate Pelagius Thomas of Capua demanded that he should march out of Monte Cassino scot-free and that the Bishops of Aquino and Alife, who had taken refuge with him, the prisoners and those faithful to the Pope should be spared. Gently flowed his speech from the Cardinal Priest's fine, full lips. The Emperor questioned him about Aristotle. Thomas of Aquino complained about Berthold of Spoleto, who had just made an inroad upon Peter's Patrimony and ravaged the frontier with fire and sword. The Emperor reprobated this and made promises. When he touched upon removal of the interdict, the Cardinal Priest became evasive ; he had no authority.

He went with Frederick from San Germano to Suessa, but, at Christmas, no further with him towards Capua. Vainly he begged the Pope to say what he wanted, settlement or war. The Emperor, who had given gifts to the German Crusaders and allowed them to depart, was made privy that Gregory was dragging out his decision merely on account of the Lombards. The Tiber, swollen by icy cold storms, lapped with its yellow

145

10

waves in the aisles of San Paolo Fuori and against St. Peter's. The Romans saw a judgment of heaven in this. The people over-ruled the Senate and besought the Pope, whom they had ignominiously driven out nearly two years before, to return. He came during the first week of Lent. The Romans gave full throat to their welcome. German Princes stood among the red Cardinals of the Lateran, the Dukes of Austria, Carinthia and Meran, the Patriarch of Aquileia, the Archbishop of Salzburg, the Bishop of Ratisbon. The Pope kept them in suspense. The wrangling still continued, concerning Gaeta and Santa Agata. Then Gregory called James of Vitry to him also and waiting Thomas of Capua. He did not on Maundy Thursday name the Emperor among the excommunicated.

The Princes were with Frederick at Foggia. He had, as sole punishment, deprived the city of its walls; a wood of evergreen oaks grew round his palace there. He celebrated Easter with the Germans. He turned towards Capua, towards San Germano. The white Dominican brought him the Pope's draft treaty. The victor offered to swear obedience to the Church. It was night when the ropes of the bells swung and they pealed out into the plain. In the cramped cathedral a buzzing multitude was gathered, the King of Thessalonica, the Germans, Archbishops, Abbots, Justiciaries, Barons. The grounds of his excommunication were read aloud. The Emperor swore, Everard of Salzburg had to justify him, Thomas of Capua to invalidate the justification. Federigo was very tired and pale.

Leopold of Austria died of a sore disease. For hours the muffled bells of San Germano jangled. The Duke's corruptible flesh was boiled from his bones. The Archbishop of Salzburg and Hademar of Kuenring conveyed them to his home, to the monastery of Lilienfeld. The Pope and the Emperor made ready to do the dead man homage. Federigo pitched a splendid camp in Ceperano, by the banks of the Garigliano. Great ones of the Church put in their appearance, among them the

KNIGHT AND BENEFACTOR

Archbishop of Arles, the Bishop of Winchester, Milo of Beauvais, who had been delayed with his French knights, in order yet to win renown in arms against Frederick, and Guala the Dominican, now Bishop of Brescia. In one of the chapels, John, Bishop of Sabina, and Thomas of Capua, Cardinals both, set the Emperor free from the ban of the Church. They kindled the candles anew, they raised the glittering pyx. Graciously did the Pope salute him who surpassed all rulers, his best beloved son. Federigo surprised him in Anagni. He had his gold embroidered pavilion at the foot of a hill, by a springing fount. Gregory had himself conducted to him. He received him and Herman of Salza in his father's house, the ochre-yellow home of the Conti. Bending down to him on trembling legs he gave him the kiss of peace. He had oozing red-rimmed eyes, and Frederick started back.

WHEN young Henry turned back with the armed knights from Trent, Duke Lewis of Bavaria became his guardian. When the Emperor was in Jerusalem, round about Christmas, the King broke with the latter at Hagenau. He accused him of being in league with the Pope. The King wished to bear the responsibility alone.

The Cardinal Deacon Otto of San Nicholas *in carcere Tulliano* journeyed as Legate to Germany, seeking an Anti-King. Henry of England was negotiating with Otto of Brunswick, who had bought his release from confinement at Schwerin. But the Lüneburg Prince did not desire to die like his uncle, deserted by the Church. By way of Meitingen and Constance the King marched against Duke Lewis and ravaged his villages and monasteries. The Bavarians threatened the Duke of Meran's stronghold Wolfrathausen with incendiaries. They were surprised; they who did not remain for dead were scattered. Duke Lewis had to furnish hostages and abjure.

The Legate was on his way from Valenciennes to the Danube. As he could not get through Staufic

Swabia, he went to Strasburg. The King appeared with an army in front of the city, against which he was wroth because of the disgrace of Blodelsheim, when the Count of Pfirt and Count Egeno of Freiburg succumbed to Bishop Berthold and the Landgrave of Habsburg. But Henry did not overcome Strasburg. His troops proved inferior to the Bishop's. The Legate proceeded unmolested to Constance, to Upper Germany. The King granted the men of Strasburg an armistice and retired to Ueberlingen. Robbers on the high roads, on the Rhine and in the Vosges plagued Alsace.

Close to the Emperor's son stood the High Steward of Waldburg, the Cup-Bearers Everard and Conrad of Winterstetten. Silently there went out into the dark Henry of Tann, the Protonotary. The young King listened to the double-tongued and gave largesse to jugglers and singers of songs. His marriage with Margaret of Austria went agly. He was at feud too with the Count of Freiburg on account of the Jews and authority over them and their money-bags. He advanced against Breisach and then issued a prohibition against embracing the cause of the steeple-hatted yeomen of the chamber against the Count. At Nürnberg he became reconciled, before the Emperor had done so, with Lewis of Bavaria. On his seal he called himself Duke of Swabia in his own right. But northwards he got no further than Gelnhausen and Friedberg.

Arrogant and impotent he held Diet at Worms. The citizens had banded themselves together against the Bishop and had built for their Council a great house of stone in the Hagengasse. As the Bishop complained, the King commanded the Court Chancellor Sigfrid of Ratisbon to abate the nuisance of the Council. Envoys from the Bishop of Liége complained against himself for confirming the liberties of that city and permitting it to form a union with Huy, Dinant, St. Truiden, Maastricht, Tongres and Fosses. Nevermore now was he to permit lordless confederacies. Not a guardian, but guardians kept watch over him. He went to

Würzburg to the Council of the Legate, who placed an interdict over Liége and Aix-la-Chapelle. The Princes of Saxony broke up the Council; the King, taking his resolution from others, agreed that a second should not be convoked at Mainz. He held Diet in Worms, and there came to it the Archbishops of Mainz, Treves, Cologne and Magdeburg, the Bishops of Ratisbon, Würzburg, Strasburg, Spires, Augsburg, Chur and Lausanne, the Abbots of St. Gall, Gengenbach, Weissenburg, Prüm and Inden, the Dukes of Brabant, Limburg, Lorraine and Meran, Counts and nobles. The King had granted the municipalities the right of coinage. On the following day he had to promulgate a Golden Bull. Every Prince was to enjoy his jurisdiction, counties and tithes in peace, according to the custom of his country. The King was forbidden to set up new towns or castles without the Princes or to strike new coins. Nor were the Imperial towns allowed to give protection to citizens living without their gates or an asylum to the excommunicated and condemned or to hinder vassals when they were on their way to join their lords again. The lords henceforward had the right of fortification over their towns. The young King was diminished and, with him, the German crown. He laughed with his singers and cup-bearers.

His brother-in-law, Frederick of Austria, fought against the hound Hademar of Kuenring and Henry, the latter's brother. They had acquired Duke Leopold's treasury, occupied the bank of the Danube near Klosterneuberg, burnt Krems and Stein and had retired to their rude castle of Dürrenstein. The Bohemians, under Ottaker's son Wenceslaus, rode plundering through the Ostmark. Now the knights were flogged, the rebellion was quenched. King Henry wished to be divorced from Margaret, Frederick's sister, who had borne him a child. He reproached the Babenbergs for not paying her dowry. He felt nothing for Agnes of Bohemia, who had been betrothed to him; but, familiar with Cligès and William of Orleans, he believed himself pining for love of her. Conrad of Bussnang, the Abbot of St. Gall, calmed Henry's unstable longings. The King feared his father, through whose agency he had been married. He sent the Abbot to Austria in the matter of the dowry. Ottakar died in the grey Vyšehrad at Prague. Agnes put on nun's habit.

In alliance with the Count of Wasserburg Duke Lewis of Bavaria had carried on a feud against the Bishop of Freising and had besieged the castle of Wörth on the Inn. He was advancing with his retinue over Kelheim bridge when a man who had been crouched in front of an image of the Virgin, gaunt, the lappet of his cloak over his red shock-head, leapt up against him and drove a dagger into his side. The Duke rattled out his ghost as the sun was setting. Servitors seized the man and tortured him with goads and pincers. He did not say who he was or who set him on. He lay dead on the river's bank, showing his teeth. The multitude dismembered him. Then the story went that the King had put the weapon into his hand, or even the Emperor; monks spread the rumour that he was a hired Assassin from the Old Man of the Mountain in the east.

POPE GREGORY had lovingly admonished Federigo when he had had the walls razed round Foggia, Civitate, Casale Nuovo and Santo Severo : " The work of peace, avowed by the oaths of so many men, turns, alas ! so quickly to woe and misery. Only see how (as is generally spoken) the two great lights have come together in order to plunge so many into the darkness of terror and affliction. They who are destined for the salvation of mankind act for its undoing ". He had warned him against suspicion and the doubting of documents. He demanded the extirpation of heresy in Naples and Aversa. The Emperor obeyed him. " These accursed Patarenes ", he said, " shall experience the passion of death for which they yearn." He sent the Archbishop of Reggio and Marshal Riccardo Filangieri, who arrested multitudes of heretics, to Naples. The obdurate they cast into the fire, the repentant into the dungeons of Monte Cassino and La Cava, with rusty gyves upon them.

Federigo was in Foggia when he gave the sign for seizing Reynold of Spoleto, who had dined with him but the day before, as if in favour. Pope Gregory interceded for him. Berthold took refuge in the stronghold of Antrodoco and defied the Emperor's men-at-arms; he escaped to Rome. Frederick's tipstaves patrolled the whole of Sicily in order to apprehend malefactors.

He called to Melfi Archbishop James of Capua to help in framing laws with the Chief Justices Peter of Vinea and Thaddæus of Suessa. "Since we alone", thus he began, savouring the sound of the words, while the notaries wrote it down after him, "have been raised on to the throne of the Roman Empire and other realms by the divine power and against the expectation of men, it is Our resolve, in humility before Jesus Christ, from whom We have received everything, to render account to the living God for the two-fold talent committed to Our keeping, by promulgating fit laws and, in especial, in that among Our realms which stands most in need of Our care. As therefore Our Kingdom of Sicily, the precious heritage of Our Majesty, has suffered much by confusion during Our infancy and Our absence subsequent thereto, We are under obligation with all Our powers to take thought for its tranquility and so We ordain these laws." At the head he placed his title of Cæsar Augustus, ruler of Italy, Sicily, Jerusalem and Arles, of Fortunate, Victorious and Triumphant. He was the god-like monarch and had the Justiciaries, the Chamberlains, the Bajuli of the towns far beneath him. There was nothing that, during these weeks at Melfi, he did not order according to his will and the planets of heaven. He spoke gaily of love-potions, such nonsense, and of capital punishment for those who administered them. Whoso sold poison for arrows was hanged. Fishermen were forbidden to pour into brook or river yew or similar herbs by which fish are killed. Ordeals, red-hot or cold, were forbidden. The adulteress and the adulterer—and Frederick, with wrinkled brow, aped the sour puisne judges—should have their noses cut off by the husband; should he refuse, the wanton was to be publicly whipped. A mother who brought her daughter to whoredom was also to be docked of her nose. The serf who lay with his lord's wife was to be castrated. "They are spotted like pards", he said of those born in Sicily. "We will not suffer them, man or girl, to marry foreigners without asking our leave." Then, with Peter of Vinea, he proceeded to delimit the Church's and the Orders' rights of property.

The Emperor read a letter from the Pope : he had learned of the laws he was preparing and had to fear that God's grace had been withdrawn from him : " It surprises us that thou lendest thine ear to counsellors who, animated by the spirit of impiety, would make of thee an enemy to God and man. May quiet reflection hereanent speak loudly to thine heart to the end that, in regard for thy fame and our admonition, thou keep each of us from the malediction of the people ". With him Gregory reproved the Archbishop of Capua; he was to refrain from further wrong. He could not excuse himself as being merely the pen. The Emperor weighed in his hand the golden augustals with the Roman eagle and his image as Cæsar, surmounted by the laurel and the gleaming diadem. "He annoys us," he said, "the Holy Father." To the Archbishop he gave friendly furlough.

He ratified the laws in a big council at Melfi. He built *fondachi* for the merchants and himself traded in corn that he had shipped. No one was authorized to sell salt but out of the State stores, silk the Jews of Trani alone. The treasurers extorted taxes which were called Collects. Date-palms were planted by Jews from Africa, cotton, indigo, henna, Syrian sugar-cane. There came yellow-wood, galingale, myrrh, terebinth, amber, musk, cardamom, rice, alum, ebony, silk, cassia, balsam, muscadel, ginger, rhubarb, camphor and cinnamon.

Wells were digged in sandy drouth. Federigo went into the Abruzzi to Lake Fucino, in order to conduct its waters into the Liris through Claudius's old level. An enormous piece of limestone, the Emperor's stone, lay on Monte Pellegrino. As long as the sun shone upon it, it was working-hours ; when reft of light, evening rest.

The Emperor himself hardly resided in Palermo more, he kept his court in the palace at Foggia. He forgot the laws, forgot the mute, devotedly mournful astonishment of Peter of Vinea, and lay with Theophano, the mother of Frederick of Antioch (of whom it was said that she was sister of El-Kamil), or else with one of his serving wenches. Eunuchs were there as in the Mansuriya, brown slaves, negro musicians with silver trumpets, Saracen girls as in Jerusalem, who, to the beat of the tambourine, danced in thin veils on rolling balls of ivory. From Tunis and Egypt came the Emperor's strange animals. He had humped camels with saddlery of red leather from Tafilet, the Sultan's elephants who trumpeted through the park in the sultry noontide, snarling Berber lions, leopards, rugged bears, lynxes, an odd strutting giraffe, ostriches and parrots. And when he set out with his beasts, the impenetrable dust rolled over the sycamores.

He was curious about all created things. In a pond beside the palace he bred the bird-species peculiar to the swamp. While hawking he observed the herons', cranes', storks' and wild geese's lines of flight. He explored the secrets of the warm springs of Pozzuoli, of the wind, the mountains of fire and the magnetic needle. Daily now he has brought to him the wise Scotsman, Michael Scotus, who had been in Toledo and Bologna, the second Apollo, the astrologer and magician. Of him he wanted to know where Hell was and Purgatory and Paradise, what the earth stood on, how many heavens there were and who guided them, how God was seated on his celestial throne, what the angels and saints before him might be doing, whether a departed soul could reveal itself. "O happy Emperor," said the Scot to him, " if one man in this world might be able to escape death, you should be he who alone among all should escape death." The Sultan El-Kamil sent him the learned El-Hanifi, and with his Jews he expounded deep Maimonides. He loved the poems of the Troubadours and Trovatori, *Palamedes* and *Merlin*. One July evening near Gioia del Colle a minstrel struck the lute and in the rustics' speech sang of the rose whose leaves were scattered. Melancholy were the beatings of Federigo's cool heart.

THEN and later began the legends about him. He had, they said, a falcon dearer to him than a city. He set him upon a crane hovering high in the air. The falcon flew still higher, saw beneath him a young eagle, stooped to him so that he fell to earth through the tree-tops and strangled him until he was dead. The Emperor hurried thither believing it to be the crane. He discovered who it was. Angrily he summoned the executioner and ordered the falcon's head to be struck off, for he had slain his lord. While hunting green-clad in the forest, where a spring gurgled, he came upon a vagabond, who spread a snowy tablecloth upon the grass and had unleavened bread and a cup of tamarind wood. The King asked him for a drink. The vagabond lent him the cup. Federigo drank without putting his lip to it, put spurs into his horse and rode away with the cup. The vagabond saw that he was one of the Emperor's knights. The next day he went to court and complained. The King took pleasure in his story and asked : " Wouldst thou know thy cup again ? " He pulled forth the cup, said that he was the knight and rewarded the man for his honesty.

A smith was accused before him of disregarding festivals and excused himself by declaring that he was forced to make four *soldi* every day by his work ; one he returned, the second bestowed, the third wasted, the fourth he used. This he explained to the Emperor :

with the first he kept his father, the second he gave for alms, with the third he fed his wife and with the fourth himself. The Emperor forbade him to communicate the solution to anyone unless previously he had seen his countenance a hundred times. He put this question of the four *soldi* to his sages. They went to the smith and he opened his mouth for a hundred augustals which they brought him. The Emperor was angry with the smith ; but the latter defended himself : he had seen his countenance a hundred times on the gold coins. A Lombard knight had wished to leave nothing behind him, lived for ten years longer than he had contemplated, became poor and appeared at court, mournful. The Emperor banished him under pain of death ; for he had grudged all the world to inherit anything good of him. Among his sages he had Messer Bolgaro and Messer Martino Gosio. These he asked whether he might give his subjects and take from them as he pleased. The first, who answered Yes, he presented with a scarlet hat and a white palfrey, such as is given to minstrels ; for he had spoken his own wish ; the other, who said Nay, according to equity, he permitted to frame a law ; and so he received the more magnificent gift.

There came to him in pilgrims' cloaks three masters of the black art and did their trick. The sky grew dark, it rained, lightened, thundered, and hail, as if of steel ribbons, came sousing down. The Emperor's knights fled into their chambers, one hither, the other thither. The sky grew light again. The magicians took their leave and begged a guerdon. The Emperor said : " Ask ". And they asked. By the Emperor's side stood the Count of San Bonifazio. They said : " Lord, command thou this man that he come to our help against our enemies ". The Count went their road with them. They conducted him to a fair city, armed him with fine weapons, and noble knights served him. He was victorious in four pitched battles, wooed a wife, had children by her and reigned for many years. He grew very old, until the magicians returned to seek the

Emperor once more in his company. They travelled a long time. Then of a sudden they were at the Emperor's court and found him washing his hands in the same water that was being poured into the basin when the Count took his departure with the magicians.

Prester John was mighty in the three Indies. He dwelt hard by Paradise and the holy rivers, which are full of precious stones. He sent messengers to the Emperor Federigo, that they might ask him what were the best thing on earth and bestow upon him three jewels with secret properties. The Emperor said to them: " The mean is the best thing on earth ". But the virtue of the jewels he could not discover. Prester John sent to him a lapidary and wonderful ornaments in order by sleight to reave from him those three jewels again. The lapidary set forth with many stones of flaming beauty and took them in his hands at the Emperor's court, before barons and knights. He did not sell them, he gave them away, so that his praise penetrated to Federigo, who sent for him and in the end surrendered even the jewels to him. The lapidary seized the first: " This stone, lord, outweighs the best of your cities ". He took the second: " This, lord, your best province ". The third: " And this is worth more than your whole realm ". And by virtue of the third he became invisible. He descended the steps and journeyed homeward to his master. Others maintain that Prester John presented the Emperor with a garment woven by salamanders, which was not consumed by fire, a bottle of water from the well which gave eternal life and a magic ring.

The story went that Federigo had fallen a captive into the hands of the Saracen Sultan. He had a garden with cruel wild beasts that guarded four precious stones. He was willing to let the Roman Emperor free if he carried off the stones. The first stone conferred invisibility, the second invulnerability, the third agility, the fourth immortality. The Emperor offered to do so, if a hole were dug in the ground and he were given a cloth.

He leapt up out of the hole between the animals and snatched the first stone. He threw down the cloth, and they tore it in pieces. But when he saw that he had become invisible he had no more fear and took the remaining stones as well, however much the creatures raged. With the stones he went his way without the Sultan becoming aware of it.

Michael Scotus, the astrologer, he tested with the question, how far distant the heavens were from the floor of his palace; and when he had named the figure he sent him away. Before he returned he had architects and carpenters lower the floor. When he was then seated with the astrologer in that room again, he questioned him anew. He calculated and said that the heavens must have been raised since or the ground sunk. Then the Emperor discovered that he was a true astrologer. The same learned man dissuaded him from being let blood when the moon stood in the constellation of the Heavenly Twins. The Emperor chose such a time for all that; the knife slipped out of the barber-surgeon's hand and scratched the Emperor's foot. He shut up a man in a wine-butt, for he wished to show that the breathing soul also perished with the body. He gave orders to nurses to serve the babes at their breasts without talking to them. In this wise would be shown what the original language of mankind was, whether Hebrew or Greek, Latin or Arabic. But the children all died away, mute. He had a carp put into a lake near Kaiserslautern with a gold ring in its gills, so that it would appear to what age it might continue.

There was a diver from Catania, who had offended his mother with sinful thoughts; and she put upon him the curse that he must ever stay in the water. He was called " the fish ". The Emperor heard of him and commanded him to bring up a golden cup from the waters of the Faro. Federigo stood watching with all his court. And Nicola twice dived for the cup; and he had to tell the Emperor about the crawling beasts of the sea, about the corals and the wreckage down there.

He besought him: "Do not send me down again; for the waves are agitated, and I shall never return". The Emperor did not condescend to mercy. The diver's neck was never raised again, he drowned in the storm.

THE Landgravine Elisabeth, in the lazar-house at Marburg, lay for hours as if dead, and yet her life endured. She saw Jesus Christ and the saints, face to face. For many days thereafter her eyes had a strange gleam. A man of the town of Marburg, who had been blind from his mother's womb, was saying his prayers in church. She helped him pray and knelt for him. Then the blind man had his sight. And afterwards the sickness of her ecstasy tore Elisabeth like the pangs of labour. But she achieved no further miracle.

She knew her end was drawing nigh and laid herself upon her deal bed. When for twelve days she had been almost without breath, one of her maids heard a sweet bird's voice twittering in her throat. Elisabeth lay with her face to the wall, turned to the maid and said: "Where art thou, sweetheart?" And then: "Hast thou heard aught?" The maid answered: "Aye". And Elisabeth: "I tell thee, between me and the wall a bird was singing so sweetly that I was wakened by it and had to join it in song".

She would admit no one to her more and said: "I will think upon Doomsday and the strict judgment upon me and my almighty judge". She sent for Conrad the preacher, who took her confession. She said, her voice dying behind her palsied tongue, that she had not sufficiently thanked God for his suffering on the Cross. She laughed like a crazed woman, bared herself, demanded new hurts from the fists of the preacher, who, his wolf's eyes narrowed, stood gigantic against the dull glow of the stove-hole. "Avaunt! Avaunt!" she yelled at him, and it was as if she meant to drive off the devil. Then, in the night, when the monster had departed with heavy tread over the stone floor, the bird's voices again sang from out her like angels.

ST ELISABETH

[face p. 158

A cock crowed, a second, a third in the black gloom of morning. The sick wept and groaned in the lazar-house, Elisabeth drooped her head as if she were asleep; but she had gone to her eternal rest. The maids clothed the dead woman in an old grey smock, as she had desired. Priests and monks brought her amid litanies to the chapel of the house. For four days she did not alter, save that she turned white and livid spots became visible upon her. In Reinhardsbrunn monastery she appeared to one of the brethren, who had the office of grinder and whose right arm had been broken by the wheel of the mills when he sought to mend it. He was praying in the night of her passing. He saw her, with royal raiment upon her and shining very clear. She asked him: "How farest thou and how art thou behaved, Brother Volkmar?" He kept silence until he recognized her and said: "Why are you wearing such splendid clothes who are wont to go in such poor and wretched raiment?" She answered: "I have changed my condition". And she touched his arm, and when he felt it it was whole and so was the hand too. But many miracles, it was said, happened after her funeral—to Isentrud of Slitzenrode's infant son who was blind from birth, with eyes like frog's spawn, and got his sight, to Lutgarde of Fronehusen's boy, who was dead and brought to life again, to the humpbacked, strumous daughter of Sophie of Bütingen, to a lame man, a drowned scholar, brought to life again, to a widow who had an ulcer in her nose and was converted from heresy, to a maniac, a woman with the stone, an epileptic and a dumb man, a girl with an issue of blood—four and thirty all told.

THE Emperor Frederick was angry with the King of the Germans, his son. He was awaiting him at his Diet in Ravenna. The King remained in Augsburg and sent the Grand Master of the Teutonic Order back to his father. The Lombards replied to the Pope, he should see to it that the Emperor travelled without an army, and again they closed the Alpine roads.

Frederick hesitated in Ravenna. He had the Archbishops of Palermo and Reggio with him, the Counts Thomas of Aquino and Berard of Loreto. He went through San Vitale, through San Orso and San Apollinare to the palace of the Exarchs and the gloomy tomb of Theoderic the Great, who, in the Teutons' superstition, had been the harbinger of the wars. Dominion over the world—the shadow of a cloud. To deceive his smouldering wrath, he gave instructions to lay bare the tomb of Galla Placidia, the Roman empress. Dully glittered the mosaics. From sarcophagi they scratched away the rubble, from the coffins of the empress, of Theodosius and Saint Elisæus. Federigo called to mind Theophano, the Arabian Greek, whom a flow of blood to the heart had killed a week before : how was the arch of her brows bent, how did she smile in the willingness of her surrender ? He had a mistress of Piedmont, Blanca Lancia, Marquis Manfred's sister. She and her brother, who had accompanied him to Jerusalem, were here in Ravenna and he had spent the nights unashamed with her, who, blue-eyed like himself, received him quaking.

There too arrived, in dejection, Herman of Salza. There came the Archbishop of Magdeburg, Count of Romagna, there came the Patriarch of Aquileia, the Archbishop of Besançon, the Bishops of Bamberg,

Brixen, Ratisbon, Worms, Osnabrück and Lausanne, the Dukes of Saxony, Meran and Carinthia, the Landgrave Henry Raspe, many Counts, Henry of Neifen, the Hohenlohes, the Bolandens and, from the court of the King of the Germans in Hagenau, the cup-bearer Conrad of Klingenberg—many by sea, many who had sneaked through the passes in disguise. Messengers from the burgesses of Worms were there : they saw with shame that they were impotent against the Bishop. The Emperor despatched to Sicily the Count of Aquino, to Tuscany Gebhard of Arnstein. At Christmas he strode into the cathedral of San Orso, the golden dalmatic with the eagles hung about him, the diadem upon his head. In Archbishop Theoderic's palace he pronounced the Imperial ban against the Lombards. And yet again he called those who remained obstinate into the cathedral. No loyal town, he ordained, might choose a *Podestà* for itself who had been born among the rebels. The envoys of Genoa heard it and murmured ; for Pagano Pietrasanta, their *Podestà* since Candlemas, was a Milanese. The Emperor was making a trial of his strength upon them.

Guala of Brescia, the white Dominican, wanted for his Order the right of tracking down the heretics in Germany and in Italy. The Emperor granted it him, in order to be serviceable to the Pope. He had summoned the Princes and his son to Aquileia. He suddenly, on learning that Gregory's legates, James of Palestrina and Otto of St. Nicholas, who had been looking for an Anti-King, were journeying to him from Bologna, set spurs in his horse. He rode to the lagoons of Ravenna, to the harbour. The south wind bellied one of his ships' sails. He swung himself aboard, was carried by the breeze into the estuary of the Po della Maëstra, near Loreo. His retinue was small ; the representatives of the Venetian Republic, who greeted him, thought it lacking in Imperial pomp. He alleged that he was asking for leave to testify to his veneration for Saint Mark. When he made his entrance into

Venice, besides Berard of Palermo, the Counts of Loreto and Giraci, Jordan Filangieri, Tebaldo Francesco and the Treasurer Richard, the German Princes and the Marquis Lancia had overtaken him. The watchman on the Campanile blew the trump, the brazen bells reverberated, the gondoliers pressed round the Bucentaur of the Doge Jacopo Tiepolo, who, in brocade and ermine, the purple *corno* with the flashing hoop on his cambric cap, was rowed out to meet the Emperor. With the Doge he knelt before the altar in the green and gold church of Saint Mark's and he made the Saint presents of gold and precious stones. To fight the Genoese he told the Venetians he would grant them what they wished of him. They asked protection for their shipwrecked goods. He paid for their restrained hospitality with concessions to their trade with Sicily and, on the mainland, bestowed privileges upon the monasteries of San Nicola and San Giorgio. The Doge, by the sea-lapped steps of the Piazzetta, wrinkled his forehead as the Emperor sailed away with his Germans.

For the last time Frederick, through the Bishop of Ratisbon and the High Steward Wernher of Bolanden, had cited King Henry into his presence. And again he had to delay in Aquileia until he he was to judge put in his appearance. Easter had come before his son drew near. He banished him to Cividale in the Friulian Alps. Twelve of the Princes had to beseech Henry to stand his mediators with his father, to release them of their oath to him if he should break his own, to promise that he would keep at arm's length all counsellors hostile to his father and thwart every plot against his majesty. Then Frederick with the lords moved over to the Natisone also. Offhand and frivolous was the King's submission.

The Emperor proceeded with the Diet to Udine. He addressed the Princes, the apples of his eyes, the pillars of his throne, and confirmed the sovereign powers which the headstrong boy had squandered upon them. Duke Otto of Bavaria was absent, also Frederick of

Austria. The Emperor awarded the Bishop of Worms the fief of Neckarau against the Wittelsbach and empowered him to pull down the Worms burgesses' court. King Henry took his leave with the Bishop of Freising, the Dukes of Saxony and Meran and the Counts. Clammy and trembling were his fingers in his father's clasp. Frederick stared after him as he rode in harness round the stone buildings of the fortress.

He went over the flat Tagliamento to Pordenone. Here Frederick of Austria did him homage, and he made him a gift of 8,000 marks, to compose the Babenberg's dispute with Henry. Alberico of Romano paid him homage, son to Ezzelino (he had become a black monk), a brother of Ezzelino the Third, the Tiger, Veronese *Podestà*, wet with his enemies' blood. There appeared envoys of the King of France, the pious Lewis, with whom the Emperor concluded a treaty, envoys of El-Asref, the Sultan of Damascus, with an orrery of gold and jewels ; on it sun, moon and stars moved according to the laws of the eternal harmony. Frederick was lost in gazing upon it ; it was to be his dearest possession, after Conrad, his son. Among the Saracens were young men from the Lebanon, with the mark of the Old Man of the Mountain.

In Padua the Papal legates negotiated with the Lombards about satisfaction for the Emperor. But the cities demanded a guarantee against the German army. The Emperor, in Pordenone, at variance with Herman of Salza too, laid an oath upon the Princes after a year's space to advance upon Italy with him, under arms. News came that Ibelin and the King of Cyprus had taken Acre and burnt Marshal Riccardo Filangieri's Imperial fleet wintering there. Frederick embarked with the Saracens on swift galleys for Apulia, menaced on the voyage by Dalmatian pirates.

HE hunted in the dark forest about Melfi and let a convict, whose life was forfeit, climb down a deep ravine against which a nest with still unfledged white falcons was plastered. He shut himself in with Blanca Lancia and Manfredi, her child. But hatred against the Lombards buzzed in his ears and uneasiness for Acre, Tyre and Jerusalem. On the day of the Hejira, on which Mahomet the prophet and Abu Bekr had fled on camels to Yathrib, he dined with the Bishops of Sicily, the envoys of Damascus and the Assassins. Then certain news was brought that Riccardo Filangieri, victor over the Cypriotes at Casal Imbert, had been almost destroyed near Agridi and Dieu d'Amour and had with difficulty got away to Hayton, the King of Armenia. Alice of Montferrat, the young Queen of the Island, had died in Cherine.

The Emperor knew that Gregory was in Rieti or Spoleto, and not in Rome, which was in a ferment against him. Since autumn an Imperial garrison had lain in Viterbo, to protect it. Federigo appointed Magister Peter of San Germano to represent to the Pope to what danger the Holy Land was exposed as the result of his enemies' wiles ; and Gregory punished the Patriarch of Jerusalem. He admonished the Emperor to crush the Romans with his triumphant right arm. In Brindisi Frederick had made preparations against Ibelin. In place of the mercenaries Herman of Salza went overseas. Then flared up in Sicily the revolt against the tyrant, who had robbed Roger of Aquila's heir, who kept the suspect in terror with the lists of names drawn up by his *sbirri*, whose taxes oppressed the whole people. Riccardo de Montenero fled from Messina before the conspiracy of Martino Balloni, the butcher who swung the chopper with muscular arm.

Federigo had no armed assistance for the Pope. But he would pretend to be his friend. This he asseverated through Henry of Morra and Peter of Vinea. He was in Aprocina, the Pope in Anagni. And he wrote to Gregory : " Far be it from us to hold the brute, stupid notion that Papacy and Empire were opposed to one another in enmity. We two, who are called one, and assuredly feel the same, will work in harmony for the good of the faith. In renewing the liberty of the Church as well as of the Empire, we will sharpen the swords entrusted to us against the adversaries of the faith and the rebels against the kingdom. The times do not admit of our indulging in sophistries. Go up into the hill of Sion, O man of God, and with your apostolic right arm raise the standard in our defence ! " Gebhard had come no more to Lodi. For Anagni Federigo gave the Crown lawyers full authority to enter into negotiations with the Lombards. He concealed his exceeding great disappointment when, after but a few days, they came to a standstill. He took Ezzelino the Tiger under his protection. In Aprocina, to the proclamation of the herald, Peter of Vinea condemned the Florentines to pay compensation to Siena. Then Gregory answered, answered as a liege lord does a vassal. The Emperor himself, he wrote, was responsible for his subjects' heresy ; for none in his kingdom dared move hand or foot without his leave. That burnt itself inextinguishably into Federigo's spirit.

The Pope returned to Rome without the warden of the Church. With gold he bought the multitude and John of Polo, the Senator. The Emperor bestowed Gaeta on five-year-old Conrad and mustered an army in Policoro. He made war upon Messina and entered the city. Martino Balloni had got away, hidden in the bilge of an oil ship. Federigo pardoned the citizens who cast themselves down before him in the cathedral. Then he went back on his word of grace. His tipstaves caught many and dragged them to the gallow's tree. Balloni, betrayed by a woman, a dyer in Malta, perished with his comrades at the stake. Lead hats were forced down on the rebels' heads, and the metal melting in the fire consumed their brain-pans. The Emperor punished Syracuse and Nicosia. So pitiless was he that even Gregory reproached him. He had Centorbi, Traina, Capizzi and Monte Albano stormed and destroyed. Their inhabitants he transplanted to Palermo or a town which he founded, called Augusta. Reynold of Spoleto and Berthold, his brother, he granted free passage from the Sicilian lands. He commanded his subjects in December to celebrate his birthday, the birthday of Cæsar Imperator Augustus and the King, with rejoicings.

IN San Germano there appeared a monk in a tattered cowl, a Franciscan. He blew into a horn, to collect the idlers round him, and yelled three times : " Hallelujah ! " The multitude replied : " Hallelujah ! " He spake to them : " Glory, praise and honour be to the Father, the Son and the Holy Ghost. Hallelujah, the renowned Virgin ! " All repeated the prayer after him, children too. He limped ahead of them, and in every place the crowd of those possessed by God increased. They screamed that peace had come, exchanged the kiss of reconciliation and sang " Hallelujah ! " In this wise too did Brother Benedetto go about in Parma, the monk belonging to no Order, called Cornetta after his trumpet. He tooted and preached ; the whole town was as if intoxicated by him.

The Dominican Jacobinus journeyed about in Emelia, and, wherever he was seen, the people, headed by the *Podestà*, greeted him with crosses, flags and music. The places of worship could not contain the devout ; so he addressed them in the market-place or in a field. The peasants in the villages pressed in wonderment about him, as about a quack or one with novelties for sale. He declared that a Dominican church must be builded in Reggio, and everyone hauled along stones, mortar and planks. He healed the sick, wakened the dead, made wine out of water. He demanded works of righteousness and mercy, renunciation of ill-gotten gains, liberation of prisoners who were languishing in the debtors' tower. " Be reconciled ", he admonished the faithful, " with your enemies." But he had nothing but deadly enmity towards the heretics.

Against the heretics the Franciscan Leo, a Milanese from the noble family of the Pereghi, showed passionate zeal. In Piacenza he interfered in the dispute between the Knights and the Popolari, led by William of Andito. Gerard of Modena—a Franciscan too—saw to it that the citizens, banished after the assassination of the *Podestà*, might return to his native town, seized the government of Parma and restored the rights of the Church, which had been diminished under the long-suffering Bishop Gracia. He stood in the middle of the *piazza* on a wooden estrade, that had been built for him, wrapped his head in his hood and held his peace, as if lost in God. Then he pulled back the hood again and continued with his sermon, as who would say: " In the spirit I have been at God's judgment seat ". Peter of Verona confuted the heretics and even in Milan handed many of them over to the flames. His secular arm was the *Podestà* Oldrado Grosso of Lodi, who had an equestrian statue voted to himself.

The Dominican Giovanni was the son of the advocate Manelin of Vicenza. The saint himself received the young man into his Order while he was attending the courses in Padua. In Bologna he preached repentance and condemned debauchery. He forbade usury with money and speculation in corn. The poor banded themselves together, threatening citizens and merchants, and destroyed the house of a money-changer. " I, Brother Giovanni," he began, " repeal and set at naught "; and all submitted to the monk's arbitrament. The heretics grew faint-hearted at his frightfulness. Ten corpses, carried past him folded in their linen shrouds, he brought to life again. When he spoke in the Council, the sign of the cross appeared on his forehead. Procession followed upon procession, incense-laden, before his face, miracle upon miracle. In the monastery church of Bologna Pope Gregory, while still Cardinal of Ostia, had interred the remains of Dominic. Giovanni of Vicenza raised them on high in the chapel of San Domenico, and the consecrated space in front of the sarcophagus, the Arca, was the site of miracles. When his power waxed menacing, Gregory wrote to the General of the Order, the Saxon Jordan, that the sower was not to wait for the springing up of the seed, but should meanwhile pass on to another field. He wished to get rid of the monk to Tuscany. But Giovanni fled darkling to Modena.

He appeared in Padua. The citizens conducted him into their city with the *Carroccio*. He appeared in Treviso, Feltre, Belluno, Conegliano and Vicenza; and everywhere the prisoners were set free. He came to Vicenza and told the Council that where he had been born, he must be Duke, Duce, and Count. They hailed him with delight and did as he thought fit. On top of his white monk's weeds he now wore his hair long, instead of tonsured, and a sword hung at his thigh. The populace was excited by him, excited were the women, who tore their garlands. Once again he went to Bologna, to Mantua, then the gates of Verona were opened before him and the banished. He preached from the tower of the municipal palace. He reconciled Richard of Bonifazio and Ezzelino; the Tiger wept tears of fury. In the Forum, the Piazza d'Erbe, by the pillared canopy of the Capitello, Giovanni of Vicenza mounted into the Carroccio and proclaimed himself *Duce*, *Podestà* and Rector of Verona. A shout of jubilation went up to the burning heavens. Giovanni of Vicenza appointed consuls, vicars and judges. Sixty men and women of the foremost families he burnt as convicted heretics on the Piazza d'Erbe and in the Emperor Diocletian's Amphitheatre, where centuries before the blood of gladiators and wild beasts had reddened the limestone.

He sent two Dominicans from Padua to Conegliano, commanded the *Podestà*, Count Tisco of Campo San Pietro, to release the still imprisoned Trevisans and took hostages and castles for surety. He invited the cities and the magnates to Verona, to the Paquara on the right bank of the Adige. They came from Padua, Treviso, Vicenza, Mantua, Brescia, Bologna, Ferrara, Modena, Reggio, Parma, also from Venice, also the Patriarch of Aquileia and the Bishops, to the number of four hundred thousand persons. The *Duce* Giovanni spoke from the pulpit in the meadows: " My peace I give unto you, my peace I bequeath unto you ". And he proclaimed eternal peace for all. The hundreds of thousands kissed one another and thanked God it had been granted them to witness this. But already on the way mocking voices were heard in the inns, and many, their clothes sticking to them with the sweat of the pilgrimage, stabbed one another with daggers, got drunk.

The *Duce* Giovanni was overthrown. The *Nobili* of Vicenza helped the *Podestà*, whom he had turned out, back to his office. Giovanni hurried from Verona to Piacenza with a troop of soldiers, took, the people still remaining faithful to him, the town-hall and threw the *Podestà* into captivity. The *Nobili* fetched reinforcements from Padua. They overcame the *Duce* after fierce street fighting round the Basilica of San Zeno. In the episcopal palace he had to lay down his arms. He went to Verona. The Veronese rose against him, so did they of Bologna. He fell into dejection. The Pope wrote him a letter to console him : the Saviour too had first been deified, then crucified. The citizens of Florence made mock of him, saying that their city was very populous and had no room for the dead which he resurrected. In the Dominicans' house at Verona he revoked his sentence against Treviso. Ezzelino made use of him until, slowly, his light went out.

When in Piacenza Roland of Cremona preached against the heretics, they quickly took action, wounded him and killed one of the slavering Hounds of the Lord.

THE Emperor had set out for Rieti, to meet the Pope. The Senator Luke Savelli had disputed the government of Rome with Peter's successor and the right by his sole power to banish a Roman citizen or punish the city with the interdict. He had, on the Romans' behalf, demanded free choice of their Senator, mintage and the repeal of dues levied on ovens and grazing. The people forced Gregory to flee to Perugia, plundered the Lateran and the Cardinals' houses, laid hands on the Papal possessions.

The Emperor had his son Conrad with him. Uneasy was his mind as he spoke to the nonagenarian, driven out yet again, who sat before him racked by calculus and, even on this May day, enfolded up to the chin in black rams' fleeces. He had need of the old man against the Lombards and, still more, against the King of the Germans. Henry had assembled the Princes in Frankfort, for the re-establishment of the King's peace. Complaints were made against him by the Marquis of Baden, who was now with the Emperor, whose demand in return for Laufen, Silsheim and Eppingen the King had cut down by a thousand marks, whose son he kept as a surety and from whom he had taken the bailiwick of Selz Abbey. Complaints were made against him by the Imperial Knights Godfrey and Conrad of Hohenlohe, by reason of the destruction of their castles by Henry of Neifen. He who had brought him himself, the child from Apulia, to Germany was now counsellor to his first-born, corrupting him. Frederick trembled in his wrath. He begged the Pope for help against Henry, offered him Conrad as a hostage. Gregory, astonished and hesitant, wrote to the Lombards that, the Apostolic See requiring secular arms, they should not hinder the passage of the German men-at-arms, to the King that he should be mindful of his written oaths, to the Archbishop of Treves that he should examine the accusations against the noble Henry of Staufen and excommunicate him if they were true. But to the German Princes he sent a secret envoy; none of Frederick's sons should ever henceforth be king.

During the summer the King carried on war from Viterbo against the Romans, in conjunction with a Papal army. Count Raymond of Toulouse, sentenced because of the Albigenses to penance under the cross, commanded the latter with Bishop Peter of Winton. With Frederick were German lords and Cardinal Raniero of Santa Maria in Cosemedin. For two months he lay before the castle Rispampani. Fowling took up his time, the victory of his eagles hardly at all. With Herman of Salza he sought out the Pope in Spoleto. Philip of Troyes and Henry of Nazareth, attorneys for the barons and burgesses of Acre, had agreed in Viterbo to a treaty with the Emperor and his Governor Riccardo Filangieri. To Spoleto Gregory called the Patriarchs of Constantinople, Antioch and Jerusalem; and in their presence, to divert him from Lombardy, he urged Frederick to a new crusade The Emperor went to Apulia, before Rispampani he left his Captain Guilelmo de Fogliano, who moved off with his company. The Germans defeated the Romans outside the gates of Viterbo. But after that the town had to recognize the authority of the excommunicated Senator.

The Emperor was in Foggia, when one of his knights died, who called himself Johannes de Temporibus. He had said that he was the *Écuyer* Richard, shield-bearer to Oliver, Roland's bosom friend, and that his sword was Alteclere, the hero's blade. He told of Fierabras, the King of Alexandria, of Agelafer, the bridge-keeper, of the Giant with the leopard's head, of the Mooress Floripas's magic girdle, of King Hugh's palace of gold and silver and glass. He had eaten at the feet of Charlemagne and the drunken Paladins. He had a parchment skin and a dyed beard—in the coffin, a dirty nest of whitish green wool. In Foggia the Emperor received news from Germany. Up yonder by the Rhine, at Boppard, his son Henry had openly rebelled, with Henry of Neifen, Anselm of Justingen, the Bishops of Würzburg and Augsburg, Landolf, Bishop-Elect of Worms, the Abbot of Fulda, a canon and a court chaplain. On their way to Italy were the Archbishop of Mainz and the Bishop of Bamberg, whom he had in humility gone so far as to assure that he had never purposely done aught to offend the Emperor's majesty. Frederick, stirred up and controlling himself, waited. The Pope had urged a marriage upon him, marriage with the Plantagenet's sister, who in days gone by had been passed over for Henry, with Isabella of

England. Men praised her beauty. The Emperor sent Peter of Vinea to London.

The Archbishop of Mainz, the Bishops of Bamberg and Eichstädt arrived ; and everything he knew was confirmed. But he heard that envoys from Henry— Anselm of Justingen and Walter of Thanberg—were in Milan to negotiate the King's alliance with that city, with Brescia, Bologna, Novara, Lodi, and the Marquis of Montferrat. Frederick nerved himself against the shock. He gave the Archbishop letters to deliver in Germany : he was minded to avenge so great an outrage and would soon be in Friuli. He thanked the burgesses of Worms for their information. " For we are Emperor and Lord of the realm." He released them from obedience, as in duty bound, to the usurper. Was the Pope lying when he directed the Archbishop of Treves to fulminate the ban of the Church against the traitor to his father, the contemner of divine ordinance ?

The winter in the south had been severe. Trees and vines, beasts and men perished with cold, carts drove over the solid rivers, not till April were the harbours free of ice. When soft winds blew, Federigo prepared for his setting out. He had no army with him, but monies from drained Sicily, administered while he was far away by the Archbishops of Palermo and Capua and the Bishop of Revello. He wrote to Gregory, who was coming to terms with the Romans. He wrote to Lewis of France, whom the Bishop of Würzburg and Henry of Neifen had courted in Paris, that he had no ground for mistrusting him because of his marriage with Isabella. In Rimini he took ship with Conrad and an exotic retinue for Aquileia and proceeded thence to Cividale and into the Alps, misty with the spray of avalanches.

THE Dominican Conrad Dorso roamed about Upper Germany with the secular clerk John, a one-eyed, hunchback cripple. They tarred on the people against the folly of the woman Lukhardis, who had said out loud that the Archangel Lucifer had been expelled from heaven unjustly and must return thither; and against other heretics. In towns and villages they seized every man and woman to whom they had a mind, dragged them before the judges and declared : " These here are heretics, we withdraw our hands from them ", and delivered them up to the stake. Many they burnt alive who even in death prayed to Jesus Christ and the Mother of God. The mighty however helped Dorso ; for a serf's property fell to his master.

Dorso and John appeared before Conrad of Marburg, who was spreading the red terror on the Rhine and as far as Saxony. Fires blazed in Strasburg, Colmar, Mainz, Leyden, Goslar and Erfurt. The monk Conrad had miscreants about him, the Minorite Gerard Lützel-kolb, the trull Alaidis and a forger called Amfried. They denounced to him everyone they suspected. Alaidis took him to Crefeld, the town in which she had been born, and pointed with her finger to her relatives, who were disinclined to make her their heiress. They were burnt on the woodpile. It was Conrad's doctrine that heretics were best detected by according complete credence to evidence against absent persons and leaving them the choice between confession and having their life spared after heavy torment. They who still abjured in their terror ignominiously lost the hair of their head through the scissors. The inquisitors applied themselves at first to the humble, then to burgesses and their wives, counts and nobles, even to clerks. Conrad no longer permitted confession or intercession. The execution took place on the same day. The wife accused the husband, the brother his brother, the child its parents, in base greed and infatuation.

When the inquisitors had the impudence to accuse the Count zu Sain of heresy, and the Counts of Solms and Arnsberg and the Countess of Lotz, Count Sain, whose previous humiliation could still be seen by his cropped head, rebelled yet again against them. He appeared before the court at Mainz ; and his innocence was made manifest. The inquisitors did not let go of their victims. Through Magister Volzo, canon of Worms, and clerks from Spires and Strasburg Sain invoked the Curia. But meanwhile the malefactors met with their requital. Near Marburg knights struck down wolfish Conrad and Gerard Lützelkolb. The Pope was wroth. The murderers, he decided, were to make a pilgrimage to the Holy Land, in shirt and breeches, ropes round their necks and birches in their hands, to confess themselves to every priest and be chastized by them. All who personally or by payment co-operated in the extirpating of heretics he promised remission of sins. Soon afterwards Dorso met his end at Strasburg ; beastly John was hanged by unknown persons near Friedberg.

The peasants of the fens about Hunte and Jade, the Stedingers, had maintained their freedom against the Counts of Oldenburg and the Archbishop of Bremen. Their land, between the black moors, was protected by ditches and dykes. They were accused of heresy. The Bishops of Lübeck and Ratzeburg deposed that the Stedingers consulted prophetesses and devils, kept, as a mockery, their own emperor, pope and bishop, worshipped idols of wax and great frogs, whose posteriors they kissed, took the spittle and the tongue of certain animals into their mouths for the symbol's sake, practised fornification of every sort and were shameless towards clerics. They had killed a priest for pushing her scanty shrove-penny into a woman's teeth in room of the consecrated host, which she had not dared to swallow. The Pope in Rome allowed a crusade to be preached against the Stedingers. They overpowered Burkhard of Oldenburg and two hundred knights. The Archbishop of Bremen wanted to pierce the dykes and drown the Stedingers like kittens. Commanded by Bolke of Bardenflet, Detmar of Dieke, Thammo of Huntorp, they went under, man for man six thousand of them, in a great battle near Oldenesche against the troopers of the Duke of Brabant, the Counts of Oldenburg, Guelders, Lippe, Cleves and Holland. Defiantly the dead stared with their glassy eyes into the misty grey sky, under the clouds of which the wild geese screamed.

THE Emperor was with Conrad at Neumarkt in Styria; and once more the Archbishop of Salzburg, the Bishops of Bamberg and Freising, the Dukes of Austria, Carinthia and Lorraine swore oaths of fealty to him. Herman of Salza greeted him with tears. He celebrated Pentecost in the monastery of Admont. In Wels on Traun Bishop Sigfrid of Ratisbon, who had been Chancellor for five years, went out in state to meet him. Englishmen knelt before him in Ratisbon, and by their side stood Peter of Vinea. He had visited Isabella in the tower, done homage to her: " Long live the Empress ! " and given Frederick's ring to her. The marriage portion was thirty thousand marks of silver, the valley of Manzara and San Angelo were the fief that awaited the bride. The Emperor saw his Court Justice's temples hollowed as by night-watches. He embraced him as his servant and friend. Duke Otto of Bavaria, whom the King of the Germans had threatened with arms, remained for long by Frederick's side.

The Emperor journeyed with Saracens and blacka-moors, camels and mules, leopards and apes and costly treasures through Franconia to the Neckar. In Nürnberg envoys from Henry bowed before him, imploring his clemency; he heeded them not. In the palace at Wimpfen the King, urged by Herman of Salza, cast himself down before him on the stairs ; he heeded him not. But he ordered the gentlemen-at-arms to keep strict watch over him. Even just before Easter Henry with Bishop Landolf had beleaguered the city of Worms. Now, on Saint Ulric's day, the Emperor made his entry into it. Twelve Bishops in full vestments conducted him to the cathedral, Landolf among them. Sharply Frederick signalled: " Away with him ". Landolf concealed himself in the house of his chaplain, later in Mariamünster Abbey.

The Emperor passed judgment upon King Henry. Dethroned, his forehead on the ground, he heard his father's sentence : he was to deliver up his castles and renounce every criminal attempt. The streets surged with the revels in the Empress's honour. She came from Antwerp with the riches of fable, with a crown of the finest gold, bracelets, necklaces, jewel boxes, soft cushions for the nuptial couch and saucepans of pure silver. In Cologne horsemen mounted on Spanish chargers splintered their lances before her, ships sailed along upheld by silk-caparisoned horses with clerks playing on organs and harps therein. Isabella doffed hat and cloak for the women who stood gaping at the edge of balconies. Young girls sang and made music until the blue of dawn in front of the Archbishop's palace ; singing she mingled among them. The Emperor advanced to meet her and the Bishop of Exeter. A cradle was given her with adornment of gold, pearls, shells and ivory. The wedding lasted four days. But the Emperor did not consummate his marriage with Isabella until the morning constellation sparkled in the heavens. Thus did the wisdom of astrology wish it. Smiling he prophecied to the Empress, kissing her limbs, that in this hour she would become pregnant of a son.

In the midst of the jollifications he had Henry arrested. He had resisted the surrender of Trifels, in which the state jewels were kept, and—so the spies whispered— had contemplated flight over the Alps into Lombardy. In the round tower called Luginsland against the city walls of Worms, as they were depriving him of his armour and binding him, he sang the song of a Swabian troubadour. The Emperor banished him to the Palsgrave's keeping in the gaol of Heidelberg Castle. He pardoned Henry of Neifen, punished with heavy fines the Cup-Bearer of Limburg, Lewis of Schipf and Lewis of Wirnsberg, his son's inconsiderable fellow-plotters. Anselm of Justingen's ancestral castle was destroyed.

The Emperor of Nicæa, the Greek John Vatatzes, Theodore Laskaris's son-in-law, had sent mustachioed knights with pearl tassels in their tunics, with puffed-out breeches and icons worth gold to the Emperor at Worms. Pope Gregory sent a brieve, that Frederick should, for the sake of Christendom and the promised land, renounce all thoughts of war against the Lombards. The Emperor sent answer through Peter of Vinea and gave the rebels until Christmas. Then he held a Diet at Mainz before more than seventy Princes. He had them raise their hands to swear that they would be ready for an expedition against the Lombards in the spring. By acclamation they swore peace to him. And the decree was read out : " Whatsoever son expels his father from his own or his inheritance or his blood or burns or robs or with his enemies conspires against him with oaths, aimed at his honour or destruction, if his father attest it before a judge by two knights whom he has despatched, that son shall forfeit his own, his fief and his movables ". The Emperor himself, closing his eyes, solemnly raised his arm to this.

The Duke of Austria stayed away ; he had invaded Hungary ; Hungary and Bohemia were chasing him back. In Mainz the Emperor invested Otto the Guelph, who bent the knee before him, with Brunswick and Lüneburg and gave him the flags. For High Mass he strode into the cathedral, crowned with the diadem. Beneath a smiling sky he prepared a festal banquet on the Wormlage. He raised the golden wine to his lips, but drank it not ; for the image of Henry, as he had seen him last, with dishevelled hair, tormented him. He contracted his son Conrad to Elisabeth, the Duke of Bavaria's daughter.

FREDERICK had wintered in Hagenau. The Jews of Fulda appeared before him, who had been charged with the murder of Christian children, whose blood they had decanted at Passover. He pointed to the decomposed corpses of the children and said : " If they are dead, go

and bury them, for they are no good for anything else ".
But he punished the Jews with a fine of gold. His
astrologer Michael Scotus had gone with him to Germany.
A stone from the wall of the Imperial palace in the
Vosges killed him, smashing the iron helmet with which
in prophetic apprehension he had sought to protect
himself. In December he bade the Bishops of Salzburg
and Bamberg take Henry, languishing in a castle of the
Riess, to the Patriarch of Aquileia. Then the Marquis
Lancia conducted him to San Felice, a fort in Apulia.

From Rieti Pope Gregory wrote to the Emperor
that the Church would not quietly tolerate violence
against the Lombards. He lamented that he was putting
off the Crusade ; and complained of the tribute levied
upon the priests in Sicily. " What, while we are at a
distance," Frederick retorted, " has been done amiss by
our officers in the Kingdom of Sicily you impute to us
as though we had been able from Germany to supervise
everything with lynxes' eyes and make ourselves heard
with a voice as if of thunder." Heresy, he wrote, had
grown to a forest in the cities of Italy, strangling the
standing corn ; why then a war against the Saracens ?
A wound in which the steel still clave was not to be
covered over with superficial salves and plasters ; for
that left but the worse scars. Nor without army or
money could he fight against so many and so brave
enemies of Christ ; Italy however had men, arms,
horses and treasure superabundantly. In May Frederick
summoned all his lieges to Diet at Piacenza. He called
the men of Sicily to his help against the Lombard
rebels, the scourings of the sewers, and bade the Bishop
of Como cite the cities, his debtors ; after that the disgrace overseas would be wiped out.

He journeyed to Marburg to the exaltation of the
blessed Elisabeth. Assembled were the Archbishops of
Mainz, Treves and Bremen, Landgrave Raspe of Thur-
ingia and his brother Conrad of the Teutonic Order,
Elisabeth's children Herman and Sophie, Bishops,
Princes and Nobles. From the old shrine the body was

conveyed into a new sarcophagus, and Frederick himself, in Franciscan habit, lifted the stone over the grave. Out of the corruption there flowed balsamic oil, which was collected in bowls as a relic for chapels and monasteries. The Emperor clad the wasted limbs in costly raiment and at the decapitated head laid his cup and crown. He honoured in her the high-born lady, not the handmaid of God ; and he did so shuddering.

He proceeded to Coblenz, the Lower Rhine, Alsace and Swabia. In Augsburg he outlawed the Duke of Austria, who sheltered Justingen, had seized the Duke of Bosnia's gifts to the Emperor and taken forcible possession of castles. Five hundred mounted and cuirassed mercenaries Frederick sent in advance to Italy under Gebhard of Arnstein. On the Lechfeld he girded his sword about him. With a thousand knights he himself embarked on the expedition. He recognized the failure of the Diet of Piacenza, in the market-place of which Peter of Vinea as his herald and harbinger had spoken to the citizens touching Isaiah's Messianic words : " The people that walked in the darkness have seen a great light, upon them hath light shined who dwell in obscurity ". The Legate James of Praeneste, Cardinal Bishop, had induced the citizens to cast out William of Andito and the *Popolari* ; now the *Podestà* Raniero Zeno, a Venetian, reigned in Piacenza, and the *Nobili*, Federigo's enemies. He cursed the Cardinal, the tearing wolf, and the cunning of the Pope.

He was in Trent, in the fiery heat of August. Ezzelino, sweating in his black harness, the curly hair of his body black as a monkey's pelt, and his brother Alberico brought him to Verona. He addressed a Cæsarean missive to the Romans, the blood of Romulus and the progeny of them who, saved from the ashes of Troy, founded the city, the envy of the terrestrial globe, the seat of the Empire. Milan's pride had set up a throne for itself in the north, reviled them instead of paying them tribute. " Ye have a King who rouseth ye, the slumbering, by perpetual admonition. But ye abide in your sleep." He betook himself with his and Ezzelino's horsemen and footmen to Vacaldo. Once more he mounted a-horse. " Pilgrims and wanderers ", he cried, " go their way unmolested, and should I not be able to travel the roads in my own Kingdom ? " Unfurling the yellow banner with the eagle, he crossed the narrow Mincio.

HE joined with the troops of Parma, Cremona, Reggio, Modena. He took Narcaria and Pontevico. He lay before Mantua for two weeks. He reached Cremona, received the envoys from Rome and from Tuscany. Pope Gregory kept silence about the Lombards—from dreamy forgetfulness, he said. Pope Gregory was wroth with the Emperor about Sicily : " If thou wouldst bear in mind that the Tree of Life standeth in the midst of Paradise, thou too wouldst keep thyself within thy confines and least of all venture upon unwisely condemning the secrets of our conscience, in which thou merely betrayest the many flaws in thine own conscience. Dost thou not see that the necks of the kings and princes are bowed before the priest ? Christian emperors shall not only be subject to the Roman Pontiff, but also shall never submit him to the decisions of other prelates. Is it not wretched madness when the son tries to measure himself against the father, the pupil against the teacher ? " Federigo's hands crumpled up the parchment in a spasm.

News came that Rivalta was threatened. Ezzelino proceeded thither, and reeled. Swift as a swallow cleaving the air Federigo marched after him. He scared the foe from the Adige to Vicenza and ordered the assault. In the night the Germans climbed the walls and forced one of the gates. They murdered and plundered ; brides and greybeards wandered naked and miserable through the streets. When day broke Federigo spared the vanquished and put in Guilelmo as *Capitano*. He walked with Ezzelino through the Bishop's garden. " I will tell you ", he said to him, " how securely to keep a city's government and administration " ; and with his dagger he mowed down the lush, green grass. Ezzelino, who was chaste in his dealings with women, had cut down a German knight who was violating a woman. " If thou ", said he to the Emperor, " hadst done such a deed before my eyes, the same would have befallen thee." The report spread that Peter Frangipani's party was inciting the Romans anew against the Pope, that the Knight Sir Godefroi de Tort, a Syrian, had come to Gregory in order to repudiate the Peace of Viterbo in the Barons' and the King of Cyprus's name. Then Federigo suddenly turned round northwards, over the Piave to Aquileia, by way of Forum Julii and Carentana, through the Alpine passes, into Germany.

The Duke of Austria, the outlawed rebel, was in the fortress of Neustadt and Vienna, taken by the Bohemian King, in the Burgrave of Nürnberg's hands. The Emperor, together with the Princes, celebrated the Nativity in Graz. He made his entry into Vienna by way of the Semmering, accompanied by the Archbishops of Mainz, Treves and Salzburg, the Bishops of Bamberg, Ratisbon, Freising and Passau, the Duke of Bavaria, the King of Bohemia, the Duke of Carinthia, the Landgrave of Thuringia. He sent Herman of Salza and Peter of Vinea to the Pope at Viterbo to the end that he might now hurry on his decision against the Lombards. In the martyr Stephen's Cathedral he took Austria, Styria and the City of Vienna under Imperial protection. By God's help, he said, they had fallen to him. He promised the burgesses justice and the exclusion of Jews from all offices in Vienna, so that they, doomed to eternal servitude, should not oppress the Christians. According to the Emperor's wish the Princes elected in Henry's stead eleven-year-old Conrad King of the Germans, as David was chosen instead of Saul. At Whitsuntide Frederick was in Spires. " Despite unceasing exertions ", wrote Peter of Vinea, " our little bark tosses between Scylla and Charybdis, between the stratagems of the Cardinals and of the Lombards."

Then the negotiations in Fiorenzuola were broken off. In August Frederick crossed the Alps, southwards again. Ten thousand Saracen bowmen from Lucera advanced to meet him through the plain of the Po.

Ezzelino was Lord in Padua. Pushing the vizor from his forehead, he had passionately kissed the Porta Torrissella; but the city trembled before him and his mercenaries. He had destroyed the houses and towns of the suspect, brought a saddled horse as a present to the Abbot Giordano Forzat of San Benedetto and taken him prisoner, desired two thousand marks of silver from Bishop Corrado. He terrified Ravenna. Ferrara and Treviso obeyed the Emperor. Federigo advanced before Goito, the Mantuan fort; he subdued it. Azzo d'Este and James of Carrara joined him, and he was friendly to all. Ezzelino hated Carrara. With half-drawn weapon he fell upon him. He would have killed him, had not the Emperor hindered him. The Count of San Bonifazio appeared, to surrender Mantua. The Emperor took Montechiari, the bulwark of Brescia. He assured fifteen hundred footmen and twenty knights of the Lombards of their freedom; when he had them, he sent them with mocking lips into captivity at Cremona. The Milanese avoided battle. They asked Gregory for help; he supported them with money. The Emperor disdained to admit the Pope's delegates into his presence.

He was encamped near Pontevico, the Milanese near Manerbio, between brooks and swamps by the Oglio. The rumour penetrated to them that the Emperor's army was dissolving into several companies. They evacuated their rain-softened caves in the ground and aimed for home. But Federigo bridged the Oglio and, with Saracens, Germans and Italics, turned on the right bank as far as Soncino. The Milanese, already scattered, were assembling in their tents near the fort Cortenuovo, to wait for the baggage. In the morning the enemy multiplied against them out of woods, valleys and defiles. Fires flared, betraying them, near Civitate. A German horseman galloped up to them: " Have a care, the Emperor himself is giving you battle ". The army bugles resounded and the battle-cry " *Miles, Roma, Miles, Imperator* ". They who fled to Gosalba were brought down by the Bergamasks. The main body of the Milanese and those of Alessandria made its resistance round the *Carroccio* which the youths of the *Società dei Ferti* defended under Enrico, the hurler of fire. Federigo was in the mellay with his son Enzio, whom he loved, and Ezzelino was wounded in the shoulder.

The German knights in their shirts of mail climbed the ramparts of the laager, they were already fighting at the thill of the *Carroccio* when dark night decreed a truce. The *Carroccio* was stuck in the mud. The youths who still survived hoped to save the golden cross at the top of the mast. The Emperor's men captured it during the pursuit. The Archbishop of Milan was missing. The *Podestà* Pietro Tiepolo, the Doge of Venice's son, was taken prisoner. Tied to the *Carroccio*, which an elephant hauled along, he served, with gyves about his wrists, as a spectacle at the Emperor's triumphal entry into Cremona. On the elephant's back weighed a wooden tower with Saracen trumpeters.

Federigo's letters of victory went forth to his brother-in-law Richard of Cornwall, to the Duke of Lorraine, to the Imperial lieges, to the Pope and the Cardinals. He would, he wrote, wear down the old dragon as long as he should still see his tail twitching'; and, in filial reverence to the Holy Father, he gave thanks to Christ Jesus. He wrote to the Romans, the Quirites, to *Senatus* and *Populus*. He presented them with the *Carroccio*. They brought the trophy on to the Capitol and placed it on five pillars of marble. In marble they carved the picture of the chariot, with distiches to Federigo's glory.

Round about Christmastide he was in Lodi. There the brown Prince Abd-el-Aziz implored his protection, the son of the Berber prince Abdallah of Tunis, whom his brother Abu Zacharia had driven out. The people of Milan suspended the Crucified by the legs, polluted the altars, ate flesh on fast-days. The city wished to buy the victor's clemency with gold and its banners. He demanded unconditional submission. The Countess Lucia of Caserta, one of his paramours, stepped forward and said to him : " Lord, you have so fair a realm ; why in God's name do you plunge into this new feud ? " He told her he could now do no other. The Milanese took back their word and burned the bridges of the Ticino. The Emperor had a triumphal arch built over the Volturno in Capua, which was to bear his statue with those of chief Court Justices Peter of Vinea and Thaddæus of Suessa.

FEDERIGO yearned for the amenity of Sicily, that pleasure-garden amid the briars of the world. " Had the God of Israel seen it ", he would say, " he would not have praised Palestine so." In Ravenna Isabella bore a son, called Henry like him who was lost, conceived under the planets of good fortune, marked with the glorious sign of the *fasces*. " A new King is born unto us ", wrote Federigo to Ezzelino from Padua, " bright is his cradle amid his father's exulting."

From Turin he summoned Conrad and the German princes to be in Lombardy in the summer with strong forces. He repeated the bloody ordinances against the heretics, the Patarenes. French Crusaders under John of Béthune traversed Italy, to reach Constantinople for young Baldwin. Baldwin had refused fealty towards Frederick. The Emperor himself had designs upon the Byzantines' gleaming crown. If the Pope, he wrote to Gregory, wished against the will of the Greeks to be head of their church, he had a still better right with their will to become head of their state. The opposition nor of man nor of fiend, the Pope wrote, might detain the Crusaders. But Frederick had Béthune taken prisoner, then let him free ; the Count died in Venice.

On Whit-Monday the Emperor was in Verona. He married Selvaggia—she too his daughter by Blanca Lancia—to Ezzelino outside San Zeno's Abbey. For

PETER OF VINEA

[face p. 184

eight days did the populace celebrate the wedding. Ezzelino lay with his bride of fourteen summers in the Count of Panico's palace, coiled her chestnut plaits round her little throat until she was breathless and was hard to her. The Emperor rode out with him, and they disputed who had the best sword. Federigo showed his, its hilt adorned with jewels. Ezzelino said: "It is excellent, but so is my unadorned one". He pulled it out, and his six hundred attendants unsheathed theirs, that the sparks flew. Ezzelino took his leave from his father-in-law, to fight for Padua against Azzo d'Este, James of Carrara, Uguccio de Pileo and the refugees. Outside the gates he overwhelmed them. Azzo escaped through the swiftness of his horse. James of Carrara, invested in his stronghold of Agna, had his life spared yet again.

In Verona the Emperor received Conrad and the Germans. With a great army they made their appearance, the Patriarch of Aquileia, Archbishop Sigfrid of Mainz, now Imperial vice-regent, power-seeking Conrad of Hochstaden, Archbishop-elect of Cologne, the Archbishop of Magdeburg, the Bishops of Worms, Würzburg and Meissen, the Duke of Carinthia, Counts and Nobles. His vice-regent warned the Emperor against Otto, the Duke of Bavaria : he had conspired in Ratisbon with the rebel Babenberg and the King of Bohemia. As Lord of the Palatinate Otto had warred against the Archbishop of Mainz for the monastery of Lorsch. Papal envoys—Rainier of St. Quentin, Archdeacon of Troyes, and Albert Beham, Archdeacon of Passau—were agitating in Bavaria against Frederick and were the Duke's guests in Landhut Castle. The Emperor had much conference with the Grand Master of the Teutonic Order, who had a sick man's pallor and heavy eyelids and had to be carried to him on pillows. He was purposed to see the doctors in Salerno.

Mules, dromedaries, elephants, the treasury and the chamberlain's office followed the army in which Vatatzes's and the Egyptian sultan's troops enrolled also and Burgundians, Englishmen, Frenchmen and Castilians.

185

Federigo besieged steep Brescia. In chains Ezzelino had sent to him the Spaniard Calamandrinos, who was expert in fashioning battering-rams and similar machines. He went to work, panther-like, with gleaming eyes. He soon fell into the hands of them of Brescia. They gave him a wife, the hot widow of a woollen-weaver, and a house facing the Broletto and the dome of the Rotonda. So he applied all his skill for the citizens' benefit. There where the walls were in the greatest jeopardy the Brescians strapped their prisoners, but the Emperor's men tied the most eminent men they had taken, such as Corrado de Concisio, to their palisades ; and Corrado called out to the townsfolk : " Remember the League of Liberty ". Calamandrinos's missiles split in two whosoever was aimed at. Day after day the rain poured down. The siege lasted three months. Then the Emperor had the towers which had been brought up burned to the ground and retired to Cremona leaving only a number of distempered horses at their pickets. The townsfolk with their coloured birettas shouted and danced on the circumvallation.

Federigo's envoys returned from Genoa. The *Podestà*, Paolo de Soressina of Milan, who since his election had been hostile to the Emperor, had let the commune vote in San Lorenzo's Church and had tampered with the Emperor's letter ; they were not minded to have his *dominium*, the answer ran, but rather to fortify the city against him. Federigo declared the Genoese rebels against the Crown. Since August he was negotiating with the Pope, through Berard, the now white-headed Archbishop of Palermo, the Bishop of Reggio, Thaddæus of Suessa and Magister Roger Porcastrella. In October Gregory once more set foot in perfidious Rome, in which his party was victorious through the senator John de Judici. Together with the forts of Bombacianus and Ægidius Boetii, houses and temples from pagan centuries, their statues and mosaics were torn down and brayed to dust ; for they were, Gregory said, the houses of Anti-Christ.

THE Emperor in Cremona married Enzio to Adelasia, who since the death of her first husband, the Pisan Ubaldo Visconti, was sole mistress of Torre and Gallura in Sardinia. The island was a Papal fief. The Pope had proposed to Adelasia an alliance with Guelfo Porcari; she broke the oath of obedience—for handsome, golden-haired Enzio's youth attracted her. With a great following of knights he sailed to Sardinia, landed in Torre, beheld the Domicella's domineering countenance. He was married to her in Sassari, there where Adelasia's brother Baresone had been murdered by the inhabitants, and called himself King of Torre and Gallura. Pope Gregory heard of this and waxed wroth. His Legate Roland excommunicated the Queen. But in truth his anger was directed against the Emperor. He authorized the Bishops of Bamberg, Worms, Vercelli and Parma to put into his hands a document comprising the complaints of the Church.

Federigo sat enthroned in Cremona on a dais with twelve steps. Beneath him sat the Archbishops of Palermo and Messina, the Bishops of Cremona, Lodi, Novara and Modena, the Abbot of St. Vincent, Franciscans and Dominicans. Admirable appeared to the monks the devoutness with which he replied to the fourteen complaints. " Churches and monasteries ", spake he, " I have not robbed, but rather restored the possessions of the Curia through the blameless notary William of Tocco; I have, however, not yet been able to travel all the provinces of Sicily. The Saracens, not I, have damaged the church of Monreale. The Bishop of Cefalù is a heretic and a villain. Templars and Knights of St. John would have obtained the whole Kingdom of Sicily by purchase, but for the law. The clergy are obliged to pay taxes like everybody. The Prince of Tunis has fled, not in order to have himself baptized in Rome, but to escape death at the hands of Abu Zacharia. I have not favoured the Romans' rebellion against the Church, though I espoused the cause of my subjects against the Senators chosen by their adversaries. Where are the knights with which the Lombards were to provide me? The Church was arbitress between them and me; she has deceived me. I do not, for the sake of the Empire's rights in Italy, damage the Western cause. According to the advice of the Church will I conduct it. But, although I have returned answer through the Archbishops of Palermo and Messina, this admonition, this impeachment of my Imperial name, has been entrusted to the prelates." He stood up and left the assembly, quick and clattering.

As Gregory grew wroth about Enzio, Federigo taunted the Pope with peevishness, because he had already matched one of his nieces for him. He said: "I have, as all the world knows, vowed to regain the members alienated from the Empire and will not slackly lag behind that vow". In January he made his entry into Padua, with Cremonese Knights, the Germans, the Apulians, the Saracens, those of Egypt too, Vatatzes's Greeks, an elephant, five leopards and twenty-four camels. Five *miglie* there advanced to meet him Ezzelino, in black armour, the citizens, with garlands of flowers about the *Carroccio* and with songs, cymbals, trombones and cithers. Arab steeds trotted, adorned with brocade and gold, the mounts of the noble ladies of Padua, who bowed before smiling Federigo, splendid in a hyacinth-red suit. Enrico Testa lowered before him the banner on the *Carroccio*: "Mighty Lord, this flag dedicate to you the loyal townspeople of Padua, to the end that, through the crown upon thy head, Justice may preserve it". The Emperor spent the night in Santa Giustina Abbey, the Empress Isabella in Noenta. Abbot Arnaldo gave gifts to him, the Empress and Peter of Vinea. Federigo was at pains to reconcile Ezzelino with Azzo d'Este. He went fowling in the Euganean Hills and along the course of the Bacchiglione.

He wrote no more to the Pope, who had turned Venice and Genoa against him, who suffered the Legate Gregory of Montelongo to work against him in Milan, but to the Cardinals. The Church, he declared, he served with heart and hand. The offender who abused the authority of his chair and through whom scandal came he would requite like with like. He granted free passage to the Crusaders who were now setting off under Baldwin for Constantinople. The Archbishop of Salzburg, the Bishops of Passau and Freising, the Abbot of Tegernsee, the Count of Görz came to Padua. They did not conceal that in Germany Albert Beham, the Archdeacon, was urging on the Emperor's overthrow.

On Palm Sunday the people were taking their walks abroad in the Prato di Valle. Federigo, on a footstool, sat in their midst in cheerfulness. Peter of Vinea praised the Emperor's benevolence to the multitude, and they clapped their applause and rejoiced. On Easter Sunday he attended Mass in the upper church and, the crown upon his poll, went back to Santa Giustina. Then it became certainly known: on Palm Sunday and Maundy Thursday Gregory had banned Federigo, among other grounds for joining Sardinia to his dominion, for not permitting the restoration of the Latin Empire in Byzantium, for repudiating the arbitrament of the Church between himself and the Lombards. To the end that the soul might be saved the Pope gave the body over to Satan. The mendicant friars however preached in all places against the Emperor. On seeing the host carried to a sick man he was said to have cried out : " How much longer will this deception last ? " and, when a Saracen prince asked him what the priest was raising up with the pyx, to have remarked : " The priests feign that to be our God " ; by a field of corn to have said : " How many Gods will they bake from this grain ? " and taken upon himself to ordain for all nations a wiser rule of faith and life.

The Emperor felt sorrow for Herman of Salza, his friend, the ploughman. Despite the physicians' art he had died in Salerno. Scotus, who used to read in the stars, was dead and Federigo lonely. In no one could he confide but this mute Peter of Vinea, who was eloquent only in edicts and proclamations, this Capuan of needy origin who, as a scholar in Bologna, had begged his bread, his Seneca who kept watch for him. Through him he called the Paduans in the hall of the municipality. He mounted the raised alabaster seat with the jewels of his majesty. Peter of Vinea spoke touching the line of Ovid : "*Quæ venit indigne pœna, dolenda venit*". "The undeserved punishment it is that hurts." He said that the Emperor was just as no ruler of the *Imperium* had been since Charles the Great. It was meet he should complain of Holy Mother Church. The Emperor was astonished that the Pope had delivered such a sentence so hurriedly and so unwisely. The burgesses went home, agitated by diverse thoughts.

Federigo went to Treviso, whose *Podestà*, James of Morra, did him homage, and took with him to Padua Alberico of Romano, who was at variance with Ezzelino, and Azzo d'Este's adherents. Ezzelino's spies noted their names on wax. The Emperor wrote to the Kings and Princes of the earth and appeased his desire for revenge upon the decrepit old greybeard. He wrote against the Elders of Babylon, against the Pope, who had been weened to live on celestial heights and who had been found out to be less than a man ; who laid open his inwardly seething fury and wickedness ; who was not worthy to be the vicar of Christ, the posterity of Christ, steward for the souls of all faithful. "Without taking counsel with the Cardinals, his brethren, pursuant to the Church's ordinance, he sits in his chamber with his pair of scales, binding and loosening in accordance therewith, his own scribe, weigher and cashier. If We look into the book of Our conscience, we cannot discover from it any reason which might so violently have excited this inimical man, unless it be that We thought it improper to marry Our son Enzius, the King of Torre and Gallura, to his niece." And then in trumpet tones : "But ye, Kings and Princes of the Earth, deplore ye not only Us, but the Church also ; for her head is weak and her *Princeps* a roaring lion, an unfaithful man, a polluted priest, a lunatic prophet. We to be sure are most nearly touched by such mischief, and We feel severest the consequence of papal misdeeds ; but Our disgrace in the end is yours too, and your subjugation appears easy as soon as the Roman Emperor is overcome. All this We write unto ye, not as lacking power to apply, but to the end that the world should recognize how with the honour of one that of all Princes is threatened ". He wrote the epistle to the Romans, the noble and burgess *Quirites*, that they were asleep, ungratefully tolerating the outrage upon him. A Franciscan wrote for him the epistle to all Christendom : " There assembled the Pharisees and Scribes and took counsel together touching their Lord, the Roman Emperor ". And the letter against the usurer, whose greedy belly not the whole world could fill : " Peter, even when he was tormented with burning hunger, would eat nothing unclean. But thou livest in order to eat, and on all thy vessels is inscribed : I drink, thou drinkest. This saying thou repeatest at table so often, that thereafter, as if rapt into Heaven, thou speakest Hebrew, Greek and Latin and, although surfeited to the brim, thinkest to hover on the pinions of the winds. Through thy fault Jerusalem laments forsaken, through thy fault the Emperor cannot hasten to the succour of the Holy Land. With the contributions of the faithful thou buildest thee houses and palaces, instead of employing them for those regions. Desist from evil, remember poor Pope Sylvester and great-hearted Emperor Constantine, do not oppose thyself to the true defender of the Church. Seven-and-seventy times, saith our Lord, shall ye forgive transgressors ; and thou wilt not spare an innocent man begging for forgiveness ? Receive charitably the son who would gladly return to the bosom of the Church, lest from his apparent slumber he rise up like a lion, stablish justice anew, govern the Church and break utterly the proud horns of the mighty ".

He was in Vicenza. A conspiracy was detected. Federigo put Saracens into the forts of the perjured. Alberico da Romano, whose daughter Adelasia he had sent with Reynold, Azzo's son, to Apulia as a hostage, betrayed him and surprised Treviso. The Emperor went to Padua again. He listened to the echo from Rome. It penetrated to him, monstrous as the challenge. " Out of the sea has risen a beast ", in such terms wrote Pope Gregory, " full of names of reviling, with the feet of a bear, the maw of a bloody lion and, in his other members, like unto a panther. It openeth its mouth for the blaspheming of the Divine name and aimeth poisonous darts at the canopy of Heaven and the Saints that dwell therein. With its claws and iron teeth it would fain rend everything, with its feet trample upon everything, and it standeth up no longer in secret, but, openly and supported by infidels, against Christ, the Redeemer of the human race, in order to raze out the tables of His laws with the pen of heretical malice. Cease therefore to be amazed if it draw the dagger of its calumnies against Us ; for it hath risen up in order to root out the very name of the Lord from the earth. To the end however that ye may be able to withstand its lies by the power of truth and set at nought its craft by clear judgment, consider carefully the head, middle and end of this beast, that calleth itself the Emperor Frederick." He, not the Pope, had provoked the recalcitrance of the Lombards. He was Simon the Mage, desirous of sullying the purity of the Church with worldly filth, the Egyptian whore, who made Joseph lewd offers and, rejected, accused him to her husband. This forerunner of Anti-Christ, this King of pestiferousness had said that the world had been fooled by three deceivers, Moses, Mahomet and Christ ; two of them had died honoured, the third however hanging to the tree. He had derided as folly the lore that Almighty God had been born of a virgin. He believed in nought but nature and reason.

The Emperor had besieged Castelfranco, raised the siege at an eclipse of the sun, by a golden bull given the town to the Paduans, devastated the neighbourhood, proceeded to Cittadella, Padua, Vicenza, Verona.

Azzo d'Este, Peter of Montebello and Uguccio Pileo took their leave of him under a pretext. In Verona, after ringing of the bell and proclamation of the crier, Peter of Vinea from his horse declared Azzo, Montebello, Uguccio, the Count of San Bonifazio under the ban of the Empire.

The Emperor made reply, reply to the Pope, the Pharisee on the chair of false doctrine, more than his like anointed with the oil of knavery ; the beast, of whom it was written : " Another horse rose up out of the sea, which was scarlet red, and he who sat upon it took away the peace of the world, to the end that the living might slay one another ". Him, the Pope, he declared the great dragon, Anti-Christ, the angel of the abyss. Never had an impiety like that of the three deceivers passed the Emperor's lips. No enemy to the Church was he, but utterly did he damn sundry persons. " Such a person is the Pope, and should he not of his own accord or according to the counsel of his brethren find again the path to truth and justice, we must and shall pursue him with the Imperial sword."

Ravenna fell away, pricked on by the Cardinal Sinibaldo Fiesco. The daughter of the *Podestà* Polo Traversari Federigo had burned as a hostage. The Emperor's army reduced to ashes forts belonging to the Bolognese, Plumatia and Crevalcore, after it had drained off the waters of the triple circle of ditches round the latter. The Emperor nominated Enzio, King of Torre and Gallura, Imperial Legate in Italy. He sent him on ahead to Jesi, his birthplace. To Jesi he wrote from Parma that it was Bethlehem, deepest rooted in his breast, the place whence had come the Duke, the Prince of the Roman Empire. He himself was the Cæsar, the son of the divine Emperor, the divine Saviour.

The Venetians were fitting out five-and-twenty galleys to conquer Sicily, a moiety at the Church's charges. Three hundred knights they were to ship across, two thousand footmen, five hundred slingers, furnished by Gregory. Only with his permission were

193

they and the Genoese to make peace with the Emperor. Federigo had search made for Gilbert de Bayrano and Walter de Popleto, who had fled from his court, he had the Bishop of Fundi banished, Dominicans and Minorites of Lombard provenance expelled from Sicily, those with whom letters from the Pope were found hanged, officials dismissed, forts and castles newly fortified.

He heard from Germany that the Archbishop of Bremen had promulgated the Church's ban upon him and that Albert Beham had suborned Duke Otto and Wenceslaus of Bohemia to choose young Abel of Slesvig as Anti-King. But in Eger the Princes swore fealty to the Emperor and King Conrad –the Archbishop of Mainz, the Marquises of Brandenburg and Meissen, Landgrave Raspe of Thuringia and his brother Conrad, who had succeeded Herman of Salza as Grand Master of the Teutonic Order. No word was uttered by the pious King Lewis of France, to whom Gregory had written that he was favoured like Juda among the sons of the patriarch. The Cardinal Deacon Otto, who demanded from the Barons and Bishops of England a fifth part of all goods to repel Frederick, had twice to give way to the exasperation of the people. A Welch Carthusian, shaking his fist, had fearlessly said in the presence of the Legate, the Abbot of Evesham and the *Magistri* of Finham, Bordeaux and Susa : " Gregory is not the Pope, he is not the head of the Church. The Devil is abroad, the Pope a heretic. Gregory, who calls himself Pope, defiles the Church, yea the world itself ".

FEDERIGO advanced against Milan. Six knights had bound themselves by oath, on great war-horses to fight with him himself. A youth of the *Società dei Ferti* ran, fighting with a German, up to the Emperor's tent. As he was very handsome, Federigo gave him his freedom and a horse. The Milanese flooded their territories with ditches from the Adda and Lambro. It did not come to a battle at the bridges of the Lambreto, at Locate, Scanasio or Langiarela ; nor against Piacenza, for the Po was swollen with downpours of rain. The Emperor went to Lodi, to Parma and over the Apennines to Tuscany. The General of the Franciscans, Fra Elia, joined him, that companion of Francesco of Assisi's, who had been a mattress-maker, a temporal prince of monkish poverty. Pope Gregory had shown him favour ; but the Minorites intended to get rid of him. He said the Holy Father gave his envoys and plenipotentiaries blank sheets with his seal and they filled them up as they pleased, for the oppressing of Christian men.

The excommunicated, the Anti-Christ, celebrated in Pisa the Nativity of the Lord. He himself mounted the pulpit in the white marble Cathedral and preached. He nominated as governor of Tuscany Frederick of Antioch, his son. The cities, the counties, the castles obeyed his will. But he had to take up loans from merchants from Rome, Pisa, Parma, Cremona and Siena and from the Jew Heinrich Baum in Vienna, in return for interest or Sicilian corn. He held his Court in Foligno, whither he had sent Count Tommaso of Aquino. He had the cross borne before him, mass said aloud and he gave the benediction to all with his right hand. He sat in judgment, the multitude kneeled before his throne. Peter of Vinea, in the presence of himself and Enzio, spoke to the delegates of the Communes and admonished them to be steadfast in their fidelity to the Emperor. Spoleto remained hostile to him ; he banished all the citizens of that town who were in Apulia and Sicilia, save them who were students at Naples, from his frontiers. The Archbishop of Messina offered himself as mediator with the Pope. Had he, Federigo asked him, forgotten the offence ? " The Lord, who did not wish that from the Sanctuary itself, from Peter's chair, the traducer of our right should arise, leads us back into our Kingdom against that traducer's wish and hope." He was in Viterbo, near the seat of the Imperium. He was already writing to the Romans to send him without delay their Pro-consuls, Count Nepoleo, John de Polo, Otto Frangipani and Angelo Malabranca, to the end that under his governance the glory of the Romulan seed should flourish again with the Roman diadem, the old Roman name again be honoured and a new, indissoluble tie be knit between them and the Roman Emperor.

In front of the Castel San Angelo the people were in uproar at the Emperor's approach. Pope Gregory was at variance with the Cardinals, at variance with Colonna, to whom he cried : " If you will not obey me, I will no longer let you rank as a Cardinal ". " Nor I ", Colonna retorted, " you as Pope." The Cardinal intrenched himself in the Mausoleum of Augustus. Pope Gregory now left the Vatican with the clergy, amid the chanting of hymns, before them, in a mist of incense, the Holy Cross and the golden shrines with the heads of the Apostles Peter and Paul. So the procession made its way to the Lateran. With feeble voice Gregory said over the heads of the tens of thousands : " This is the Church, these are the relics which ye are to defend to the death ". He took the tiara from his head and laid it on the coffers with the words : " Defend ye then the city, ye Saints, since the Romans will not defend it ". The people sobbed, they tore from their garments the eagles, the insignia of Anti-Christ, they kissed the Pope's flabby fingers, to receive absolution from him and the sign of the cross for war against the Emperor. Federigo wrote to the King of England that Gregory had conjured young lads, old women and some paid troops with prayers and weeping. But he did not attack Rome. By way of Montefiascone, Toscanella, Montalto, Corneti, Sutri and Viterbo he turned to Apulia, Capitanata, to Foggia and Lucera.

He held a Diet in Foggia, in order to obtain money by taxes. San Angelo had revolted ; he had the walls forced, the mutineers killed or their noses cut off. He was called to Blanca Lancia, who was dying. He had himself married to her, so that Manfredi might be his legitimate son. He left Isabella in the palace, under the care of the Saracen eunuchs. She was pregnant. He diverted himself hunting herons. He gnashed at the loss of Ferrara, whose gates Salinguerra, swindled by lying promises, had opened to the besiegers—the *Podestà* of Bologna, Polo Traversari, Azzo, Alberico and Richard of San Bonifazio, the Doge Tiepolo of Venice. They had seized Salinguerra at a banquet. But Ezzelino still raged in Padua. He tortured the Lords of Vado ; they died of starvation in gaol. Executed on the block were the boxer Zugno and he whom Ezzelino hated madly, James of Carrara, dressed in black.

Federigo was with hired mercenaries in Capua. He pushed forward as far as Salarati, to the bridge over the Agno. With the heat of the summer he fell sick in the swampy coast-land of the March of Ancona. There died in Rome Conrad of Thuringia, the Grand Master of the Teutonic Order. Then Bishop Wala of Brixen reported to the Emperor that the Pope purposed summoning the Kings' plenipotentiaries and the Prelates to a synod, that peace might be restored. Would he, the Emperor, grant the Lombards an armistice ? " Hypocritically does he speak of peace ", said the Emperor, "so that meanwhile our enemies, reinforced, may rebel all the more securely. The Archbishops and their suffragans are to be a tool in his hands against us. Not peace is the purpose of this Council, but discord." He learned that Gregory was obliging the Bohemian King to guarantee the Archdeacon of Passau's journey and prohibit the passage of everyone with Imperial leanings.

He advanced with Germans, Tuscans and Apulians to the walls of Ravenna ; for Polo Traversari was dead. Morasses and ditches were drained, the outer city was stormed and burnt down. Sliding on their knees the men of Ravenna implored mercy. Federigo—at his back Fra Elia, Francesco's successor—granted it ; the Archbishop he sent into captivity. He besieged Faenza and imagined he would humble it in a few days. But the citizens under the Venetian Michele Morosini defended themselves for months with extreme bravery.

October set in with cold, hail and rain. In place of the tents Federigo had a town of timber run up round Faenza. By the sea-coast he hanged Pietro Tiepolo, the Doge's son.

The Emperor wrote to the King of Bohemia that the Pope sold everything, clothes, pallia, crosiers, mitres, marriage, worship, yea even the Kingdom of Heaven. He wrote to the Duke of Bavaria that he should root Albert Beham, the offender against his majesty, out of his land. Pope Gregory was negotiating with Genoan ship-owners about the Prelates' passage from France. The Emperor wrote to King Lewis that he was forced to take counter-measures. Pope Gregory had offered the German crown to Robert, Count of Artois, Lewis's brother. The King's envoys were with Frederick outside Faenza. Weeping with anger he cried out to them: "Friends and beloved neighbours, him who thirsts for my blood, him, mine enemy, may the God of vengeance punish!"

THE Emperor, so an English clerk gave warning, had, a second Nero and Herod, occupied every coast and many ships in Pisa, Corneto, Naples and Gaeta. If the priests of the Church got to Rome nevertheless, new dangers lurked for them there: the broiling heat of the sky, foul water, coarse, unwholesome food, countless gnats and scorpions, the poisonous reptile brood of the catacombs, a dirty, repulsive, corrupt and brutalized race of men. And whoso survived Rome still had the dangers of the return journey. Not gentleness or charity had moved the Pope. Overcome in his fight against the tyrant, he required crushing imposts. He held the clergy an unstable reed and cast them in ever tighter bonds and servitude. But in March the Prelates assembled in Genoa and Nice, Bishops from England with the Cardinal Deacon Otto, that wild boar in the vineyard, Bishops from France and Spain. The Emperor assured them of safe conduct by the land route, in order that they might hear his reasons from him.

They saw through the wiles of the ungodly man. But many quietly turned back.

Federigo still lay before Faenza, the town which had once killed a knight for resembling him, the Emperor. He had not four ounces of gold in his coffers as journey-money for a court page whom he wanted to send with a falcon to Apulia. He paid with augustals of ox-hide, of which on the one side was stamped his image, on the other an eagle. Famine overtook the citizens of Faenza. They asked that their women and children might go free. Federigo gave a harsh No : " Am I to feed the women that the men may be spared, whom before God and the whole world I must accuse of high treason ? Did they not aforetime shut every gate and loophole to catch me ? Did they not slay a man like unto me, arrayed in Imperial arms, and believed full of joy to have murdered in such shameful wise me, their Lord and Emperor ? Did they not do my mother, when she travelled through Faenza, manifold dishonour, regardless of her sex and dignity, and, senselessly cruel even towards animals, mutilate the privates of her palfrey ? For that they shall reap what is due to them ". Through yet another embassy, the citizens implored the Emperor to suffer them to emigrate naked and unclothed and settle in some region or other. Yet again he refused to grant them forgiveness. Walls were sapped, mines opened up. Then the citizens surrendered, their swords round their necks. But suddenly Federigo pardoned them.

Out of the harbour of Genoa, on St. Mark's day, to the sound of trumpets, seven-and-twenty ships put to sea with the Prelates. The Admiral, James Malocello, let the fleet sail as far as Porto Fino, then, days later, to Levano. It was reported that the Imperial Vicars Uberto Pallavicino and Marino of Eboli had invaded Genoese territory and that Pallavicino was besieging the castle of Zolaschi. The Genoese wanted to return ; for the Doria were Imperialist, an Imperial letter had been discovered in a wax loaf and the unrest among the people kept secret until the sailing of the *Podestà* Guilelmo

Surdo. The Genoese declared they must proceed to Zolaschi. But, the Prelates urging, they sailed on as far as Porto Venere. There they received the news that twenty-seven Imperial galleys and forty belonging to the Pisans were lying outside Pisa. The Genoese counselled those with them to wait for eight new ships which were now almost built. The Prelates were confused and insisted on greater expedition. It was possible to make a westerly course towards Corsica and thence, while superfluous ships were steered towards Pisa, on in the direction of Civitavecchia or Ostia. James Malocello however sailed against the enemy.

The Emperor's Admiral, Ansaldo de Mari—he a Genoese too—and the Pisans', Ugolino Buzacherini, sought battle. They hid near the rocky isle of Meloria. Fiercely the fleets rushed together on Holy Cross day. Yells rushed together in the bluish air. Three ships of Genoa were sunk with sprung hulls and splintered masts. What had been aboard them drowned in the waters, among them, dragged down by his bellying velvet cloak, the Archbishop of Besançon. The Genoese seamen, not yet accustomed to war, were slower than those of Pisa, who bored grappling-hooks into the crashing galleons, those fish-tailed mermaids. They and the Imperialists laid about them with oars, poles and swords and captured ship upon ship. They took two Cardinals, the Deacon Otto and James of Praeneste, four Archbishops, those of Bordeaux, Rouen, Auch and Milan, the Bishops of Carcassonne, Nîmes, Agde, Tortona, Pavia and Asti, the Abbots of Clairvaux, Cîteaux, Clugny and Prémontré and, in so far as they were not dead, the Lombards' ambassadors; moreover, money and valuables, together with what the Cardinal Deacon Otto had collected in England. Many rode about Monte Christo and Giglio on planks in the crimsoned waves and lamented: " O Vierge Marie, Madonna ". Two thousand corpses floated about, face upwards. The Spaniards got away at the very beginning of the battle already—the Archbishop of Tarragona, the Bishops of Astorra, Oria, Salamanca,

Porto and Plasencia and, with them, Archbishop Jean de Baussan of Arles. James Malocello escaped, who was called Ubriaco among the Genoese, the toper. The Emperor's men and the Pisans bound the captives who were still struggling in irons, according to the custom on galleys they rubbed vinegar and salt into them. As the prize was rich, Ansaldo and Ugolino forbade the sailors to gamble for it with dice. They therefore gambled on planks which they daubed with circles of chalk and, from high to low, raced their lice against one another. The galleys made for the estuary of the Arno, by which King Enzio stood in the evening sun.

The prisoners were forwarded by way of Pisa to Federigo at Faenza; thence to San Miniato and again by sea to the castle at Naples and to Melfi. They suffered from thirst and sickness and the roughness of the sailors. The harshest treatment was meted out to James of Praeneste. Through Magister Gualtieri de Ocra the Emperor sent a letter of triumph to the King of England. "So the divine judgment", he exclaimed, " has not failed against that man of Palestrina, who has so often directed hatred against us. May he, the wolf in sheep's clothing, know that God is with us, sitting upon his throne and judging according to righteousness. We, however, will conclude our victorious progress to our glory and that of all Princes."

In Germany Albert Beham was on the run, the pestilential knave—for that is what he was called by the Archbishop of Salzburg, who trod a brieve from the Pope underfoot. Bishop Rüdiger of Passau had struck him in the fat face when he disturbed his church service. He concealed himself in forests. He fled to the Rhine, to Worms. He required of the citizens the fifth part of the ecclesiastical revenues. The Emperor wrote to Worms against the dissembler in priest's garb, wrote in the spirit of the prophet Elijah when butchering the infamous priests of Baal. From the Alps blew the gloomy Föhn. "Help, Lord, we perish" sounded through the western world.

THEY had slit eyes, thin bandy legs, beardless cheeks with knubbly bones, pigtails at the back of their shorn skulls. They bestrode shaggy ponies, which were hardy and could go a long while without food and climb unshod over rock, hill and dale, like goats. Their bucklers consisted of neat's leather, several layers pressed on top of each other. They had helms of leather or iron, curved swords, their bows strapped round them with the strings taut. In their quivers stuck frightful arrows, four inches longer than those of any other people, with heads of iron, bone or horn that cleft shirts of mail unfailing. They waved little flags of black and white with a hank of wool on them. When they dismounted, instead of bread they consumed milk with horses' blood, which they called *kumiz*. They ate too the flesh of clean and unclean beasts, cats, rats and mice. They slept in tents of felt and leather. Like dogs their horses followed them to their resting places. As they rode onwards the water of rivers did not hinder them from crossing in the saddle. If a water-course was really too wide, they took a weft, half basket, half skiff and inflated skins and with their help swam to the further bank. If they came upon a hostile army, they surprised it by stealth. They fought mutely, without battle-cry, making hissing sounds. If they had to retire they did so in ordered files. It was dangerous to pursue them. For they would turn round and suddenly shoot behind them. When one of them was killed they brought his corpse into safety at once. They were inventive and clever in sieges.

The Mongols had had a leader, Temudjin, the Gingis Khan ; and now it was Batu. Their generals were Ordu, Shivan, Tangkut, Cuyuk, Cadan, Buri, Paidar, Subutai and Vaghatur. They took the capital of the Russians, Kiev the Golden. Prince Michael of Chernigov fled to Duke Conrad of Masovia and then into Silesia. The Germans in Sereda killed his granddaughter and plundered the treasures she was taking with her. The hordes of horsemen flooded Volhynia and Podolia.

They were only five days' march from Hungary. In Saracen script Cuyuk wrote to King Bela, who had let the baptized Cumans into his country: "I, Cuyuk, God's emissary, to whom he has given power upon earth in order to exalt those who humble themselves before me, to cast down his adversaries however, am amazed at thee, thou kinglet of Hungary, that, when I have sent thee ambassadors to the number of thirty already, thou neither sentest one of them back to me nor otherwise didst let a message come to me. I have learnt that thou hast taken the Cumans, our subjects, under thy protection. I therefore charge thee for the future not to keep them with thee, if thou art not minded to have me as thy adversary on their account. It is easier for the Cumans to escape than for thee; they, without houses, vagabonds in tents, can avoid me, but thou dwellest in houses and hast fortified cities and castles; how shouldst thou not fall into my hands?" He sent a letter to the Emperor, that he should submit to him, as king of the earth, and promised him a place at the Mongol court. The Emperor jested that he knew his way about with birds and was fitted to be the Khan's falconer.

King Bela had sought to obtain information through Franciscans and Dominicans; they were slain by the Volga. He convoked a diet at Buda. A courier from the Palatine hurried into the hall. The Mongols were already at the Carpathian pass of Ruszka and had destroyed the barriers of pines and oaks. The Palatine himself arrived, his robe of state in tatters. To the sabres and arrows of the hissing hordes all who fought under him had succumbed except himself and a few knights. The King commanded the Archbishops, Bishops, Counts and Barons to call out their men and ferried across the Danube to Pest, the German city. Through the plain the Mongols' vanguard under Shiban, Batu's brother, came dashing onward. They scorched up the villages round Pest. Others took the town of Vacz and burnt canons, women and infants who had fled into the church and the episcopal buildings.

The people in Pest cursed Cuthan, the Cumans'
Prince, believing that the Mongols were Cumans too.
Hungarians and Germans shouted : " He must die ".
The Cumans defended themselves with a hail of arrows.
They were overpowered. The people hurled their
decapitated heads through the windows. The Cumans
in the country revenged themselves upon the peasants
and murdered nobles, women and children who were
journeying with the Bishop of Csanad. He alone,
ill in his litter, was spared by rapid flight. They
filched money, horses and cattle and turned towards
Bulgaria.

The Duke of Austria had come to Pest to help King
Bela. He went, hurt by his arrogance. Archbishop
Hugolin of Kalocsa wanted to attack Shiban. After
sustaining losses on the ground flooded with March
rains he turned back. Then the King's army moved
against Batu on the north-east by the reed-grown swamps
of the Sajó. It had its camp on Mohi moor, surrounded by a rampart of wagons with ropes and chains.
During the night the Mongols were on the move, cat-
like. They came crawling up to the Hungarian bank.
Koloman, the King's brother, scattered them ; a part
of them were cut to pieces. The Hungarians laughed
and drank. But Batu pelted the only bridge with stone
blocks from seven catapults and with arrows, and when
daylight had come the hordes crossed in terrifying
swarms there and by a ford.

Koloman's Hungarians fought in a wedge, with
fierce bravery. The Archbishop accused the King of
irresolution and reproved the magnates. The French
Templars and their Master remained dead on the spot.
The Mongols had closely surrounded the camp ; now
they forced the ring and all wanted to get through. The
King, whom a faithful retainer had saved from one of
the slit-eye's blows, swam over the Sajó on horseback
and careered into the protection of the woodland
thicket. The Slav Vochu kept watch through the nights
at his head. The Mongols stabbed the Archbishop of

Kalocsa, severely wounded, to death. Koloman, crowding out the women, fled in a boat across the Danube. He died in Croatia and was buried in the monastery of Casma. Uncounted were they who suffocated in the rain-swelled pools. The peasants took refuge in the fortified churches. The Mongols set fire to the roofs, hundreds groaned, until there was a fearful hush. In their furs black with smoke they rotted under the stalks of maize and sunflowers, from which the seeds fell rustling.

The people of Pest, mad with terror, wanted even now to fortify their town. The Mongols took it by storm. They slaughtered the populace by thousands. The Danube no longer carried down water, but red blood. Thousands screamed in the monastery of the Dominicans as the fire consumed them. They of the slit-eyes piled up mountains of corpses. They speared children on their lances and carried them on their backs along the Danube strand, mowing and chattering like fishes.

Mounted hordes, while King Wenceslaus was marching through the Riesengebirge and the part of the Neisse towards the Elbe, burst into Moravia. They devastated the cities and monasteries, and killed men, women and children. They descended into the plain of the March. They besieged Olmütz. Burgrave Zdislav of Sternberg surprised them and captured Cadyu, who had ventured too far. On their forays they beleagured Brno and destroyed Littau. Then they too turned towards Hungary. They appeared in Poland and dragged away from Cracow many men and much gold and silver. They appeared before Breslau. The inhabitants themselves burnt down the town and pressed into the castle, which lay on an island in the Oder. The Mongols rode to Prussia and to Lithuania, Prince Bezeramban's land.

Near Liegnitz they were opposed by Duke Henry of Silesia with Duke Miecyslaw of Oppeln's and Sudislaw of Cracow's troops, German gold-diggers and French Templars—nine brethren, three chevaliers, two sergeants and five hundred men.   The hordes surrounded him.   He waited for King Wenceslaus, who was still a day's march away.

They killed the Duke of Silesia and his barons on the battlefield.   They cut his head off.   His mother Hedwig, the saint, who was in Krossen Castle with her daughter, the Abbess Gertrude, and Duchess Anna, heard of her son's death without a lament.   Duchess Anna recognized her husband's trunk and limbs by the six toes of his left foot.   He was buried in Saint James's at Breslau.

THE world startled.   No one, men wailed, would escape the impious hands of these barbarians, who also went by the name of Tatars or, from hellish Tartarus, of Tartars.   The vine-dressers in Burgundy, the herds-men of the Pyrenees startled.   In every church the prayer went up : " From the fury of the Tatars, good Lord deliver us ".   The Jews began the first year of the sixth millennium and awaited from the east the coming of the Messiah, of King David.   The story spread that the Tatars were Jews of that tribe whom once, at Alexander the Great's request, the Lord shut up in the Caspian mountains ; that the Jews had bought up weapons in the west and packed them in barrels, declaring that the Tatars drank only wine packed by Jews and that this wine was poisoned.   But by the bridges in Germany the circumcised had refused to pay toll ; then the arms were discovered.   They tortured the Jews and put them to death.

King Bela begged the Emperor through Bishop Stephen of Vacz to make peace with Rome and equip an army against the Mongols.   If he saved him he promised he would swear him the oath of allegiance. " We have ", the Emperor answered the Bishop, " sought to win over the exalted Pope by much complaisance and courtesy and done everything serviceable to that end. We have sent a special embassy to the Papal See that he may remove the many obstacles which by word and deed he has raised before us and permit us to set forth to the defence of Christendom." Gregory however wrote to the Duke of Silesia's sons : " When we consider that through these Tatars the name of Christian might utterly perish, our bones shudder at the mere thought, our marrow dries up, our body dwindles, our spirit and strength are undone ; it causes us so much terror and so much grief that we do not know to whom to turn ". He praised and commended to the Lord the Duke of Carinthia, who had taken pains to move him to peace with Frederick, the alleged Emperor. " In case he should show himself worthy of peace with the Church and inclined to fulfil the conditions indispensable to the honour of God, we will gladly open the bosom of our apostolic fatherhood to him who returns full of humility to the bosom of Mother Church." But to King Bela he wrote that the alleged Emperor must submit in contrition.

In Merseburg Princes and Lords decided to take the Cross by reason of the great peril. King Conrad took it at Whitsuntide in Esslingen until Martinmas. They collected money and slingers. Victuals were to be taken into the strong castles, not to the Rhine. There were prohibitions against the sitting in inns and wearing of costly clothes. Knights endowed churches and monasteries for their souls' health. Jacobins and Minorites wandered about to markets and fairs preaching the Cross. Albert Beham, however, smuggled a letter through to the Bishop of Ferrara to the effect that messengers from Frederick had been seen with the Tatars, and in some regions of Germany people maintained that he had sent for them.

After fruitlessly negotiating with Rome, the Emperor sent from Spoleto a missive to the King of France, to the Counts, freemen and ministerials in Swabia, to the Romans. " With pain ", he began, " we report it and remember it with tears. The malice of the old, venemous serpent shows itself so superior to our prudence that, spreading ruin over the whole world, it has turned our subjects' loyalty into disloyalty and the Church has withheld the breasts of motherly affection." So he would hasten his march upon Rome and, when the son should then have found with Gregory the Priest what was the Father's, he, Augustus, the Catholic Emperor, the renowned tamer of the rebels, would pledge his person and his power for the defence of the Christian faith. Had not this Roman priest once before fallen upon his rear, he, our dearest father, invading Sicily with troops of the Milanese and their copesmates, while he himself was in the Holy Land to lay low the Saracens? The obstinate man, unable to control the slippery course of his tongue, the Roman Pharisee, he called him. Through his legates he, the Pope, had a crusade preached against him, the arm and warden of the Church, instead of the Tatars. The Emperor wrote to King Lewis, who, by the mouths of the Abbot of Corbie and Gervais d'Escrennes, his Cook, demanded the liberation of the French prelates. The Empire, he wrote him, surpassed all other dignities, even as the beasts had to be in terror of the footprints of the lion. And wrote him : " We must stand amazed that the cleverness of the French is blind to the Pope's wiles and purpose. His insatiable ambition, after humbling the crown of England, is directed towards subjugating all Kingdoms and with proud presumption to bow the head of the Empire beneath his will ".

The Bishop of Vacz returned to Bela at Zagreb. King Conrad put off his Crusade. They who had made a vow of participating were ordered by Albert Beham to stay at home until the Pope should call them out against the Emperor Frederick. The Bishops and the Princes divided the monies between them. The Mongols drew nearer to Austria. They slew the peasants by the Danube. The first swarms threatened Vienna. Then, from the top of the Leopoldsberg, where the Marchioness Agnes's veil hung in the branches of an elder-bush, they beheld many troopers approaching. It was an army under the Dukes of Austria and Carinthia, the Patriarch of Aquileia and the Marquis of Baden.

The hordes of the slit-eyed vanished. Others, more powerful, destroyed German Wardein, ravished women, desecrated graves. They crossed the winter ice of the Danube, pressed on to the Adriatic, surrounded King Bela on the Island of Arbe, appeared outside Spalato, plundered Pest and Esztergom. Then they departed, because their Great Khan Ogdai had died in Karakorum. They dragged away many captives, Germans among them, who were digging silver in the mines of Transylvania, also a girl from Metz and a goldsmith from Paris, whom, decades later, William of Ruysbroek found in Karakorum.

FEDERIGO lay before Terni, before Narni, which he did not take, and before Rieti. His brother-in-law, Richard of Cornwall, returned from the Holy Land. He had arrived outside Acre when, near Gaza, the Counts of Bar and Montfort had succumbed to the Egyptians and he had concluded a treaty with the Sultan Malik-es-Saleh, El-Kamil's son, in Ascalon, the citadel of which Richard Cœur de Lion had built, a castle reared with stone blocks and towers and in the charge of the Imperial lieutenant Walter Penaupie. He anchored in Trani. Federigo sent him to the Pope in Rome, in order to speak for peace at his discretion. The Roman citizens made mock of him. The Pope even now wanted nothing less than the submission of the reprobate he had banned. " I rejoice ", thus did the Emperor receive the Earl of Cornwall, " that you yourself have experienced what we moreover prophesied."

The Emperor lay before Tusculum, before Tivoli. It opened its gates to him, and he tarried by the waterfalls of the Anio, beneath the olives and cypresses surrounding the temple of the prophetic Sibyl. He took Albano. For, from Praeneste, he was receiving the help of Cardinal Colonna, who occupied Monticelli with Sicilian troops and whom he thanked for furthering the *Imperium*, for the fire of his noble blood.

He stormed the walls round the monastery of Farfa. Borgo was abandoned ; he reduced it to ashes. He stormed the fort of Monteforte, which the Pope had erected for himself and his relatives with money raised for crusades. He halted in Grotta Ferrara, nine miles east of Rome, and devastated the neighbouring places.

Pope Gregory had, while the Romans were investing the Mausoleum of Augustus, elevated Matthew Rossi of the clan of the Orsini to the Senatorship. He wrote to the prelates who were captive : " Let not yourselves, ye faithful, be stunned by the changing present. In misfortune be not afraid, not proud in good fortune. Trust in God and show patience in his trials. Peter's ark from time to time is carried away by tempests and driven against rocks. But soon and unexpectedly it dives up again out of the foaming waves and sails undamaged upon the levelled surface ".

Pope Gregory, nearly centenarian, was wont during these weeks of summer to take the baths of Viterbo for his calculus. Now he was far away and he used to groan o' nights too in the sultriness of the *scirocco*. He reared himself up. At the gate of Rome stood his enemy. With horribly changed countenance he collapsed inanimate. The hundreds of clerics hurried about in scared confusion ; every bell of the Eternal City knolled out.

The Emperor, who still had Cornwall with him, received the news at Grotto Ferrata with a happy man's tranquillity. "He then," he wrote to the Kings of Europe, "who rejected all peace, all negotiations for peace and merely contemplated universal dissension, who wished to cast down the Emperor, Augustus, has not survived the end of the avenger August. Dead is he indeed through whom the earth returned not to peace, but discord continued and many stood in peril of death. Albeit we are stirred up to hatred against him by manifest wrong and hostile persecutions, we regret his death and wish that heaven had lengthened his days until our venerable Mother, Holy Church, and the Roman Empire, at whose head by the grace of God we stand, had become

GREGORY IX

[*face p.* 210

reconciled and the greatest scandal of these latter (which he provoked) had been removed. As a comfort to lamenting Christendom, the Creator of the Universe, who knows the privy schemes of the wicked, will ordain to St. Peter's chair a man after His own heart, who will make straight again what Gregory left crooked, make good again his misdeeds, give peace to the whole world and receive us lovingly again into our Mother Church."

He removed from the vicinity of Rome into Apulia. He heard that Admiral Ansaldo de Mari had penetrated with the fleet into the harbour of Genoa, but had retreated before the fiery signals of the Genoese, and that in Germany, at Budenefelde, Archbishop Sigfrid of Mainz with Conrad of Hochstaden, him of Cologne, had conspired against him; the Dukes of Brabant, Lorraine and Limburg knew of it, the Counts of Guelders, Jülich and Loos. He sent Roger de Amicis, Captain of Sicily and Calabria, to the Sultan Nogdem-eddin-Ayub at Cahira. He set free the Cardinal Deacon Otto and James of Praeneste for the Papal election, but only until then; unless Otto were chosen they were to return to custody.

The Senator Matthew Orsini assembled the Cardinals to conclave like thieves in a dungeon. They were kicked and buffeted, dragged round the Palatine over the sharp stones of the street. They were Ægidius of Santi Cosma e Damiani, Stephen of Maria trans Tiberim, Raniero Capoccio of Maria in Cosmedin, Giovanni de Calonna of Sancta Praxedis, Galfrid Castiglione, a Milanese, Richard Anibaldo, Sinibaldo Fiesco, Robert of Ostia, Romanus, Bishop of Porto, the Englishman Robert de Sumercote, Otto and James, the captives. They had to sit in the Septizonium of Severus, a single hall with an apse, surrounded by a cordon of soldiers, who used the floor above them as a latrine, so that, with the rain, the stinking excrement poured through the cracks in the ceiling. Too weak a majority voted for Galfrid, the others for Romanus. The Emperor refused the Bishop of Porto, for having put pressure upon the

University of Paris, for having imputed what was improper to the Queen of France and taken part in the quarrel between himself and Gregory. Once more the conclave began. Robert de Sumercote died in the pestilential air. The soldiers carried him on to the roof, spat at him, sang dirges to him and, while the breath was still in his body, threw him into the corpses' corner. Sinibaldo Fiesco fell ill. The Senator Matthew Orsini threatened that, if they did not elect one out of their midst, he would dig up Pope Gregory again and seat him in the Septizonium, between the cells. They agreed upon Galfrid Castiglione, who was eighty years old. He called himself Celestine the Fourth.

He was Pope for seven days only. He had not yet been consecrated when he died too. A part of the Cardinals fled to Anagni. Three of them remained, adversaries to the Emperor. Matthew Orsini, who, with the Cross borne before, wanted to massacre all the Emperor's partisans in Rome, had Calonna seized. It had no head, the Church of Christendom.

THE Empress Isabella had died in Foggia, after giving birth to a daughter, Margaret ; and Federigo buried her. Then he learnt of the death of Henry, his first son. His keepers were taking him from San Felice to Neocastro. He was once more to change his abiding place. Hemmed in by a lazy, heedless escort, he was riding along towards Martorano. He spurred his horse by the edge of the precipice and lay smashed in the abyss. He was buried in Cosenza, by the door of the cathedral, in a marble sarcophagus and wrapped in a dalmatic with eagles. A Minorite preached about the sacrifice of Isaac: " *Arripuit Abraham gladium, ut immolaret filium suum* ". The Emperor wrote to the Barons of Sicily : " The loving father's grief vanquishes the judge's sternness and sends forth from within a flood of tears, which the recollection of insults endured has hitherto checked and the solemnity of justice. Hard fathers perhaps will marvel that the Emperor, unvanquished by public enemies, should succumb to domestic grief. But a ruler's spirit, how steadfast soever, is subject to the dominion of nature ". Of David he spoke, who bewailed Absalom, and of Cæsar's sorrow for his son-in-law Pompey. Masses for Henry's soul were to be said everywhere and all customs observed.

He yearned for Conrad, his second-born, and adjured him to be virtuous and wise. Fowling and hunting were not to make him all too intimate with servants, whose vain talk lowered a king's dignity. His brother should be a warning example to him. Then, unrecognised, he betook himself to him in Germany. By the Rhine Conrad of Hochstaden was fighting against the Count of Jülich, Archbishop Sigfrid against Otto, the Bavarian Duke and the Palsgrave, also against Worms. Near Lechenich the Count of Jülich had surprised Conrad of Hochstaden and brought him, severely wounded, to Niedeck. To ransom him, they of Cologne sought to capture the German King, who was proceeding from Aix by way of Coblenz to the Main. The Emperor saw him in Frankfort. He made Henry Raspe, the Landgrave of Thuringia, who put in his appearance with Elger, the Prior of Hohenstein, his vice-regent and the King of Bohemia his procurator in the Germanies, to appease him for the loss of the succession in Austria by the marriage of Gertrude, the Babenberg's niece, to his son Vladislav of Moravia. English friars appeared in his presence, Dominicans and Franciscans, and implored him by his anger not to prevent the Papal election. " Who prevents the election ? " he answered. " It was not I, but the stiff-necked pride of the Roman church and her insatiable greed. Even now she is minded by any means to drive me from the throne and never ceases from acquiring money and enemies for my destruction." In May he crossed the Alps once more.

The Senator Matthew Orsini had allied the cities round about Rome against him ; Spoleto and the March of Ancona were in uproar. The Emperor advanced from Civita Nova into the plain of Scurcola and before

Avezzano by Lake Fucino. He marched to the gates of Rome, to set free his friends among the Cardinals, and, desisting from that, went with his army into his kingdom. He had released the Abbot of Clugny, then all the French prelates. Now he gave Cardinal Deacon Otto his freedom. James of Praeneste and Magister John of Toleto, an Englishman, he sent to the Rocca Jani near San Germano.

In July a writing against the Cardinals was broadcast, running: " Through your dissension the Church is in confusion, the faith in which ye live is shaken. The sound of your mouth, which aforetime resounded throughout all lands, is now hushed or transformed into a ridiculous echo. Your hands are still ready to receive, but they of Sheba have no more money for you. Ye have feet no longer for ambulation, whereas the hands of the mighty weigh heavy upon ye. O disgrace: the least of creatures excel ye in wisdom, for the birds fly not without a leader, nor the bees without a queen. Would ye but read in your conscience, how many accusations would ye find therein ". Lewis of France wrote to the Cardinals in Anagni, whether they stood in fear of the Emperor's tyranny: " Choose ye a Pope, who may justly be chosen as Christ's successor, a pure shepherd, a preserver of the Church, whose purity and light is brighter than the sun, to lighten all Christendom. But let there not thereanent be much speech or taking of counsel, but, roused by the grace of the Holy Ghost, let the sleeping lion rise from his lair, that the Princes of the world may tremble at his voice ".

Vercelli refused to surrender to King Enzio. With six hundred Milanese knights Cardinal Legate Gregory of Montelongo made his entry into the town. The Emperor sent Enzio against the Lombards and once more showed himself outside Rome with an army that, he vaunted, was no smaller than that of Hannibal, the Libyan. His ships were anchored at Ostia. He had discharged also James of Praeneste; for Romanus of Porto was dead. Through the Archbishops of Rouen and Messina, the Bishops of Reggio, Brescia and Modena, the Abbots of Clugny and Clairvaux, the Cardinals who were in Rome begged him to withdraw his army and allow them a passage to Anagni. He did so and wrote to the King of France : " Although the striking of our camp meant self-restraint to us and our lieges, we yet evacuated Roman territory, against the public and our private benefit, merely to advance the Papal election. We are in hopes that the Cardinals, by reason of the promise they made us, will harmoniously show solicitude for God's Church by doing away with this open breach ".

In Anagni, after a mass, the Cardinals invoked the Holy Ghost. Then they voted for Sinibaldo Fiesco, the Genoese Count of Lavagna, Cardinal Priest of San Lorenzo in Lucina, the expounder of the Decretals and pupil of the Bolognese jurists Azzo, Accursius and John of Halberstadt. Innocent the Fourth was henceforward to be his name. Federigo ordained a thanksgiving for the Kingdom of Sicily.

INNOCENT, consecrated Pope, reigned. He wrote to the Bishops that they should join with him in prayer, to restore peace in the Church, to preserve her from the fury of the barbarians and the wickedness of the heretics. The Emperor sent to him at Anagni Gerard of Malberg, the Grand Master of the Teutonic Order, the Grand Justiciaries Peter of Vinea and Thaddæus of Suessa, Magister Roger Porcastrella and the pirate from the rocky island of Meloria, Admiral Ansaldo. He would say to the step-motherly Church : " Mother, here is thy son, whom thy bosom has nourished, he will be obedient unto thee ". Heaven had bestowed upon the Pope the name of Innocent, that through him the guilty alone should be punished, the guiltless protected. The choice had fallen upon an old friend of the Emperor's, a noble of the realm ; his power was at his service.

Innocent, both Fiesco and Lavagna, replied through an embassy to Melfi, made up of the Archbishop of Rouen, the Bishop of Modena, the Abbot of San Facondo.

The Pope and his brethren likewise were wishful of living at peace with the Emperor. He was to release all clerks still in his custody and suggest atonement for the things because of which he had been excommunicated. Should the Emperor believe himself in no wise to have done harm to the Church, then an assembly of all Kings, Princes and Prelates should decide. But the peace must comprise every friend of the Church. The Emperor complained of Gregory of Montelongo, that he should be removed from Lombardy, of the nomination of Sigfrid of Mainz and the Archbishop of Avignon as Legates and that the Pope had made no detailed explanation to the Grand Justiciaries. But a few short weeks afterwards Innocent wrote to Gregory of Montelongo that the Emperor had declined the articles of peace. Never would the Church desert the Lombards.

Calculating with Genoese frigidity, he made the Cardinal Deacon of Maria in Cosmedin, fiery Raniero Capoccio, Bishop of Viterbo. The Gatti had carried it away in the revolt against the Emperor, the people of Viterbo murmuring against the tyrant set over them, the Governor Count Simon of Theate, and declaring that by the side of his palace a gaol had already been built for housing free citizens. The Governor threatened to requite such mutiny. With mercenaries from Rome, exiles and bandits, Capoccio gained possession of Viterbo. Count Simon maintained himself in the citadel of San Lorenzo, which had seventeen towers, and by messengers desired help from his tardy successor, Count Richard of Caserta : " You justify yourself by declaring that you are waiting for the Emperor's arrival, in order to hasten to us, but the proverb will be fulfilled that while the grass grows, the steed dies ". The Pope sent Capoccio two thousand five hundred ounces of gold, to pay the mercenaries.

The Emperor himself, on a bay charger, came to the walls of Viterbo, like a lioness, a she-bear from whom her young has been stolen, like a whirlwind from the North, a courier lacking all royal pomp, to destroy the city. This Capoccio told the men of Viterbo : the Emperor was merely deluding them with his offers, for he had sworn : " And even if I stood with one foot already in Paradise, I would draw it back, if I could only be avenged upon these men of Viterbo, who have offered violence to my followers and destroyed their houses ". Peter of Vinea divided the companies for storming the ramparts. Federigo swung himself from his horse and fought with a four-cornered shield. But merely the palisades of the outer works were loosened. Then Federigo gave the signal for a second charge, and they in San Lorenzo joined in the fight. Through Viterbo the legend ran that voices from heaven had announced victory. The blessed Rose, the miracle-worker, a child of ten, went in front. The Imperialists had iron wagons with bridges, ladders on wheels, torches and Greek fire and threw brushwood and fascines into the ditches. They in Viterbo poured vinegar upon the flames and blew them into the besiegers' faces, set the brushwood under them alight, so that, in the north wind, a sea of fire surrounded them. With stones a woman knocked the helmet off a German's head and put it on her own ; a girl of nine, carrying stones, was hit in the arm by an arrow, drew it out with her teeth and persevered in her task. The Emperor vanished in the hellish heat. Men said that he had been shot. He sat in his tent after the battle, full of ugly thoughts.

Cardinal Deacon Otto went to him and demanded in the Pope's name that he should discontinue the siege of Viterbo. He agreed to do so if Count Simon's three hundred knights might leave the fortress of San Lorenzo unharmed. But before Capoccio's eyes the people of Viterbo fell upon the exhausted garrison and struck down a number of them. At peril of injury the Cardinal Deacon exerted himself to cover the knights. In Viterbo, in Vico and Capranica those who still adhered to the Emperor were stripped of everything. Federigo, not yet himself again, complained to the Cardinal Deacon : " What is to happen when the fidelity of men is thus trodden under foot and modesty and conscience are thus stifled?" The Marquises of Montferrat and Malaspina rebelled; likewise the town of Alessandria.

Pope Innocent returned to Rome, to the Lateran. The merchants, to whom Gregory owed forty thousand marks, wanted their money and even molested the Holy Father when he was at meat in the Triclinium of the third Leo. He sneaked into the inaccessible chamber with the relics from Jerusalem, with the pillared table on to which the priests had paid Judas Iscariot the thirty pieces of silver, with the stone on which the legionaries had diced for Christ's coat, with the doors from the house of Pilate, with the scissors by means of which Domitian, in mockery, had given Saint John the tonsure. A little silver cradle was the bed of Nero's frog-child. When he had wanted to bear a child and had threatened the doctors with the sword unless they saw to it, they had given it to the Roman Emperor in a draught and he had spat it up again. Tenderly did Nero love his frog, he kept a nurse for the croaking reptile until, on one of the Tiber bridges, it jumped from the gold-wheeled carriage down into the waters. Pope Innocent dined alone amongst this lumber, far from the light of day.

Then, with the patience of his countrymen, he disposed of his creditors. From her palace in the stronghold of Goceano, the consort of Enzio, King of Sardinia, Queen Adelasia, had petitioned the Pope for the dissolution of her union with Enzio, which he had broken. Pope Innocent commanded the Archbishop of Arborea to lift the ban from her. He wrote to Lewis of France that, at his request, he had removed the excommunication laid upon Count Raymond of Toulouse. He wrote to the city of Bologna that the Emperor was now prepared to make peace according to the dictate of the Church.

In Aquapendente, whose citadel he reduced to ashes, Federigo gave full authority to the Grand Justiciaries Vinea and Thaddæus of Suessa. It was on the same day that in Germany, at Weimar, Archbishop Sigfrid published the Emperor's excommunication. Then Federigo, once again in Aquapendente, let the Grand Justiciaries and Count Raymond swear to the peace and affirm it by his soul. Not from contempt had he regarded Gregory's ban as non-existent. Soldiers and money he would agree to, alms and fasting, erection of churches and spittle-houses, liberation of prisoners, invalidity of all punitive sentences, renunciation of vengeance upon all who had been at odds with him before Empire and Church had fallen into dissension, peace even with Gregory of Montelongo. The peace was ratified by oaths on Maundy Thursday in Rome, in the presence of Baldwin of Constantinople, the Senate and the *Quirites*. Pope Innocent received the Emperor as his son and as a Catholic Prince. The Emperor wrote to King Conrad that soon the Pope would bless him too. He invited the Germans to his court at Verona. But about Whitsuntide already Innocent repudiated the peace, for the Lombards' sake.

POPE INNOCENT advanced Henry of Raspe, the vice-regent of the Germanies, to be Count-Palatine of the Lateran and, as greatly obliging the Apostolic See, he praised whoso should be minded to raise him still higher. Instead of obeying, the Emperor had preferred to go back on his oath. Pope Innocent appointed three Bishops, three Priests and six Deacons Cardinals, among them John of Toleto, who had been incarcerated with James of Praeneste. Pope Innocent let the Emperor tarry in the Campagna, in Interamna and Narni, and sent Cardinal Otto to announce to him that unless a remedy were found for that concealed distemper, the Lombards' cause, there could nowhere be peace. He said aloud, before the ambassadors from England and France, that even after absolving the Emperor he would support the Lombards against him. The secret negotiations he had written down ; for sixpence they were on sale, for anyone to buy, where the fortune-tellers' starlings twittered by the Lateran.

He pretended to await Federigo in Rieti. But Bojolo the Minorite went to Genoa with a letter to the *Podestà* Philip Vicedomini, the Visconti : the Pope was surrounded by the Emperor's hosts, so that he daily feared to be taken prisoner. To save his life, the Genoese fleet should fetch him at Civitavecchia or Corneto. Twenty-two ships put to sea, with the Papal kinsman Alberto, Jacopo and Ugo Fiesco. Innocent was in Sutri. He learnt that two hundred of the Emperor's knights were riding up to the town. Simply attired, in a leathern soldier's jerkin, his cloak up to his eyes and the beard on his cheeks, he fled on horseback in the night, to Civitavecchia. Only young Cardinal William of San Eustachio—also one of his nephews—and his chaplain Nicolao de Corbio were with him. Five Cardinals travelled after him the next morning, seven proceeded by land to Susa. Wind billowed the sea, the ships were driven out of their course to the Pisan island of Capraria. Toilsomely they made Porto Venere, on the seventh day the sun-lapped harbour of Genoa. The bells rang, a choir carolled : " Blessed is he who cometh in the name of the Lord ". The Cardinals made response : " Our soul hath escaped like a bird from the snare of the fowler, severed is the cord and we are free ".

Federigo heard the news in Pisa. " The unjust man has fled away ", he cried, " and none pursues him." Then : " When aforetime I played at chess with the Pope, I usually checkmated him or at least took a rook of him ; now the Genoese have put their hands on the chessboard, and through them I shall lose the game ". After Fra Elia had been with Vatatzes the Greek, he had married his and Blanca Lancia's daughter Anne to the Emperor of Nicæa ; in Brussa they now celebrated their wedding. He begged Raymond of Toulouse to go to Genoa for him ; the Count in Savona merely sent messengers to Innocent who answered them ungraciously. The Emperor sent to Cîteaux, to Lewis of France, who was intending the betrothal of his sister to Conrad, still King of Germany. But the Pious, following his

Barons' advice, would not grant even the Pope an asylum.

Innocent fell sick in Genoa. The Cistercians of the monastery of San Andrea nursed him. He disclosed to the *Podestà* and his brother Opizo Fiesco that his goal was Lyons. He blessed Genoa and had himself carried on beds to Varaggio and to Stella, the Marquis of Carreto's castle. The physicians' arts were vain. But he prevailed through the toughness of his constitution. On a mule he rode to Cartamiglia and to the Monastery of the Holy Apostles outside Asti. He passed the snowy Mont Cenis. From Chambéry he sent thanks to the King of Bohemia, who had again made submission to the Church. By the pale flowing Rhone stood his servants with a litter. A great city swarming with people began, Lyons, and in the bloodless old Archbishop's granite palace by the Saone the Pope laid himself down.

THE King of France had himself scourged by his confessor with little chains which he carried in an ivory box at his girdle. For long he had worn a hairshirt on his bare skin, he fasted much and daily said a mass for the dead or, even on horseback, recited the prescribed words. According to the calendar he eschewed the sin of the flesh with Margaret, the Queen. If none the less desire plagued him, he walked up and down in the bedchamber, till his body grew calm. From the Emperor Baldwin he acquired the relics from Constantinople, the splinter of the Cross, a bit of the sponge, the thorns of Christ's crown ; in a procession he brought them from a shrine in Sens to Paris, he, his brother Robert of Artois and all his Knights with naked soles. He honoured the begging friars, washed the feet of the sick, in the morass of the Compiégne road he kissed a leper's scurfy hand. He never lied. For the love of God the clerks in Clugny Abbey gave bread to a knight, limping on crutches. He caused the learned Rabbi of the Jews to appear before the Abbot and asked him whether he believed that the Virgin Mary had borne Jesus by a virgin birth. When the Jew replied that he did not believe that, the knight hit him with his crutch on the ear so that he fell down. To this King Lewis said that a layman might not dispute with the Jews. If he should hear the Christian faith mocked, he should smite them with the sword, in the belly, as far as ever it would go. He himself burnt a blasphemer's lips with red-hot iron. He sat in judgment upon the people in the forest of Vincennes or in his garden in Paris, on his head a hat with a white peacock's feather. " *Beau Sire Dieu*," he prayed to God when they crowned him, " I commend myself to thee."

He was thought dead in Pontoise, and, his mother Blanche and Margaret, the Queen, having gone, the layer-out was already drawing the sheet over him as a dead man, when he opened his eyes and said : " The light of the East has spread from Heaven through the mercy of the Lord of hosts and called me back from death ". The Bishop of Paris had to fasten the cross of red silk upon his shoulder, the symbol of the Crusade, of the fight against the infidels. " Verily ", the King retorted to the Bishop of Paris, as his mother and several of the Bishops and Barons were dissuading him, " I will enjoy no food until you have recognized me as a soldier of the Lord."

About the time that this befel in Pontoise, there came to the Emperor Frederick a messenger from the Patriarch Albert of Antioch : hordes of Chorasmian Turks had taken Jerusalem, ravaged the holy places, desecrated the graves of the Kings of Jerusalem and burnt their remains. At Christ's sepulchre they had beheaded the Bishop of Siunia and three priests with him, so that the blood spurted, and added : " It is meet that the blood of them be spilt who so often spill wine here for the God who hung on the cross ". The Emperor informed the Princes of the West. He jeered at the Patriarch of Jerusalem, the new athlete, Bishop Robert of Nantes, who had been hostile to him since Apulia and designated the Templars' hatred as the root of the evil. In February the Patriarch of Antioch himself came to him. Near Gaza the Chorasmians and Egyptians had defeated the Christians' and the Sultan of Damascus's army. Only thirty-three Templars, twenty-six Knights of St. John and three German Knights had not been killed or captured. The Emperor wrote to Richard of Cornwall, that Satan was busy and Simon sleeping. He had wanted to protect the Holy Land, but the reprehensible perfidy of the Patarenes, the Lombard heretics, weakened his arm. Only after he had won back his ancestors' rights in Italy would the Imperial eagle be able to stretch its pinions again. Through the Patriarch Albert, he then wrote to the Pope, a light shone beckoning to him from the dark welkin; for the last time he turned peaceful phrases.

Pope Innocent was a nuisance to those of Lyons. A draper knocking at the portal of the palace was refused admission so rudely that the burgess smote off the porter's hand with his sword, and the judge passed only a half-hearted sentence upon him. The Pope appointed his relatives, the Fieschi, to the prebends of Lyons Cathedral. The Canons revolted; nor would they have budged if one of the former were drowning in the Rhone. Fire broke out in the Papal wardrobe. They of Lyon said that the damage had been expressly done to extort new tribute. Lampoons were affixed to the walls of the palace : " Pecunia, the Empress of the Romans and the whole world, to her well-beloved sons and attornies greeting and abundance of the dew of heaven and the fat of the land. I dwell on every hill, I let my voice be heard on every road, I have journeyed through the sphere of heaven, I cause the deaf to hear and the dumb to speak. Verily I say unto you, before Abraham was, I was, clothed in gold, girt about with manifold adornment. O all ye that pass by, take heed and see whether any honour is equal to that paid to me. To me all kings of the earth have recourse and all peoples, the court of Rome is my servant. Here will I abide until the end of time, the court of Rome have I chosen to be my own. What greater pleasure can I enjoy than that the Cardinals should bow their necks before me and run after the perfume of my salves and my incense. Never does the Church refuse me her bosom, the Pope joyfully clasps me in his arms. I will give you abundance ; to the preservation of it my sweetest friend will gladly consent, to wit, Avarice ".

The Abbot of Clugny made presents of much money, costly vessels, twenty richly appointed horses and for each of the Cardinals a saddle-horse and a pack-horse. The Pope rewarded him with the mitre of Langres. He appointed the Provencal Philip Archbishop of Lyons and the Archbishop of Rouen a Cardinal. He punished the Paris clergyman who had said to his congregation : " I am ordered, to the knolling of bells and the burning of candles, to publish the excommunication of the Emperor Frederick. Unknown to me is the reason, but not that violent dissension and irreconcilable hatred exist between him and the Pope. I know also that one of the twain has done the other a heavy wrong ; but which of the two I do not know. Therefore I declare him excommunicated who is guilty and absolve him who suffers the wrong so pernicious to all Christendom ". The King of England, whom Innocent had asked whether he would entertain him, was opposed by the Barons : the purity of England was already abundantly soiled by the usury, spoliation and simony of the Italians and Romans ; all that was wanting was that the Pope should come in person to spoil and squander the goods of Church and State. The knight Sir Fulke threatened Magister Martin, the Legate, that they would all be cut to pieces, unless he with his train left the realm at once. The Magister embarked at Dover. The Pope in Lyons exclaimed : " We must come to an understanding with the Dragon, the Emperor, or crush him under our heel. After that we shall soon have tamed these snakes, these petty kings ".

POPE INNOCENT had convoked a Council to debate the dispute between the Church and "the Prince". On Maundy Thursday—the Archbishops of Mainz and Cologne present—he pronounced anew his ban upon the Emperor, Enzio and the Marquis Lancia. At Easter he cited Federigo to Lyons. Spent was the Patriarch of Antioch's last effort. The Emperor despatched Thaddæus of Suessa, Gualtieri de Ocra and Berard, the very ancient Archbishop of Palermo.

To the Council journeyed seventy-one Primates and Metropolitans, four hundred Bishops, eight hundred Abbots and Priors—most of them Frenchmen and Spaniards—envoys of the rulers, envoys of Venice, envoys from Genoa, Hugh Fiesco and Simone di Marina. There appeared the Patriarchs of Constantinople, Antioch and Aquileia, the Emperor Baldwin, the Counts of Provence and Toulouse and among the Germans squint-eyed Albert Beham. Pope Innocent proceeded to the monastery of St. Just for the assembly. To the right of his throne sat Baldwin, to the left the Cardinals, the Counts, on one side the Vice-Chancellor of the Roman Curia with scribes and notaries. Opposite the Pope were the seats of the Patriarchs of Constantinople and Antioch. Amid uproar the priests overturned the chair of the Patriarch of Aquileia, who claimed the same honour for himself. The shepherds of the flock sang the "*Veni creator Spiritus*", knelt and prayed. Then the Metropolitan of Constantinople told of the distress to which he, his suffragans and the Latin Empire were exposed. Innocent kept silence. The English prelates stood up and demanded the canonization of the Archbishop of Canterbury. Innocent interrupted them: more important things were now to be deliberated.

There rose, while the feet of the clerks scraped the stone flags, the Emperor's envoy, bald Thaddæus of Suessa. Through illness, he said, his master was prevented from coming. But he offered peace and friendship, the restoration of the Latin Empire, help against the Mongols, Chorasmians and Saracens, restitution of ecclesiastical property, satisfaction for the injuries he might have done. The Pope looked around : " O these many and great promises which were never and nowhere kept, which never can be kept ! Nor have these promises any other purpose than by baffling and deceiving the Council to turn away the axe already laid at the root of the tree. Where shall I catch the Proteus who ever changes his countenance ? and, if I should grant him everything, where is there a surety to compel him to carry out his part when he refuses ? " " The Kings of France and England ", said Thaddæus of Suessa, " will stand surety." The Pope bowed his head under the mitre. " I do not want them ; for if the Emperor, as so often, fails to keep his word, we should have to punish the sureties. Then the Church, instead of one enemy, would have three enemies, and those the mightiest in Christendom." Thaddæus of Suessa said not a word, and the Bishop of Beirut made a speech about the Holy Land.

On the vigil of Saints Peter and Paul the Council met in St. John's Church to the sound of organs and inharmonious chanting. The Pope, crowned with the tiara, spoke sobbing to the deep silence : "O see ye whether there be any grief like unto mine. Even as Christ was pierced by five wounds, so I am overwhelmed by five-fold grief, at the inhuman cruelty of the Tatars, at the Greeks who disdain the bosom of Mother Church, at the heretics, at the godless brood of the Chorasmians and at the Emperor, who is an adversary to all Christ's servants, a perjurer, a disturber of the peace, a robber of churches, a violator of sanctuaries, a heretic. He takes the treasures of churches by force, puts taxes upon the clergy, has let prelates languish in durance, even persecuted the Popes. But this idol, who means to extirpate all worship of God, is also a worshipper of idols. In his realm he founds not holy monasteries, but Mohammedan cities. In mockery of Christendom he gives the Holy Land as a fief to a Mohammedan. Mohammedan eunuchs have guarded Christian women in his Gomorrhan labyrinth. He has married his daughter to the excommunicated heretic Vatatzes. He honours Mohammedan observances and does not shrink from commerce with Saracen harlots. Here are the documents to which he has put his hand with solemn oaths and against which he has blasphemed ". He raised them on high in a hand that was stiff with jewels.

Thaddæus of Suessa replied and pointed to the parchment of the Papal Bulls : " Were these accusations as true as they are heavy, it would go hard with the Emperor, my master. Who can reproach him for not letting himself be excluded by an unjust ban from the beatific communion of the Church ? Whether he is a heretic, none can know but he himself ; he alone, by his confession, can decide of that. But that he at least in his realms permits no usury bears witness against such an assertion ; so does his failure to protect the Lombard heretics as, to universal scandal, the Pope does. How dares anyone rebuke him for a robber of churches since he merely desires what is Cæsar's ? The Holy Father has forgotten how often the Church has approved alliances in the Holy Land between Christians and Saracens. There have been Saracen girls at the Imperial court, not however for lewd intercourse, but for the sake of their artistic skill and feminine deftness. But to the end that my lord may furnish me with full powers touching these accusations or may come hither himself, a sufficient time should be allowed ". " Never ! " cried the Pope, " I fear the gins which I have scarce escaped. If the Emperor comes, I go. Not yet am I minded to be a martyr with my blood or a prisoner."

But as the attorneys for the Kings of France and England decided for an adjournment, Innocent and the Cardinals were fain to consent to a delay of twenty days.

FEDERIGO marched with an army, with mules and camels, with leopards and elephants past Viterbo to Parma. He distrusted the families connected with the Pope, the Rubei, Lupi, Correggi, Soragna, Salimbeni and Cornazani and Guarino de San Vitale, Fiesco's brother-in-law, of whose six sons one was now Bishop in Parma. He distrusted Fiesco's other brother-in-law, Orlando Rossi, who dreamed of the Scipios and whom, when he brandished his iron club, the monk Adamo Salimbene compared with the Frankish Emperor Charles the Great. Federigo went from Parma to Verona, to a court of the German Princes.

There arrived in Verona King Conrad, the Emperor Baldwin, the Archbishop of Salzburg, the Bishops of Ratisbon, Passau, Freising, Brixen and Bamberg, the Abbots of Kempten and Ellwangen, the Dukes of Austria, Meran and Carinthia, the Counts of Tyrol, Ulten, Habsburg and Helfenstein, the Grand Master of the Teutonic Order, Henry of Hohenlohe, with his brothers. Ezzelino too followed the Emperor and the shy Infante Federico of Castile. The Bavarian Duke and the Palsgrave were absent. The Patriarch of Aquileia had sent the Emperor a message to Foggia, that the Duke of Austria was not averse from marrying his niece Gertrude to Frederick; the Emperor sent him a royal ring to Vienna. Now the Babenberg came, but without Gertrude. A devout Christian, she would not give her hand to an excommunicated bridegroom. Ezzelino's men barred the towers and gate of Verona. They threatened the Babenberg's men and killed one of his knights. Without bidding the Romano farewell, the Duke departed.

The Emperor proceeded to Cremona, to Pavia, where he dubbed the sons of Jacopo de Andito. The Infante Federico, his nephew through Beatrice of Swabia, got away to his enemies in Milan, as he was withholding his heritage from him. "What", the Emperor wrote wrathfully to Ferdinand of Castile, "will he be in his old age, after perpetrating so young treachery unheard of and impudent, untouched by so many admonitions from his father and benefits from his uncle?" With the Marquises of Montferrat, Ceva, Carreto, Federigo proceeded to the Count of Savoy in Turin. Thence he

sent to Lyons Gualtieri de Ocra and after him the Grand Master of the Teutonic Order Henry of Hohenlohe, the Bishop of Freising and Peter of Vinea.

Ringing accusations had in the meantime been framed by Cardinal Capoccio, with the words of Isaiah as preamble : " But woe unto the ungodly, for they are perverse, and they will be requited as they deserve ". He was the prince of tyranny, they said, the master of cruelty, the corrupter of the century, the hammer of the earth. With festering ingratitude he had requited the Church for all her favours. He had denied Peter's power of the keys, sought, another Lucifer, to climb above all the constellations in the Church's heavens, in order to be the equal, yea the superior, of the Almighty's vicar. He was Gregory's murderer, had meant to take the present Pope prisoner in Narni or Rieti. He had blasphemed God, Moses and the Saviour. Renewing the heresy of the Sadducees, he and his companions maintained that with the body the soul crumbled to nothing. He was the great Dragon, the raging Nimrod of fornication, a bloodthirsty villain, more wicked than Nero, viler than Julian, the Apostate. A desert because of him was the *Patrimonium*, the Land of Bliss. More than a hundred had been dragged away in Aquapendente by the agents of Peter of Vinea and Vitalis of Aversa, those two vessels of infamy, while the fairest women had been handed over to the lust of the Saracens. In Verona, he, the man of blood, had wanted to bring a Council into being, in order to dissolve that in Lyons to which he was withholding access. Whoso had stolen pallia, silver images of saints, crosses, chalices, censers, treasures of the Church and the clergy, and with such booty bought the favour of Kings and Princes, what torment had such an one merited ? " Spare ye then no missiles against this infamous king! Cast him out of the sanctuary, that he may no more reign over a Christian people. Deliver him who is drunk with the blood of so many saints over unto everlasting reprobation. Root out the name and the scions of this Babylonian. Forgotten be his

name by the Everlasting Mercy." The accusations said moreover that the Emperor had compassed the death of Henry, his first-born ; by his cooks poisoned, after lives of torment, his three wives. Like the Bethshemites, Uzzah, Uzziah, the company of Korah, the Babylonian Belshazar, who died in the same night as the prophetic fingers wrote *Mene tekel upharsin* on the wall, he must be punished with merciless death.

THE Council met again, and in the glory of the tiara Pope Innocent sat above the red-stockinged rows that whispered of an army's approach from Savoy. Bishop Peter of Cales stood up. The designs of the Emperor had, from childhood, been infamous. He wished to make the Church as poor as she had been in her earliest days. Thaddæus of Suessa reproved him, that he should hold his peace, so that his lies might not be spread abroad ; for by a formal sentence his brother had been hanged for treason. In bad Latin the Archbishops of Tarragona and Compostella, the Spaniards, yelped their cries of distress. The Pope cut short their speeches. He let the prelates sign the *Transumpta* concerning the privileges of the Roman church. Whoso laid hands upon them, him would the wrath of Almighty God chasten and that of the apostles Peter and Paul.

The third, the great assembly began with a high mass. He read ordinances touching help for Palestine and the feast of the Nativity of the Virgin. Thaddæus of Suessa rose, urging that they must wait for the Magister of Ocra. "I appeal", he cried, "from this Council, at which so many prelates and laymen have not appeared, to a general, impartial Council. I appeal from this Pope, who bears my master a hostile mood, to a future Pope, of Christian and more charitable mood." And Innocent, coolly replying : all had been summoned, the absent kept away by the tyranny of Frederick himself. Neither by pride, nor by malice and deception would he suffer judgment to be further stayed.

From the Englishman's bench, by the side of the Earls Roger Bigot, William de Cantelupe, Philip Basset, and Ralph, son of Nicholas, rose the clerk William of Poveric, complaining of the Italians, that they had squeezed not only Peter's pence, but more than sixty thousand pounds from his poor country. Without a sound, dropping his piercing black eyes, Innocent listened to the Barons' document. " The matter requires consideration ", was all he remarked ; and, as if nothing had distracted him, he spoke about the proceedings against the Emperor. He shouted at the Patriarch of Aquileia, who wanted to excuse the Emperor, that he would demand his ring back. More softly, in humility, that he had loved Frederick, and wished, even now, to be reconciled with him. Thereupon, nevertheless, he read out a Bull with one hundred and fifty seals, the Decree of Deposition : " We absolve and release all who are bound or engaged to him by oaths of allegiance or in any other way for ever from these duties and these oaths. In the plenitude of our apostolic power we strictly forbid that henceforth he be obeyed as King or Emperor. Whoso, contemning or circumventing this command in any way, yet obeys him or supports him with word or deed, the ban of the Church is upon him. The Princes in Germany entitled to vote may proceed to the election of a king. Touching the Sicilian kingdom we, with the advice and support of our brethren, the Cardinals, will decree what may be necessary ".

Frederick's ambassadors turned pale and tore their breasts and shanks. Thaddæus of Suessa cried : " This is a day of wrath and wretchedness. Heretics and Chorasmians will rejoice, the Tatar spawn overwhelm the Christian peoples ". Pope Innocent retorted : " I have done what I needs had to do. May God bring it to a conclusion according to his will ". He intoned the first words of the *Te Deum*. The prelates sang it with him and quenched their smoking torches on the stone flags, the sparks leaping up crackling, dull red.

Two days away from Lyons was Magister Gualtieri de Ocra, three days away Peter of Vinea, with the Grand Master of the Teutonic Order and the Bishop of Freising. But the Bishop of Bamberg, who put himself at the Pope's disposal, said, on departing again from Lyons for Germany, that Frederick would be murdered by his familiars.

The Emperor at Turin declared in frightful majesty : "The Pope has deposed *me* in his Council, taken the crown from *me* ? Whence such temerity ? Bring hither my crowns that I may see whether they have been lost in truth ". On his long grizzling hair he pressed the iron crown of the Lombards. " Mine still are the crowns, which no Pope and no council shall take away from me without bloody strife. This low vanity presumes to hurl me, who have no peer among the princes on earth, from the pinnacle of my Imperial eminence ? But my lot has thereby waxed better. Hitherto I was constrained to obey or at least to venerate him. Now however I am exempt from all love and honour and every obligation to keep peace with him."

The Emperor wrote to the Earls and Barons of England touching the injustice of the proceedings. In a sermon merely had this Pope cited him to Lyons, not summoned him in person. It were ridiculous to sentence him, the fount of all laws, to secular punishment, him, who in secular matters had no man above him, but God alone. He wrote to the Kings against the priesthood : " O that we had but had the good fortune to behold a warning to ourselves in your fate, ye Christian Kings and Princes, rather than that we should now warn you on account of the indignity put upon our Imperial eminence. The clerks, fatted with the fat of the mighty, mean to play the oppressor. The very sons of our vassals, forgetful of their duties to their fathers, cast off, so soon as ordained Apostolic fathers, all reverence towards Emperors and Kings. We have a clean conscience, and it tells us that God is with us. Ever have we striven to bring back priests and, in especial, those

of the topmost rank, to the condition of the first Christian Church. In those days the clergy raised their eyes to the angels, shone through miracles, made whole the sick, raised the dead, made Kings and Princes subject to them, not with arms but with their holiness. But now they are smothered in delights. To withdraw from them the harmful riches which burden them to their own undoing is a labour of love in which all Princes should eagerly participate ".

Through Richard Posianus, his scribe, Pope Innocent sent a letter to the Germans, to the electoral college : the more the Hohenstaufen sought by excuses to deny the accusation, the more he entangled himself like the bird in the snares of the fowler. He was like unto a man who should wipe his mouth with dirty hands. As the wolf with the lamb, hypocritically kissing her he bit Mother Church to death.

FROM Turin, to defend the German crown, the Emperor sent King Conrad north, with Sicilian mercenaries and monies. Bishop Philip of Ferrara went, by way of Milan, into the German provinces as Papal Legate. He was the son of a sexton in Pistoja, had as a poor scholar learnt the Black Art of an old Spaniard in Toledo, studied theology in Paris and become treasurer to Bishop Garsendino. To father and mother he said, like Jesus : "I know ye not ". He was gloomy and vengeful. When in prayer he stumped through the room, he had goblets with sweet yellow wine in a bucket of icy water by his side. His daughter, who was beautiful, he had wanted to give to Jacopo Bernardo in marriage, but he had disdained her. The Pope commissioned the Legate to find a king in Germany. The ambassadors of Venice came from Lyons—Renier Morosini and John of Canale. The Count of Savoy took them prisoner ; Federigo procured their liberation. They came to him to thank him : "Lord, we went to the Council at our Doge's behest. But were grieved at what befell there and see therein the death and destruction of all Christendom". He chid them for the harm the Republic ¡was preparing to do him, though deriving so much advantage from its trade with him. John of Canale agreed, Renier gave his imprudent fellow a wink. Federigo saw it and laughed: "O, I know all that very well". Then he spoke about the peace: " By God, so be it ".

He was with Peter of Vinea in Parma, then in Cremona. The townsfolk followed him as far as Borgo San Donnino. Then he rode to Fontanaviva, seven miles from Parma. He slept in the monastery of the white Cistercians. Someone unknown had concealed documents in a fresh hole in the wall. In them stood written of peril for the Emperor, for Enzio and Ezzelino. The Berici of Padua intended murdering him at a banquet. The Pope's kin, Bernardo de Rubei, Bernardo de Cornazano, Gherardo da Correggio and the brothers Mons, Guido and Orlando de Lupo, fled to Piacenza, which gave the conspirators a joyful welcome. The Emperor wrote to the faithful communes that hitherto he had been the anvil, now he would be the hammer. With Germans, Tuscans and Sicilians, with horsemen from Parma, Cremona, Lodi and Bergamo he proceeded to Pavia. He sent Peter of Vinea and Gualtieri de Ocra to the French Barons. In person or through Conrad, alone or with King Lewis, he would reconquer Jerusalem, if Lewis would mediate honourably between him and the Apostolic See.

On the right bank of the Ticinello the Emperor lay encamped, together with the Marquises Lancia, Montferrat and Malaspina ; Enzio and Ezzelino halted by the Adda. To put an end to their junction with Federigo, the Milanese, under Gregory of Montelongo fortified themselves to the left of the Ticinello. The Emperor advanced to Bufalore, to Casterno, could get no further. Near Gorgonzola Enzio had an encounter with the Milanese. He was on the point of victory when Panera de Buzano thrust him from his horse and caught him by the spurs. Panting he sat in a local church. Simone de

Locario and a Genoese exchanged him for Genoese bow-stretchers. But thirty-eight of them suffered the loss of their right eye and right hand. King Enzio rode to the Emperor at Lodi and punished faithless Reggio. A hundred lost their heads, many disappeared in dungeons.

The King of France had had a meeting with Innocent at Clugny. Now he sent ambassadors to Genoa about a crusade; also to Frederick at Grosseto. The Emperor refused to submit to his judgment at Lyons. The Pope hearkened to the advocates of Federigo, that simple Christian, to Archbishop Berard, the Bishop of Pavia, the Abbots of Monte Cassino, Cava and Casanova. Unarmed, he said thereupon, the heretic would have to justify himself before him. Reluctantly did the Emperor terminate the negotiations. The town of Viterbo went over to his side, surrendered to them whom it had expelled, and at the open gates they cried rejoicing: " Peace! peace! "

The Emperor celebrated Easter in Grosseto. Discovery was made of a conspiracy in the Kingdom, between Robert de Fasanella, Guilemo de Eboli, Robert de Capano and other barons, and the San Severini family to boot. They had won over Pandolfo of Fasanella, who had been Vicar in Tuscany, and Jacopo de Morra, the Grand Justiciary's son. They had assigned the crown of Sicily to Tebaldo Francesco of Parma. The news was already given out in Apulia that Federigo was dead. The Countess Lucia of Caserta warned him and the astrologer Guido Bonatti, who, from his tower in Forli, beheld the disorder of the stars. A rain of blood plashed down, the red dust of the African desert, scattered by the trade wind, the earth grew dark, the discs of sun and moon turned livid. Pandolfo and Jacopo fled from Grosseto to Rome; Tebaldo Francesco and Guilemo de San Severino escaped into their castles of Scala and Capaccio. With German mercenaries the General Marino de Eboli defeated Cardinal Raniero and the rebels from Perugia and Assisi near Ascoli; five thousand prisoners were led away. The Emperor annihilated those who had dared to touch the apple of his eye. He gave orders to unsight and torture them. Scala fell, the fall of Capaccio was certain. From Salerno Federigo bore witness against Innocent, that the Pope had instigated this conspiracy of murder. He was appalled, he wrote, at those men, with whom he had dwelt in the halls of his court, whom he had about him as the wardens of his life, those beasts and parricides.

King Enzio arrested sixty knights in Parma and razed the strong houses of Orlando Rossi and the Lupi. But Piacenza he did not storm. When the battlements tottered, when thirst and hunger tormented them, the conspirators in Capaccio surrendered. Thirty-two maids, wives and widows were saved up for the subterranean dungeons in Palermo. Dead were they, the living. Before the men were fetched before the Emperor's face, the smoking iron explored their eye-sockets; their noses, hands and feet were chopped off. Divers were burnt to death, divers hanged, divers bound to horses behind which their torn bodies slid over the ploughed field, divers sewn with squirming poison-snakes into leather sacks and hurled into the sea. Tebaldo Francesco and five more, before being broken on the wheel, were driven blinded through the kingdom, on their foreheads the Bull to the Sicilians, in which the Pope declared himself languishing in the servitude of this second Nero. "*O felix Asia*," Federigo wrote to Vatatzes, his son-in-law, "O happy potentates of the East, who have not to fear the daggers of their subjects or the crafty wiles of the priests. *O felix Asia*."

He was weary of the Emperor's throne and yearned for the innocent peoples of the sunrise, for the great cosmic sleep.

POPE INNOCENT had promised the Landgrave Henry Raspe to help him in his project. He paid him through his treasurer Bonvicino fifteen thousand marks of silver; six thousand of them were from

England.   To the King of Bohemia he wrote, to the Dukes of Bavaria, Saxony, Brunswick, Brabant, the Marquises of Meissen and Brandenburg, to the Bishop of Würzburg, that they should unanimously and without delay elect the Landgrave, who was willing for the honour of God and the Church.   In Veithochheim near Würzburg he, brawny Raspe, was chosen by the Rhenish Archbishops, five Bishops, Counts of Thuringia and, feloniously, by the Swabians Henry of Neifen and Conrad of Winterstetten, the Cup-bearer.   Wenceslaus of Bohemia, the Dukes and Marquises did not come.   In Germany they reviled Raspe as the parsons' king : for he was old already and childless and accepted with the simple words : " Thus will I obey, even though I know I had not a year more to live ".

With King Conrad sided the German cities : Worms, Spires, Frankfort, Augsburg, Ratisbon, Nürnberg, Aix-la-Chapelle, Kaiserswerth and Treves.   He had absolved the Frankforters of all their offences against the Jews, the yeomen of the Royal chamber ; for they had killed one hundred and eighty of them by the sword or an incendiary fire.   He pitched his camp by the Nidda, with Swabian footmen and horsemen and ships from Worms.   On St. Oswald's day he came upon Raspe's army.   Then the Counts Ulric of Wirtenberg and Hartmann of Grüningen suddenly went over to the enemy with two thousand knights and cross-bowmen.   The Legate Philip had promised them Swabia, when partitioned, and the Pope bought them with six thousand marks of silver.   Conrad's chivalry was shattered.   An undisciplined band ran out of the alder-wood into his flank, he had to flee to Frankfort sans tent and baggage. Thence he went to Augsburg.   King Raspe however wrote to Milan and Genoa of his hopes, after the example of the Roman princes and heroes, to triumph over the father as now over the son.

He held Diet in Frankfort, and Philip of Ferrara boasted of the many who did homage to his most exalted majesty.   But the Bishop of Hildesheim laid down his crozier rather than damn the Emperor and went into the monastery of Schöna. The Legate threatened the clergy who had not yet appeared that they would be forcibly summoned to Lyons. He was wrath with the Bishops of Worms and Utrecht and, most violently, with Archbishop Everard of Salzburg. It was ill-received at the Papal court, so Albert Beham wrote cooingly to the Archbishop, that his representative had appeared with completely empty hands. He advised him to bestow presents upon the Cardinals, his particular friends; for in the whole of Gaul there was no bishop or abbot so poor that during the last years he had not had a free gift for the Roman curia. Prelates greater and less had remarked at Lyons with amazement that it was an unheard of thing in Gaul, Germany or Spain for a mighty and noble prince, so wise and respected and so far advanced in life, to suffer the Papal censure for so many years. Every other German prelate had made a benefaction of ecclesiastical property, bells or chalices, merely to be free of the ban. Sad and firm, the Archbishop of Salzburg died, an excommunicated man, as did, despised, the Bishop of Ratisbon, who had deserted the Emperor and was refused burial by council and burgesses.

The Duke of Austria met his death in battle against the Hungarians, through the thrust of a Frangipani's lance in his eyeball. His mother Theodora died of grief. The King of Bohemia sued for the hand of Gertrude for Vladislav of Moravia, his son. At Vohburg near Ingolstadt Conrad, aged eighteen, was married to Elisabeth of Bavaria. The Legate Philip of Ferrara, the turkey-cock, banned Duke Otto. King Conrad proceeded from Augsburg by way of the monastery of Neresheim, which he had burnt to the ground, to the Palatinate. In Trifels Isengart, the High Steward of Falkenstein's wife, handed over to him the Imperial insignia and the relics preserved in the castle. He advanced to the autumnal lower Rhine. There was fighting in Alsace, in Swabia, by the Main and the Danube. In Aix-la-Chapelle the warlike Count of

Jülich promised King Conrad support against every attack.

King Raspe held his second Diet in Nürnberg. Then he besieged Swabian Reutlingen, to which Frederick had shown favour. The inhabitants told his messenger that the oath of allegiance which they had sworn the Emperor remained unchanged after its remission by the Pope; they would build a church for St. Mary if she would preserve their town to them. Like them the men of Ulm were defiant. King Raspe retired before the frost and, Duke Humphrey providing the commons, from Swabia to Zeilitzheim. He was sick of a bloody tumour at his fundament. He hurt himself falling off a horse. In the Wartburg he lay on his deathbed, there where he had humiliated Elisabeth the widow with blockish roughness.

The Legate of Ferrara, being frightened, fled into a house of Minorites at Erfurt. The Guardian brought him to the town gate, which was shut. They were about to return to the friary through by-lanes, when the Bishop saw a hole in the wall, through which a mangy dog was crawling. The Legate crawled after him, but remained stuck in the middle. The Guardian gave him a kick in the breach and thus expedited him into freedom.

THE Emperor, who had hostages from both parties of the Florentines, Guelphs and Ghibellines, advanced Frederick of Antioch, his son, to be Vicar of Tuscany. The latter forced thirty-six palaces of the Guelphs in Florence and, in the market-place, the Palazzo of the Tosinghi with the marble pillars and the lofty tower. From Naples the Emperor wrote to Lewis of France. The story had spread that Gualtieri de Ocra had hired a liegeman, Ralph, to murder Innocent in Lyons. The innkeeper Reginald had made confession and, on the rack, Ralph had admitted it. Two Italians were said to have confessed that they had conspired with forty others of like mind to hew the Pope, the defiler of the

Church, in pieces. Innocent, frightened, no longer went out of the Archbishop's palace. The Emperor wrote that such plotting was quite unworthy of his victorious posture ; and again he accused Christ's deputy of murder.

At a court in Naples he had his nine-year-old son by Isabella, Henry, baptized. He left the Sicilian affairs of state to Count Richard of Caserta, Lucia's son, whom he had married to Violante, one of his illegitimate daughters, and to Pietro Ruffo, who from lowly birth had risen to the office of Marshal. From his Kingdom he went to Tuscany, to Siena, San Miniato and Pisa. He avoided Florence, the blooming ; for Michael Scotus had prophesied to him that he would die " *sub flore* ". He learnt of Raspe's death. He proposed to go to Germany with the Italian knights, to a court of the German Princes. By way of Parma he proceeded to Cremona. He gave Jacomino de Carreto for wife Catarina de Marrano—her his daughter likewise, Enzio's sister. He secured the power of his house by the betrothal of his sixteen-year-old son Manfredi Lancia to Beatrice Countess of Saluzzo, daughter to the Count of Savoy. The whole region from Pavia to the Apennines and to the Genoese coastland and, later, Arles were to be Manfredi's fief. He created Peter of Vinea *Logothete*, by that Byzantine title, and Proto-notary, Keeper of the Great Seal.

Then however he went to Turin. What enigmatical project lay hid beneath his mildness ? The Count of Savoy and the Count of Vienne made ready the Alpine passes for him ; Chambéry was the place where he held his next court. Lyons was the Emperor's goal. Now he disclosed as much even to French barons, Hugh of Châtillon and Count St. Pol : he would clear himself in person before the Pope of the charges against him. He would conduct the cause of justice powerfully before his adversaries and the transalpine peoples, he wrote to the Captain of Sicily. Innocent was already in despair, saw Gregory's fate in Rome lurking all round, begged the pious King of France to send an army against that Evil Spirit as soon as he, the Pope, let him know the decision of the Papal See. Then news reached Frederick, a shrill cry from King Enzio.

The King had been besieging Quinzano, a fort near Brescia, when seventy noblemen, exiled from Parma, Gherardo da Correggio, Bernardo de Cornazano, the Lupi, the Iziola and San Vitali, rode from Piacenza to Noceto. It was a Sunday in June. Bartolomeo Tavernieri, the Imperial Captain in Brescia, was celebrating his daughter Mary's marriage to a man of quality from Brescia, and all were full of fiery wine. The seventy exiles halted in a meadow and chose as their leader Ugo de San Vitali, the Pope's nephew. Ghibert de Gente and Gherardo de Arcili encouraged them to be brave unto death. Tavernieri and Enrico Testa, the *Podestà*, were the first to come to their senses in the town. They ran out into the streets, but the citizens did not follow them. On the left bank of the Taro, near Borghetto, they and the German mercenaries collided with the seventy. There fell Enrico Testa in fierce fight, Manfredo de Cornazano in single combat with Bernardo, and Ugo Manghirotti. Tavernieri, bleeding from wounds, escaped to Costa Mezana ; and a company turned about to the exiles. The seventy entered Parma, in the sign of the cross, and called to the people : " For the love of the Saviour and the Virgin, who is Lady of the City, take us in, who have innocently been banished. We return with peace and justice for all ". Tailors, bakers, cobblers, money-changers, sculptors and sign-painters stood gaping in front of their booths. Gherardo da Correggio was elected *Podestà*. From everywhere allies came pouring in, two hundred knights under the Count of San Bonifazio, four hundred from Piacenza, three hundred cross-bowmen of the city of Genoa, three hundred of the Fieschi, forces from Ferrara under Azzo and from Reggio and Bologna. From Milan a thousand knights advanced thither under the Legate Gregory of Montelongo and Orlando Rossi. He knew that Federigo

16

would not pardon him. " Sir Orlando," the Emperor had said to him smiling one day, as they were riding side by side and Orlando's horse stumbled, " I promise you a better horse, that will not stumble." The better horse, that was the gallows-tree.

King Enzio burnt the machines outside Quinzano, took counsel the whole night through until the dawn of day and proceeded to the outskirts of Parma ; but he camped near Bianconese on the Taro, awaiting the Emperor. Federigo approached from Turin, the avenger. In Cremona he joined with Ezzelino. Uberto Pallavicino came, the Marquis, Ezzelino's friend, of whom, in the cradle, a cock had hacked out one eye and whose other eye gleamed like a black coal. Once he had ridden a screw, now he was so rich, that, bread and wine not reckoned, he spent twenty-five pounds of silver daily for his household. He had put away his unfruitful first wife ; two sons and three daughters were his by the second. There came wounded Tavernieri, Ugo Boterio, *Podestà* of Pavia and kinsman of the Pope, whom Innocent could alienate from the Emperor not by flattery nor by threats, Frederick of Antioch and a levy from every province of Italy. There were Burgundians in Federigo's army, Calabrians, Apulians, Sicilians, Neapolitans, Greeks and the Saracens of Lucera. He camped by Claudius's road near San Pancrazio. He wrote to the King of France that Parma would soon be taken, but he did not invest it.

He sent Enzio, Ezzelino and Pallavicino to Reggio and Modena. They fought with the Count of San Bonifazio and Opizo Malaspina near Montecchia and took sixty knights prisoner. They brought in hostages too, chained hand and foot, merchants from Reggio and the scholars from Parma who were students in Modena. With Pallavicino King Enzio overpowered the fort Berceto and Filatiera, with Ezzelino Brescello on the Po, where the Lombards had put together a bridge of boats in order to supply Parma with victuals ; Brescello and the bridge of boats were burnt down.

Young Cardinal Ottaviano de Ubaldini had enlisted mercenaries for Innocent round about Lyons; the Count of Savoy barred him the way over the Alps, and, the money being done, the mercenaries dispersed. Ottaviano got to Milan alone. Now he wanted to relieve Parma with Alberico da Romano and Azzo, with fifteen hundred Lombard knights and ships from Mantua, Ferrara and Chioggia. But he did not cross the Tagliata. The report went that he was an Epicurean luxuriating in gold and jewels, composing sonnets, and that he was hand in glove with Federigo. " Make way for the man who is betraying the Roman court ! " someone shouted as he went past. Ottaviano did not punish the fellow, he made him a present ; and the fellow climbed a height and called out that there was no worthier man than the Cardinal of the Roman See.

The Parmesans fed themselves with bread of linseed, with roots and herbs. Mantuans and Ferrarese, opening the locks, brought up by way of Brescello spelt, buck-wheat, barley and salt. Quarrels sprang up between the clans in the city. In front of the town hall Jacopo de Beneceto murdered the notary Andrea de Borgarelli. The murderer's house was pulled down, destroyed too were the houses and towers belonging to Gherardo de Canale, who was with Federigo and whom he distrusted. The Emperor had him dragged off to Apulia and, a millstone round his neck, sunk into the sea. On the meadow outside Flanzano he had twelve Parmesans beheaded, two a day. In a skirmish near Osimo Bishop Marcellinus of Arezzo was taken. The Saracens bound him, dragged him at a horse's tail to the gallows, hanged him who, before dying, still sang a *Te Deum*, dug up his corpse again, which Minorites had buried, polluted it and once more hitched it to the gallows, until the Emperor bade them desist.

The Legate Gregory of Montelongo employed begging friars for a stratagem. They had to write letters reporting help for the city and, covered with dust as if they had come from afar, hand them over to him as he sat with the Parmesans at table. The rich subscribed for a model of Parma in chased silver and offered it, in a procession, as a sacrifice to the Queen of Heaven. The Emperor made preparations for a winter siege. The astrologer Guido Bonatti had to observe the planet Mars for him. With the plough the ambit of a new town was drawn between the Fragnano road in the south and Claudius's in the north—a new town of wood and tile, with eight gates, walls, ditches, draw-bridges, a market-place, water from the Navilio canal and water-mills, churches too and, as the largest among them, that of Saint Victor. For Vittoria was the name Federigo gave the new town, Victory ; and he had the *vittorines* struck, coins with his stern Cæsar's face. He had enclosures fenced for his exotic beasts and gardens for the Saracen dancing-girls of his harem.

Cardinal Ottaviano disbanded his army and went back to Mantua. King Enzio attacked the Mantuan ships ; the Emperor's men broke up with axes the palisades at the mouth of the Tagliata. Three hundred prisoners were hanged by Federigo's order on the banks of the Po. Envoys from Parma implored him to spare the city. " I advise you ", he mocked, " to spare your corn, for as long as I live Parma will never eat but what is in the city." He went hunting with his hawks by the Tavo, whilst Marquis Lancia drew up *sbirri* from Milan and Piacenza towards Colligio. Then the Parmesans, incited by the Milanese Baccalupo, charged along against Vittoria on the San Pancrazio road, the people, women and children, together with six hundred Mantuans, over them the banner of the Madonna. " The mice are coming out of their holes ", sneered Thaddæus of Suessa. But the Parmesans smashed up the palisades, pressed into the town, overwhelmed the men-at-arms, the women pulling them down from their horses with the teeth of their wool-combs and sickles on poles. Wooden houses flared up, fire rolled through every quarter. Thaddæus of Suessa, wounded with the sword, was taken. Taken were three thousand—the court-officials and treasurers to boot—killed fifteen hundred.

The Parmesans captured Federigo's treasure, gold, silver, pearls and gems, a statue—Venus or Aphrodite, to whom, so they said, he prayed,—astrological charts of Beelzebub and Astaroth and the *Carroccio* of Cremona. They captured the girls and eunuchs of the harem, the beasts, the Emperor's head-bands, the seal of the kingdom, the sceptre and crown of state. A cripple picked it up, Cortopasso, Short Leg ; he was carried shoulder-high thus to Parma. The city bought it for two hundred pounds and preserved it in the sacristy of the cathedral, for which a picture was fashioned, with the Madonna, St. Hilarius, John the Baptist and the inscription : " The enemies flee, for the Virgin is Parma's ward ". Thaddæus of Suessa, who had already lost both hands, they cut into pieces.

Federigo, forgetting his falcons, had seen the glare of the fire from the Tavo. He hastened to Vittoria, where the Marquis Lancia was fighting, but the rush of the rout carried him along. On his favourite horse, the Dragon, he galloped to Borgo San Donnino and on, late at night, as far as Cremona. Weeping, the multitude threw itself down before him and thanked God that he was alive. On the fourth day Enzio defeated the Legate Gregory and the fleet near Brescello and took many ships. Federigo besieged Berceto. Near Fornavo the Marquis Lancia cut off Orlando Rossi's road. In a hand-to-hand encounter Orlando fell to the ground and was, with a hundred of his men, decapitated forthwith.

FOUR weeks after King Raspe's death, Pope Innocent sent to Germany Cardinal Peter Capoccio, a relative of Raniero's, the Deacon of San Giorgio *ad velum aureum*, the Christian church from Roman times. He was to be an angel of peace, to plant and root up as seemed well to him. The Legate Peter Capoccio offered the German crown to Count Henry of Guelders, to Richard of Cornwall, to King Haakon of Norway, to the Duke of

Brabant. People said he had even tried King Conrad, provided he would separate from his father. But Frederick's son had replied: "Of a truth, not to please you traitors will I be untrue to my father or myself".

The Duke of Brabant recommended his nephew, the twenty-year-old Count William of Holland, son of Floris the Fourth and Mary of Brabant, who had been under the tutelage of the Bishop of Utrecht. In Neuss he was elected by the Archbishops of Cologne and Mainz, Henry of Guelders (now Bishop of Liége) and Otto the Halt. King William was dubbed knight. With "*hera her, spera Sper, wurra wei*", clumsy men-at-arms fought a French tourney, there was sumptuous banqueting, fanfares were blown for the progress to Aix, the coronation city. William of Holland showed himself to all people with arrogant smile under the helm from which his plume nodded yellow and red and from beneath which flowed the locks of his flax-white hair. Them of Neuss he had to exempt from all tolls; never was he to go thither with an army or to hold Diet. The Pope wrote to the German Princes that divine inspiration had guided their choice, while yet the reprobate generation of the Emperor that had been vainly laid claim to the *Imperium*.

The Roman Empire was in confusion. The Duke of Brabant died. King William pawned Nijmegen to Otto the Halt and went into icy Zeeland to war with Margaret of Flanders for her son Guillaume Dampierre, his brother-in-law. King Conrad was besieged in Swabia by the Counts of Kiburg, Sigmaringen, Grüningen and Frohburg and the Abbot of Reichenau and scarcely eluded captivity. The Duke of Meran and the Patriarch of Aquileia fell away from the Emperor. Margaret of Austria, King Henry's widow, who had lived in the nunnery of St. Catherine at Treves, was urged by the Pope to marry the Count of Henneberg. For Gertrude, whose spouse Vladislav was dead, the Legate Peter Capoccio found a new husband in the Marquis Herman of Baden. With manly courage, he wrote,

SIGFRID OF EPSTEIN WITH THE ANTI-KINGS

should Gertrude, inflamed by the ardour of the faith, oppose the Church's foes; and as dowry he assigned to the Marquis the Duchy of Austria. Count Otto of Eberstein went with Austrian and Styrian office-holders to Italy, to beg Margaret's little son, Frederick, of the Emperor as their Duke. Some were taken up by Philip, the Archbishop of Salzburg, others could not get beyond Verona. The Emperor, lying before Parma, paid no heed to the request for Henry's son. As Governor of Austria he nominated the Bavarian Duke, of Styria Count Maynard of Görz. Herman of Baden was in possession of Vienna, was negotiating with the Kuen-rings. At harvest-time, burning down the stooks of rye, Bela's Hungarians crossed the Leitha. Herman of Baden died, the widow Gertrude fled away to Meissen.

The Count of Jülich submitted to King William; the city of Aix and the Burgrave Gernand in Kaiserswerth resisted. The Pope caused priests and monks to proclaim that whoso should help subdue disobedient Aix need not go to Jerusalem or Kahira, but was discharged of his vow and should receive abundance of blessings too. Frisians came and erected below Aix a dam of such height that people rowed in boats through the streets and the waves washed the lower storeys of the houses. Then the Imperial Bailiff and the emaciated citizens surrendered, recognized William for their King, and he confirmed all their liberties and rights. On All Saints' day William was anointed in the cathedral of Aix by the Archbishop of Mainz and consecrated by the Archbishop of Treves. He was crowned, not with Charlemagne's crown, but with an imitation of poorer metal.

In Kaiserswerth the Burgrave Gernand surrendered. King Conrad was at war with the Archbishop of Mainz in the region of Spires and Oppenheim. In camp outside Ingelheim Sigfrid of Epstein fell sick and died in Bingen. The wish his successor, Provost Christian of Weissenau, sent after him into the grave was that he should be whirled into hell.

The begging friars preached against the Emperor Frederick : he had, in a church, under the picture of the mother of God, done violence to a virgin, was breeding murderers in subterranean vaults and feeding maidens on poison, so that they might infect those to whom he married them also. In Hall in Swabia lay heretics preached that, unless they themselves had come, God would have made the stones to speak, so that the true faith might not be lost ; the Pope and the Bishops lived in vice and deadly sin, were heretics and dealers in benefices, without power to bind or loosen. They tolled the bells, opened the barred churches, prayed for the Emperor and Conrad, those righteous and excellent men. King Conrad was fighting Bishop Albert of Ratisbon, who then came, feigning peace, into the city. In the monastery of St. Emmeran the King was asleep with five followers. Conrad of Hohenfels and other officers of the Bishop penetrated into his chamber. They believed him to be there with four others only, murdered two in the dark and bound three. King Conrad ducked under a bench and so saved himself. The white-washed walls were spattered with red blood.

THE paid German knights in Frederick's army grumbled. Since his treasure was captured by the Parmesans, he had no money left. He turned to his son-in-law John Vatatzes. The Emperor of Nicæa was unfaithful to the Empress Anne, bewitched by the love-potions of one of her Italian women, the Marchioness Ippolita, who arrayed herself in purple like the *Basilissa* and rode on a palfrey with purple reins. In pamphlets Blemmydes the Abbot of St. Gregory Thaumaturgus near Ephesus, cursed Ippolita as the queen of immodesty, the disgrace of the world, the mænad and harlot. During mass she made her way into the monastery. Blemmydes bade the priest who was kneeling at the altar be silent and banned the Marchioness from the sanctuary. Drimys, one of her officers, put his hand to his sword, to cut him down ; but hard as he pulled, the sword clave to the sheath. John Vatatzes was afraid of the man of God; and repentance seized upon him. He helped his father-in-law with magnificent cash-balances. A hundred and thirty thousand ounces of gold did Federigo get from Sicily, twelve thousand pounds of silver from merchants of Siena.

He took Vercelli and Orte in Montferrat and made his natural son Richard of Chieri Vicar in Romagna and the March. From Asti he sent ambassadors to King Lewis, who was now in Lyons. The King begged the Pope to receive the Emperor into the bosom of the Church again. But Innocent answered that as long as he lived he would stand by France against the schismatic Frederick, whom the Church had damned and the General Council deprived of his throne. " I have wanted to calm the old serpent," the Emperor wrote to the King of England, " but that good shepherd of the Church did not give us peace." Through Cardinal Stephen of Maria *trans Tiberim* the Pope fulminated his excommunication against the sons and grandsons of the Emperor, the Marquises, Counts and Barons, his vassals, and against Ezzelino, the instrument of the devil. Like unto the trumpet were the crusading preachers' voices to resound, the victorious banners of the King of Kings be unfolded against the tyrant's fury. No human clemency might reverse the divine judgment of deposition; nor the dominion of Christendom remain with him, whom the breath of his good fortune had so puffed up that, not remembering himself to have been engendered by human beings, he raged inhumanly and rebelled against the creator of the human race. Everyone must rejoice at the retribution exacted on behalf of all from the enemy of all and wash his hands in the blood of the sinner. He exhorted them in the March of Ancona and Spoleto to liberate Sicily, the wilderness. He invested Frangipani, the Count Palatine of the Lateran, with the principality of Taranto. Dominicans and Franciscans, who had had papal bulls upon them, and Simone de Montesarculo Federigo punished with torture and death at the stake.

The Lancias, the Marquis Manfred and Galvano and Federigo, his brothers, accused the Logothete Peter of Vinea that, from avarice, he was falsifying accounts. He had amassed riches, a handsome palace in Naples, in the Capo di Piazza quarter, two gardens there outside the Porta Monachorum, a house and a church near Capua, a plot of land in San Pancrazio belonging to the monastery of Monte Cassino, and possessed more than ten thousand pounds in *augustals*. He was in Apulia for the exaction of gold taxes. The Emperor, in Asti, warned him. " I acknowledge, Lord," Peter of Vinea wrote to his pensive and choleric master, " that thy words are full of thy great favour, unless, to the contrary, they charge me with sloth and negligence. Should this be the case, then innocence contradicts it, and whether it be man or angel that should flatter himself of its justice, under what name soever, he must be put to silence among the sons of truth. I too am certain that, however high he may be placed who brings me in ill repute, if only the Almighty prosper my services which I perform at thy feet, the wrong done unto me will redound unto that man's perdition. May the Lord make a speedy end to these slanders and restore the righteous son to his father." The Emperor went to Casale. He held his court in Vercelli. The Counts of Savoy, Amadeo and Thomas, and the Count of Vienne did homage to him, and he celebrated the wedding of his son Manfredi and Beatrice of Saluzzo.

He went by way of Pavia to Cremona, was bent for Tuscany, for Sicily, for Germany. He fell ill, the physicians prescribed a purge for him and a bath against his fever. Nicolo Smeregho, a physician taken prisoner in Parma and exchanged against a Parmesan nobleman, mixed the purge. Beside him stood Peter of Vinea, the friend of whom Federigo doubted, the bearded Seneca. The Emperor took the cup : " My soul trusts in you, I pray you, give me not poison instead of medicine ". Peter of Vinea said : " Lord, how often has your physician given you wholesome medicine ;

what fear you now ? " The Emperor said to Nicolo :
" Drink, and give me the other half ". Nicolo feigned
as if to stumble, fell down and spilt a part of the medicine.
Federigo shouted " Bind them " to the soldiers behind
the curtain. The soldiers seized the physician and Peter
of Vinea. The Emperor had what was left in the cup
poured into the throats of malefactors who were
awaiting death. In convulsions, with foaming lips,
they died.

Federigo, in the horror of loneliness, groaned the
words of Job : " I am an abomination to all who are
faithful to me, and those I love have turned against me ".
The Sun of Power Peter had called him in trembling
panegyric, whom not Plato, not Tullius Cicero could
proclaim full throated, the Eagle of Ezekiel, the Prince
of Fortune, St. Frederick. Now the incense of adoration
turned to dirty dust, to grinning deceit the rhetorican's
pomp. He gave orders to torture Smeregho by day
and by night, on Sundays and festivals too, to put out
his eyes and mutilate him and to transport him to Sicily
for execution. Peter of Vinea was taken to Borgo
San Donnino. The Emperor wrote to the Count of
Caserta : " What here has betided may be a lesson to thee.
Remember the base counsel, the scandal of every kind
which Peter has caused, the traitor, the new Simon, who,
to stuff full his money-bags, turned the staff of Justice into
a serpent and with the rascalities habitual to him plunged
the Empire into an abyss which would have swallowed
us up with Pharaoh's army and the war-chariots of the
Egyptians. The man who, sprung from the land of
fruitfulness, saw himself fructified beyond his hopes by
a superabundance of possessions, he to whose office it
belonged carefully to watch over our life, but with
malice aforethought offered poisoned drink to the ruler
on whom the safety and welfare of so many repose.
And since a considerate statesmanship should uproot the
generation of traitors, our Imperial Eminence, interpreter of the divine will, ordains in accord with the great
ones of the state, that this traitor be driven from town

to town with contumely and torments until he suffer the last pain of death. It is mercy in the requital of such a misdeed to be merciless ".

The Logothete Peter of Vinea cowered in the gaol of Borgo San Donnino. He saw his wife no more, nor his nephews, Guilelmo, the justice at court, and Giovanni, the priest in Capua. He had cheered his aging lust with elegies in the taste of the *trovatori*, because his master loved them, the Emperor. Adulators he had, as he himself adulated—the babbler Nicolo de Rocca, who lauded him as a Moses of Mount Sinai, as a second Joseph, the keeper of the Empire's keys, whose melodious voice, sweeter than honey, dropped into all hearts the magic of his eloquence, to whom by divine prompting was revealed what lay concealed under the mantle of the sun and for whom the book with seven seals had no mysteries. He howled out oaths that he knew naught of Smeregho's poisoned potion; he was a venal philosopher, a pig, but no assassin of Majesty. On the back of a psalter he wrote his Lamentation: " Unjust hatred have my own cast upon me; they who ate my bread have laid snares for me. Of the favour which I enjoyed my fellow officers have robbed me. They pierce me with their spears and dice for my coat. O that the father would rise in the glory of day and pour upon me the radiance of his grace that, already believing myself extinguished, I may breathe again. Not so incurable is my pain that I might not be made whole by a pious hand. Whoso has lost all his strength, may a strong arm catch him up. None dare hinder the father from comforting the son with the sparkling morning-dew of his favour. To the last breath I will embrace them, his blessed feet ".

The Emperor delivered Peter of Vinea, the Peter who had denied him, as the Galilee fisherman had his Lord, to soldiers whom he sent to San Miniato, the Imperial castle. The Guelphs of the town would not let in armed men. Federigo had word sent them that prisoners only were coming. The soldiers gagged themselves, as if they were Lombards, passed into the castle, the pinioned Logothete at their head, fetched their swords from the baggage on the mules and slew the Guelphs. Peter of Vinea was sentenced by a verdict of the Marquises and Barons. The red iron burrowed into his eyes. First he was to come into the power of the Pisans. Blind, he groped about in his cell. He asked his gaoler, whether there was aught betwixt himself and the wall, and dashed his skull against it.

FEDERIGO had wedded King Enzio in Cremona to a niece of Ezzelino's and bade him farewell. He went to Pontremoli, to Pisa, to Fucecchio on the Arno, where he heard of the Logothete's end. In Pisa he embarked for Apulia. The Pope appointed Raniero Capoccio liberator of Sicily.

King Enzio hanged a hundred exiles from Reggio. He ravaged the country between the rivers Enza and Parma, besieged Cavriago and returned to Cremona. The Bolognese assembled an army with Azzo d'Este and the Mantuans and advanced against Modena. They halted near Castelfranco. With his bodyguard and Cremonese knights Enzio hurried to the bridge at Bugno. The foemen approached as far as the Scotenna. Inhabitants of Oliveta were working on the bridge of San Ambrosio. The King, on a hot hour of the afternoon, surprised them as they were bathing with their sinewy limbs and swimming. The Bolognese came, treading on the piles, and the knights from the ford at Ceresa. They spurred their mounts through the shallows and caught Enzio's men-at-arms in the flank. The Council of Bologna had, through Antonio Lambertazzi, had the order conveyed that the battle must be fought. The *Podestà* Filippo Ugone detached a third part, which was to fight there where by chance the Imperialists might press forward. Every man fought as he could, in disorder. Towards evening, when the blue shades grew longer, Lambertazzi rushed against Enzio and killed his horse under him. Germans helped the King from the

ground and put him on another horse.   But the Moden-
ese were discouraged.   They fled.   Vainly did the King,
Marino di Eboli and Boso de Doara seek to discipline
them again.   They were surrounded and captured,
along with two hundred.   The Bolognese led Enzio
to Castelfranco and into Unzola castle ; and, in triumph,
they brought him into their city.   He walked in golden
chains, past the six churches of San Stefano, past the
towers Garisenda and Asinelli ; the populace hooted
and snatched at his fair hair.   They beat to their knees
Buso, Marino di Eboli and the German Count Conrad
of Solimburg.   In the *Podestà's* palace, a brick building,
a hall with barred windows was opened up.   On high
hung a chamber, a cage of wood with gratings.
Sobbing with shame Enzio threw himself on to the
bare floor.

The Emperor, in Benevento, was in tears for his
young hawk, his Falconello.   He wrote to Modena that he
had received the tidings with equanimity ; for sons in
plenty had been granted him.   But he would destroy
the rebels, to show the world how empty was their
boasting, how pitiful their resistance.   He threatened
the Bolognese that their laughter would turn to mourning.
" The might of the Roman Empire ", he wrote, " is not
weakened, as you seem to imagine ; ever watchful and
unwearied, it cannot sink into sleep.   Ask your fathers,
they will remember how our exceeding victorious
ancestor Frederick, faithful to his purpose, drove the
Milanese from house and home, rent their city into three
townships.   Open not your ears too wide to the Lombards' whisperings ; they will drag you into the pit
with them, so that naught may avail you."   He commanded them by his disfavour to release from captivity
Enricus, his beloved son, King of Sardinia and Gallura.
The Bolognese however scoffed : not always did the
wolf gain his prey.   They were not like the reeds of the
swamp in the wind or like the hoarfrost that consumes
in the heat of the sun.   " We will gird ourselves with
the sword and resist courageously, like lions.   Nor

will innumerable multitudes profit Your Highness, for where there are many, confusion comes easily, and, according to the proverb, a boar may be held by a little dog."

Federigo, the feeling of fatigue upon him, meditated on a new marriage with the daughter of Duke Albert of Saxony. No one was left him but Ezzelino ; and he was insubordinate and a lunatic. Ezzelino da Romano, outwitting the Imperial Captain, gained possession of Monselice castle. He made his nephew Ansedisio de Guidotis *Podestà* in Padua. The knights and townsfolk, through one among them, read aloud Æsop's fable of the doves, who, when the vulture persecuted them, chose the hawk for their king, soon however, persecuted more by him than the other, repented their folly. Ezzelino arrested the Delasmanini ; he was no hawk, he said, but a father, hunting scorpions and toads, crushing the heads of vipers. He tortured men and women, merchants and monks, soldiers and princes. Many bit off their tongues on the rack, so as not in their anguish to name the innocent. Many in gaol quaffed their urine because of the thirst upon them. One whose eyes had been put out tore the tyrant's arm with nails and teeth until they killed him. In Padua—Selvaggia, never touched by him, being dead—Ezzelino married Beatrice, the daughter of the Knight Bontraversio de Castranovo. He was fifty-five years old, like the Emperor. Immediately after the wedding he advanced by way of Verona against Este. Vitaliano de Arelda betrayed it to him, miners from Carinthia undermined the walls of the Rocca for him, and it surrendered.

The Emperor in Foggia delegated the war against the Patriarch of Aquileia and Archbishop Philip of Salzburg to Count Meynard of Görz. He went to Sicily, to the Palermo of his childhood. He armed and he wrote to the despot of Epirus, Michael Angelos Komnenos Dukas, that he was collecting an army from divers races, among them the Greeks, who were the best Christians and whom the Pope called godless and heretical. His faithful son-in-law, the Emperor John, was sending him his bowmen and heavy troops. Komnenos's pure love might vouchsafe them passage to Durazzo for the crossing to Brindisi.

HOLY King Lewis of France called all his Barons to Paris and caused them to swear their allegiance, should evil betide him on his crusade. There set out with him his brothers Charles of Anjou, Robert of Artois and Alphonsus of Poitiers, the Duke of Burgundy, the Counts of Brittany, Flanders, St. Pol, Bar, Marche, Montfort, Dreux, Soissons and Vendôme, the Lords of Bourbon, Courtenai and Coucy and Joinville the Seneschal. A clerk had killed three sergeants of the Châtelet, because they stole and plundered in the dark streets of Paris. The first he shot with a cross-bow in the heart, the second, who was about to climb over a fence on a moonlight night, had his leg slashed to ribbons with a knife, the third his head cleft to the teeth. Lewis took the priest with him on his crusade. The people prayed to God that he might grant the King a long life and bring him back rejoicing. From his castle on the Rhone, Roger de Clarège fell upon the crusaders: Lewis punished him as he deserved. But he paid no heed to the hostile mood of the citizens of Avignon and Marseilles.

In Aigues-Mortes the crusaders stepped on to the boats chanting the "*Veni, Creator Spiritus*". For a whole night they drifted about round a mountain on the African coast and in the morning were again before the same mountain. And that befell two or three times, until they arranged a procession round the ships' masts, and then they saw the mountain no more. They landed in Cyprus. They stored up wheat and barley, which sprouted like green grass in the rain. There came messengers of the Mongol Khan Erkalthai from Persia and reported that their Prince was friendly to the King and wished to help him in freeing Jerusalem from the Saracens. He sent the Khan a tent of red scarlet, within which was embroidered the Annunciation and the Passion of the Saviour. Eighteen hundred ships went from Limisso under sail. A storm cast them back again against the island of Paphos, and out of two thousand eight hundred knights only seven hundred remained with the holy King. On the fifth day a lookout in the crow's nest saw Damietta. Four of the Egyptians' galleys attacked the French; three were sunk. The Crusaders swam to the shore. The King himself leapt into the sea up to the armpits, with shield, lance and helmet. Above him waved the banner of St. Denis. The Egyptians lit Greek fire and murdered their Christian slaves. But they abandoned Damietta, for they believed their Sultan Eyub, who was sick, to be dead. With naked feet St. Lewis, at his side the Pope's legate and the King of Cyprus, went into the great mosque. It was cleansed and called Notre Dame after the celestial virgin in Paris, and all praised God.

The Sultan Eyub condemned the commander of Damietta to be executed for his cowardice. He offered the King battle on a fixed day and a fixed spot. St. Lewis responded: " Not on a single day and spot will I fight, but daily and everywhere, until the Sultan confesses the Lord who opens the bosom of his grace to all ". The Sultan asked mocking why the Franks had brought ploughs with them. The King said: " I have made oath to journey hither, but not of my return ; that is the reason that these tools have been brought with us ". The Egyptians' horsemen skirmished up to the camp and cut off the sleeping soldiers' heads, whose price was a bezant of gold every time. The Barons in the town caroused with wine and flesh and wenched with the women from the houses of ill-fame, a stone's throw from the King's pavilion. Englishmen put in under the Earl of Salisbury, Templars and Knights of Jerusalem.

St. Lewis was waiting for the Count of Poitiers and the rearguard. Then he took counsel with the Barons, whether they should march to Alexandria or to Babylon.

The Count of Artois was for Babylon, capital of the Egyptian kingdom ; for that seemed to them the name of Kahira. The King followed his brother Robert's advice. They set out towards Kahira. The Templars formed the van. "*Or à eux*", their Marshal Renaut de Vichiers called as they fought the Saracens and drove them into the river Nile. The Crusaders heard that the Sultan Eyub was dead and his son Moattam still in Asia. They camped between two arms of the Nile. Across the smaller, which flowed towards Tanis, the King had a bridge built and, against it, two towers, two *chats-châteaux*. The Saracens dug canals, into which the waters poured. Their commander was the Emir Fakruddin, the same whom the Emperor Frederick had dubbed knight and who bore in his flag the Emperor's heraldic beast, the eagle, beside those of the Sultans of Aleppo and Babylon. They destroyed the *chats-châteaux* with their Greek fire, that was like unto the flying dragon. As often as the King beheld the green flames, he raised himself in his bed, wept and prayed : "*Beau sire Dieu*, defend us ! " To the Constable Imbert de Beaujeux there appeared in white burnoose a Bedouin who offered to reveal a ford in the Nile, if he was paid five hundred bezants. The Crusaders waded through ; almost drowned were their horses. The Count of Artois rode with the Earl of Salisbury and the Templars after the Saracens into the town of Mansura. Vainly did Renaut de Vichiers warn him : abuse was his part. Killed was the Earl of Salisbury, killed the Count of Artois, who sank in the Nile with his heavy armour. One Templar and one Knight of St. John alone fled away, as heralds of disaster, and soldiers, who threw themselves naked into the Nile. The King asked after his brother. " He is in Paradise ", Henry de Ronnay, the Prévôt de l'Hôpital, called to him. St. Lewis replied that God must be thanked for all, and his tears trickled.

The Crusaders advanced amid yelling, trumpets and drums, in their midst the King in a gilded helmet, a German sword in his hand. The Counts of Poitiers and Flanders were hard pressed. Six Saracens caught the reins of Lewis's war-horse. Twenty times did his knights charge up. Late at night the French remained masters of the battlefield. But already at daybreak, the cry went up: "*Aux armes, aux armes !*" Count Charles of Anjou yielded to the Saracens' infantry, who burnt Greek fire in front of the horses' nostrils. The King's meiny cut him out. The French kept their position. But frightful was their distress. The corpses in the Nile came to the surface on the ninth day, blocked it and collected at a bridge. The King had hired a hundred fellahin to fish them up like carp. The circumcised Saracens they hove away beyond the bridge, the Christians into pits, hugger-mugger. The French ate nothing but fish which fed on the corpses. And for that reason and because of the parching oppressiveness of the air a distemper broke out. The flesh of the legs dried up, the skin got spotted with black and earth-coloured like an old shoe, the flesh of the cheeks rotted, the barbers scraped off the purulent abcesses from inside. Whoso had the illness had to die as soon as his nose bled. The Saracens pulled several of their galleys into the river, so that no ship could get through with provisions ; they had destroyed eighty in Damietta.

St. Lewis ordered the retreat. He sought an agreement with the Saracens, to whom he wanted to restore Damietta in exchange for the kingdom of Jerusalem. They demanded the King's person as a pledge. They killed the sick by the river bank and pierced the dams of the Nile. St. Lewis had the army's distemper and dysentery so grievously that they had to cut away the seat of his grey woollen breeches, so often had he to evacuate. With Geoffroy de Sargines he rode on a little bay horse in the Lord of Châtillon's rearguard. They brought him to a village, and it was as if he could not live till evening. Philip of Montfort was negotiating with the Emir, who pulled off his turban and his finger ring, about the cessation of arms. The Sergeant Marcel shouted to the knights to unbuckle their swords ; they did it, thinking it to be the King's will; and so they were prisoners with him.

The Saracens demanded of St. Lewis that he should surrender the castles of the Templars, the Knights of St. John and the Barons to them. When in his sickness he refused, they threatened to squeeze his knuckles to a jelly in the block, in wooden boards with nails, which were strapped together with thongs of neat's leather. As they could not cow him, they demanded a million gold bezants for his ransom and Damietta, where Dame Margaret was, the Queen. She agreed to the treaty. Then the Sultan Moattam was attacked of a sudden by the Emirs of his Halka, his bodyguard, by the Bayarites. He fled with a first wound into his castle Fareskur and, when it was consumed by fire, to the Nile. In its waves they killed him with arrows and spears, dragged him to the bank and tore out his heart. With bloody hands one of them, Faresseddin, came to St. Lewis and asked him how he would reward him. St. Lewis made no answer. They demanded an oath of the King, in these terms : " If I do not keep what I promise, I am to be looked on as a perjurer, a Christian that denies his God, his law and his baptism, who in the contempt of God spits upon the Cross and spurns it with his feet ". The King refused so to blaspheme. The Emirs bound the eighty-year-old Patriarch Guido of Jerusalem to a stake in a pavilion and pinioned his hands behind him so that the veins of his finger tips burst and the blood flowed. "Swear", he called to St. Lewis, "I take the sin upon myself and my soul." But the King still remained steadfast.

The Saracens stuck their flags on the towers of Damietta, got drunk with wine and butchered the sick in the houses. Damietta burnt for three days. The Templars would not lend thirty thousand pounds for the ransom ; by force the Seneschal Joinville fetched it out of their treasure-chest. The King was angry because Philip of Nemours cheated the Saracens in the weighing of the gold. A galley sailed with him to Acre. He lay on a mattress in deep mourning for his brother Artois.

Charles of Anjou was playing dice with Walter of Nemours. The King reproved him and pushed table and dice into the sea. He decided to remain in the Holy Land, until the prisoners were rescued. There was plague in Acre. Queen Margaret had borne a son in Damietta, who was christened John; but on account of the great affliction they called him Tristram.

THE Emperor wrote to Lewis at Acre and sent messengers with remittances for him and letters to the Sultan Moattam, of whose death he was unaware. The Ghibellines in Florence celebrated the Crusaders' defeat with fireworks, and the Pope's party diligently spread the rumour that the Emperor had prevailed upon the Sultan to keep the King in custody.

Through the Counts of Anjou and Poitiers, who were homeward bent, Saint Lewis urged Pope Innocent to make peace with the Prince of Princes. They made their appearance in Lyons, they and the Duke of Burgundy—Charles of Anjou behaving rudely and curtly, with his greeny pale face and his great nose. The Pope received them without the Cardinals, much cast down. " O false Orient," he exclaimed, " O wretchedly darkened Egypt! O Jerusalem, Jerusalem for whose liberation innumerable have died, when wilt thou at last vouchsafe Holy Church, in place of bitter grief, the joy she yearns for ? " However, the King's brothers responded with reproaches : Frederick had sent the Count of Poitiers a thousand bushels of corn and fifty war-horses ; " But you, Holy Father," he said in unseemly tones, " have brought about the pilgrims' distress by avarice and withdrawal of the shrove-monies, which you raised for the Crusades and amassed in Lombardy and in Sicily. You are the culprit, by reason of your stiffneckedness and unchristian enmity towards the Emperor ". They threatened the Pope to have him removed from Lyons, if he would not pardon Frederick. When they were gone, Innocent begged the King of England for an asylum in Bordeaux.

A runaway monk, the Cistercian Jacques, excited the French church, a man of sixty preaching the Cross. He announced that angels or the Virgin herself had laid it upon him; but only to the humble, not to the great and the clerks, who were rotten with pride and vices. Peasants were his congregation, shepherds, thieves and whores, the mob of the wretched. In Orleans a parson opposed him, the Master of Hungary, as he called himself. Jacques's adherents murdered him and twenty-five besides and drowned them in the Loire. Then they attacked laymen and then the Jews. In the region of Bourges the Master of Hungary and they bewitched by him suffered death by clubs and swords. People said that in the monk's pockets Arabic letters from Saracens had been discovered.

Through a collect the Emperor Frederick wrung from every Sicilian a tax of one *taro*. His troops fought in the March of Ancona under Gualtieri de Paleario, Count of Manupello, a nephew to that Bishop of Catania who had been the corrupter of Federigo's childhood, and were victorious at Fermo and Cingolo. There died Cardinal Raniero Capoccio. The Romans furiously demanded the return of the Pope. He had sent ambassadors to Nicæa, to break the Emperor's alliance and to unite the two churches, the Catholic and the Greek. " We prevail daily over our enemies ", Federigo wrote to John Vatatzes. " How could the Pope send a few quite insignificant friars and heralds to thy Imperial Majesty, that they might treat with the arch-priests of thy holy majesty's church ? How came this alleged high priest of the priests not to blush, who yet in thy presence, daily and by name, excommunicates thee and all thy Greek subjects, who shamelessly gives the orthodox Greeks the name of heretics ? How can he, who in manifold forms rehearses the malice towards the Greek world which, from time immemorial, was implanted in the high priests of Rome by demoniacal influence, promise to remove it in an instant with childish words and the deceitful proposals of simpletons ? Is not he the man who, in a strange design, excommunicated before the Council our Highness as heretical, because of the union between thy Majesty and our well-beloved daughter? Whence do the priests obtain it, that in place of the holy mass-vestment they put on mail, wield lances instead of the pastoral staff, the bow instead of the pen, arrows bringing bitter death instead of the cross? One orders the phalanxes, another leads a company, yet another blows up the embers of war. Some are commanders of hosts and standard-bearers and others wielders of halberds and bearers of the meteyard. Are these the disciples of Christ? Alas for the folly of the multitude, that attributes holiness to them and invents saints as myth did the giants! In Christ's church there are no high priests, but thieving wolves and wild beasts. Their unlawfulness was made manifest, and he who is puffed up, hiding his disgrace in a corner, was accused before all as the father of deceit. How many thousands have perished because of him, whose remnant since recently rests in Egypt, in the waves of the Nile? This too is known to thy Imperial Majesty, how on oath he asseverated our death, that he might seduce our faithful followers from us, as he forced the slaves of the slaves of our Imperial Majesty in Germany to turn against us. As long as the holy vessels and the revenues which he forcibly took from the Church were used in their campaigns, they showed the things as upon a stage, and their mind, pregnant with reefs, lay hid under the sea. Since however all are cast down, they turned fugitive, the one here, the other there, in terror of the threat of our right hand." The Emperor kept Vatatzes's ambassadors, who were on the way to Rome, back in Apulia.

News was brought that Uberto Pallavicino had avenged the day of Vittoria upon the Parmesans at Agnola; hundreds met with death, the *Carroccio* was captured. Peter of Gaeta had sunk sixteen ships belonging to the Genoese near Savona. In November, in Foggia, Berardo Caracciola, the notary of Bari, knelt before Federigo with but six hundred ounces;

" Lord," said he boldly, " if my services displease you, give me a successor; the land is impoverished ". Federigo dismissed him and issued the decree that whoso had not paid the tax within a fortnight should be punished with labour in the galleys. But a caravan from the Orient landed at Brindisi, twelve camels laden with gold and silver.

The Emperor had a fainting-fit at Foggia. When he awoke from it, he listened to his pulse, which crept hesitant. He wanted to go to Lucera, the town of the Saracens. But he descended from his litter outside the fort Fiorentino ; with him were Manfredi, his son, like him in chin and mouth, Archbishop Berard, Count Richard of Caserta, the German Marquis Berthold of Hohenburg, the Grand Justiciary Riccardo de Monte-nero, the Marshal Pietro Ruffo with Folco his nephew, the *Magistri* John of Otranto and Robert of Palermo, the sewer Occursio and the physician Giovanni da Procida from Salerno, who had written about the philosophers of antiquity, about the wisdom of Zede-kiah, Hermes, Homer, Solon, Pythagoras, Diogenes, Socrates, Plato, Aristotle, Alexander, Ptolemy and Gregory, a learned hypocrondriac.

The Emperor had hardly yet been in this fort. It was smaller than the eight-towered Castel del Monte, forbidding in the waning yellow November light. " Fiorentino," the Emperor jested, " here Scotus would permit us to die, *sub flore*." He was feverish, as so often during the last weeks, and his bowels bled with the flux. Giovanni da Procida had to read to him from Averroes. He dictated a chapter of his book on hawking, on swans', pheasants', storks', owls' and ducks' lines of flight. He faltered out words at random from the Arabic dialogue of the Apple, about the contemptible-ness of death and about immortality. " Not lament should the wise, when they go forth from this filthy lodging, but rather hasten joyfully to their perfecting." Then a fit seized upon him and he dropped his head mute against the wall that was wet with rain.

He was, it seemed, out of danger. But he made his testament. "We, Frederick the Second," he said in the candle-lit room smelling of opiates, "by the grace of God Roman Emperor *semper Augustus*, King of Jerusalem and Sicily, in regard to the transiency connate with man, have, at the bourn of life, sick of body, yet clear of recollection and healthy of spirit, so provided for Our soul and made such disposals for the Empire and Our Kingdoms that We shall seem still to live when We shall already be removed from visible life and that thereby every occasion for offence shall be taken away from Our sons with whom God's mercy has blessed Us and who shall consent to the present ordinance, upon forfeiture of Our blessing." Conrad, so he declared, should inherit the Empire and Sicily, Manfredi be Governor in Italy and Sicily and Prince of Taranto. He spoke of Henry, Isabella's son, and of his grandson and of the rights of the Church and the Empire. The traitors alone were not to be received into the great peace of the world. All witnessed the Emperor's will. In the night he questioned Herman of Salza whether he was wrestling with the hideous ghost of Peter of Vinea and he wept for dead Henry and living Enzio.

On the following day he had a longing for *violata*, a sweetmeat made of violets that he had met with in Syria, with sugar from Sicilian shrubs. He desired the warm, scented limbs of a Saracen dancing-girl from Foggia. Then however his brow waxed pale in the shadow of the apprehension of death. He called for the nonagenarian Archbishop Berard. "Give me your blessing," he said hoarsely, "as you stood by my father in death." "In the name of the Church I absolve you from your sins and your excommunication", murmured the Archbishop. Federigo took the Lord's Supper, had himself wrapped in a white Cistercian's cowl and stretched himself out immovable. He died towards morning, on Saint Lucy's day, in Manfredi's arms. A rolling earthquake shook the ground at that hour.

They went with the dead man to Taranto, ahead the Saracen guards, the bier upholstered with crimson cloth, then six troops of knights, the nobles and the bailiffs, the *bajuli*. In Taranto they stepped with the coffin on to a black ship; it sailed out to Messina. Pope Innocent wrote to Berard that he was tender to his white hairs and wished he might not go to hell in confusion, but rather repent in tears and utter contrition. He wrote to the Barons of Sicily : " The heavens must rejoice and the earth be glad that the tempest of thunder, with which the wonderful and terrible Lord all this time hath visited your community, should in his unspeakable mercy turn into a mild thawing wind, now that he is out of the world who unceasingly under the hammer of persecution hath crushed you above all in the number of the faithful and hath hurled God's church into calamity ". But the begging friar John of Winterthur prophesied that, even though his earthly part be burnt to ashes, the saviour Frederick the Second must come again ; with such fury would he punish the degenerate priests, that they would cover their tonsures with dung, lest they be known for priests ; he would sail over the sea and stablish God's kingdom on the Mount of Olives.

AT the *studium generale* at Padua Albertus Magnus, born in Lauingen on the Danube, the son of a gentleman of Bollstatt, had steeped himself in the wisdom of the world, which is the wisdom of God. He heard the German Jordan, the Dominican General, who had come from Bologna, and threw himself at his feet with the words : " You have seen into my heart ". He was a poor monk, in a coarse white cowl of white wool, with shorn head of hair. He studied the *Sentences* of Petrus Lombardus, the writings of the Latin Fathers, pseudo-Dionysius, Chrysostom and Johannes Damascenus and combatted the heresies of Arius, Sabellius, Berengarius, Gilbertus Porretanus and David of Dinanto. His Order sent him to Germany, to Cologne, as teacher of the natural and sacred sciences, to Hildesheim, Strasburg, Freiburg and Ratisbon. He was already a light, a glory of the Church.

When he mounted the oaken cathedra at Cologne, a Sicilian became his pupil, Tommaso of Aquino, a nephew of the Count of Acerra who followed the Imperial heretic Federigo. Sinibaldo was his second brother, Abbot of Monte Cassino, Landolfo, Tommaso's father, Lord of Loretto and Belcastro, the third. Young Tommaso went to the University at Naples and secretly entered San Domenico Maggiore. The Countess Theodora, his mother, had hoped he would become a great prelate. The Abbot of Santa Sabina wanted to let him get away to Paris. At Aquapendente his brothers caught him, Landolfo and Rinaldo, captains in Federigo's Tuscan army. In his Dominicans' cowl Rinaldo brought the monk to Roccasecca, where his mother received him with tears. Gentle Tommaso answered her that the grace of God had guided him and that naught could sever him from his choice. He was kept under guard in a tower. With the help of a courtesan from Naples his brothers sought to tempt him to a breach of chastity : with a firebrand he warded her off, who clutched at the wall, pale as death. Italy resounded with the rumour of his virtue. His sisters helped him to flee in a basket, which was pulled up to get books into his cell. He had audience of Pope Innocent. Johannes Teutonicus, who was now General of the Order, undertook to convey him to the teaching of Albertus Magnus. He kept silent among his companions for Cologne, and they called him the great Sicilian ox. But in an obscure passage of the Dionysian writings Albertus Magnus discovered Tommaso's talent for scholasticism, and he spake : " This ox will some day fill the whole earth with his mighty bellowing ". He loved Tommaso greatly.

Albertus Magnus journeyed as Doctor of Divinity to Paris, with the Sicilian. With straw under their feet the students sat in the open before him, in the Place Maubert, as the rooms of the Sorbonne were too small. The blessed Albertus condemned the Jews' Talmud, its abuses, blasphemies and ungodliness. In the guise of a monk, while he was poring, the devil came to him, the old serpent. He went with Tommaso to Cologne again, until the latter should return to Paris as Bachelor, and taught logic, physics and Aristotle's metaphysics. Fire having destroyed the Romanesque cathedral, Archbishop Conrad of Hochstaden wished to erect a new basilica in Cologne. The blessed Albertus, the story went, had a vision of four men in white surplices, with golden crowns, the compasses, the carpenter's square, meteyard and level in their hands, and in spirit he imagined the draft of the wondrous structure. People say that William of Holland paid him a visit at Epiphany. The blessed Albertus invited him to take a recreation in the garden of the Dominican monastery. It was terribly cold. But when the Count crossed the threshold into the garden, spring air and the sweet scent of flowers

CONRAD OF HOCHSTADEN

[*face p.* 268

was wafted towards him, butterflies fluttered over the blossoms, gaily feathered birds twittered in the branches, the rays of the sun were broken in the gorgeous opalescence of a playing fountain. Boys served at a table with costly dishes. And hardly had grace been said after meat, when the charm was broken and the company stood there in the winter cold. Albertus had a workshop in a remote place. Thomas, a Dominican, observed him as he carpentered, hammered, filed and turned the lathe there. Once, when the Master was absent, he made his way into the room. There were strange beasts there and artificial instruments, and, behind a fiery red curtain, Thomas discovered the magical image of a girl who with clear voice offered the salutation : " *Salve, salve, salve !* " He struck at this emanation of sorcery and cried out : " Away, Satanas ! " The Master came in and said to him in grief and anger : " Thomas, Thomas, what hast thou done ? In a moment of time thou hast destroyed the labour of thirty years ". The tale went that Albertus had burst the bonds of Pietrisyla, a daughter of the Duke of Saaz, who had nine youths for her paramours and by means of a small secret board plunged them into a lake. He walked lustily on the water, and the arrows which she hurled at him turned into birds. Then she confessed her guilt and became a nun. The tale went also that Albertus Magnus had wafted the King of France's daughter through the clouds to Cologne, had ridden the devil to Rome to keep the Pope once from sinning, had travelled through all lands with Alexander of Macedon and had been in purgatory, to bring news even of that region to mankind.

A T Easter there appeared in the Pope's presence at Lyons the flaxen-headed Count William of Holland. He lifted the Holy Father's foot into the stirrup, as a groom serving his lord. Loutishly he laughed : with the Bishop of Metz he had defeated Conrad by the Rhine. But, to supply his return journey, he had to

pawn Arles, Besançon and Lausanne to the Duke of
Burgundy for ten thousand marks of silver. With a
proud train, forty coaches and two hundred men on
horseback, the Pope rode out of the city of exile over
the bridge that spanned the Rhone. " My friends,"
he said through the mouth of the Cardinal Priest Hugo
to the disrespectfully yelling populace : " great, since
we came hither, have been our usefulness and beneficence.
For on arrival we found three or four brothels ; now
however we leave only one, but that one stretches from
the eastern gate of the city as far as the western ". He
gave King William the Bishop of Embrun as a travelling
companion and Hugo as his Legate, to preach a crusade
against Conrad.

He set out to Vienne, to Marseilles, to Genoa.
With all the Cardinals, the Count of Fiesco and Lavagna
made his entry into his native town, under the gold
fringes of the baldachino, which the *Nobili* carried.
Carpets were spread on the road and hung from the
balconies. All the *Podestàs* and the heads of the clans
relating to the Fieschi pressed into San Lorenzo, Cardinal
Gregory of Montelongo in a gleaming new suit of mail,
voluptuous Ottaviano de Ubaldini in velvet and silk
of Cyprus. Count Thomas of Savoy did submission
to the Pope, who married him to one of his nieces.
Innocent celebrated the feast of the Holy Apostles in
Alessandria. He was outside Milan ; in endless procession the clergy went with him to the doors of San
Ambrogio. Then the Milanese wanted payment for
his outstanding debts. He shrugged his shoulders like
a banker in the exchange, the Zecca ; the Church was
still in financial difficulties. He hurried to Ferrara and
Bologna. The procession went past the house of the
Podestà, above the flat roof of which the white tower of
the Arringo rose up. The *sbirri* pushed with their
staves a fair-haired captive to a barred window, King
Enzio. Pope Innocent looked into a brutish face. He
moved the citizens to give Boso de Doara his freedom ;
but the places Medicina and Argelata they did not give

up to him. He avoided going to Rome. He dwelt in Perugia, in Anagni.

Manfredi, Prince of Taranto, concealed as long as it was possible the Emperor's death. He wrote to his brother in Germany : " Mourning befits not only you, who are flesh of his flesh and bone of his bone ; the eyes of all other living men fill with tears also. Gone is the sun, which shone upon the nations, the sun of righteousness, he, the judge of peace. But a rich consolation is left us ; for our Lord and Father lived happy and victorious until his end, in the strength of his Divine Majesty ". The barons and towns of Sicily had, he reported, sworn the oath of fealty to him, their Governor.

The Germans were to keep watch over Troia. With Hegan, their Captain, they noised for their pay in front of the palace in Foggia. The Prince Manfredi told them that if they used force he would oppose them in arms ; then they would recognize that he was the Emperor's son. He was on the way from Andria to Lucera, when Foggia revolted. Swiftly he turned about ; in the morning he showed himself before the gates. With loosened hair the women prayed for mercy. He tumbled down the circumvallation and punished the town with a money fine only. He advanced to the gates of the rebellious Baroli. The Barolese did not open, they shot whizzing arrows. He dismounted, led the assault, pressed, a youth still unbearded, through the streets into the market-place. The walls of Baroli fell, Avellino fell at the hands of Berthold of Hohenburg. Aversa and Nola fell. The Prince of Taranto camped outside Naples on the tufa-hills round the steaming volcanic round of the Solfatara. King Conrad was in Verona, with Ezzelino in the fort of Goito, in Cremona, where Uberto Pallavicino did homage to him, and went by way of Venice to Istria. On sixteen galleys the embassy in his honour sailed to Pirano—Berthold of Hohenburg, the Chancellor Gualtieri de Ocra, Folco Ruffo and Filippo Chinardo. In Pola harbour, in front of the Romans' amphitheatre, Conrad embarked. He landed in Siponto, which had sunk in ruins during an earthquake. His brother, the slim, handsome *trovatore*, welcomed him, helped him into his stirrup. They walked together under the canopy. But the German King, golden-brown, prematurely ailing and serious, made Pietro Ruffo, who was ill-disposed to the Lancia, Count of Catanzaro, Governor of Sicily and Calabria and Hohenburg's brothers Otto and Lewis barons and counts. He appointed another justiciary to Taranto than him whom Manfredi had put in and took from the latter Blanca's heritage. Conrad had a bad fever. The pliant Lancia declared: "How much rather would we crown Manfredi than him. Manfredi's charm would win the world". Then Conrad banished Galvano and Federigo Lancia the kingdom. The Marquis Manfred, the oldest of the uncles, came to an understanding with Milan. Galvano and Federigo sought the court of their niece Anne, the Empress of Nicæa.

King Conrad took Naples; during the fourth month only rotten meat, sea-nettles, mallows and fig-leaves stilled the hunger of the famished. To the Pope at Perugia he sent Berthold of Hohenburg, the Archbishop of Trani and Gualtieri de Ocra, to the end that he should confirm him as his father's successor in Empire and Kingdom. Pope Innocent refused. The tyrant Ezzelino seized the notary Ottone Volpo, to whom a letter from a bishop in Romagnola had been brought. The gibbous messenger had handed it to Ziramonte, the tyrant's withered bastard-brother. It stood written in the letter that Ezzelino would not be able to hold his own for three years more in the war for the March of Ancona. The tyrant killed Ottone and his family. He tortured to death the Cremonese Magister Michael and the weak physician Monario, who had healed him of a rupture contracted at Cortenuova. In Padua he negotiated for house property; then he reft it from the owners, together with their lives. Twenty and more were often carted to the place of execution. By night wolves dragged out their corpses. Pope Innocent threatened

Ezzelino with inquisition and crusade : but, to win him away from Conrad, he extended the time for him to justify himself. The King nominated Uberto Pallavicino Vicar-General above and below Padua. Gnashing his teeth, Ezzelino swore in Verona that he would stand Pallavicino's friend.

Through Magister Albert the Holy Father offered the crown of Sicily to Richard, Earl of Cornwall. The Earl retorted upon the Legate, that that was like someone selling him the moon and telling him to climb and fetch it down. Envious Charles of Anjou offered himself to the Pope. He was married to Beatrice of Provence, whom the Emperor Frederick had asked in marriage for Conrad. Crowns adorned her sisters—Margaret that of France, Leonora that of England. She complained of being the lowliest. Her husband said, green in the face : " Be calm, Countess, soon you will be a greater queen than they ". Pope Innocent empowered the Legate Albert, according to the conditions of a bull, to invest the King of Sicily, the Lord Charles of Anjou, the true champion of Christ : by All Souls at latest he must in person advance to his task with a large army ; every fifth year he was to deliver to the Pope a well-appointed white horse, to ride through the kingdom. But Charles of Anjou was niggardly and demanded forty thousand *turoneys*.

The Roman Republic had chosen for Senator Brancaleone degli Andalo, Count of Casalecchio, a friend of Ezzelino's and Pallavicino's. He had come, absolute for three years, with Galeana his wife, in a scarlet-red, fur-lined robe, a biretta on his head like the Doge of Venice, riding up the shallow steps to the Capitol. High-born young Romans had been surrendered to him as hostages. His hand was peremptory and hard. The nobles who opposed him dangled from the battlements of their towers. Brancaleone humbled Tivoli. He wrote to Innocent : Rome was astounded at his wandering uncertainly now here, now there, intent on naught but money, with never a care for Rome or the Holy

273

See ; he was the Pope of Rome, not of Lyons, Perugia, Anagni or Assisi ; he should come back to the Lateran, now or never. The Genoese was celebrating, in the church of Assisi that spanned Francesco's grave, the *poverello's* Feast, and, with his Cardinals, he proceeded through Sabina to Rome. In San Lorenzo *fuori le mura* he had the high altar set up and at the Vatican palace, next to the basilica of St. Peter. He made gifts to the prelates. But Brancaleone had to protect him against the insolence of his creditors.

King Conrad despatched to Innocent his uncle, the Count Montfort. The Pope accused Frederick's son of inciting the Romans against him with money, kept him in suspense. He offered the crown of Sicily to Henry of England for Prince Edmund. The Plantagenet, in Gascony, eagerly snatched at it, scraped into a heap what was in his treasury, what Richard of Cornwall and the barons lent him, the Jews' gold coins and the silver which his officials, the jackdaws and magpies, had looted, and sent it to the Holy Father as a war-subsidy. King Conrad appealed to God, the Pope to come, a Council, the German Princes, to all kings and rulers of the world, yea to all Christendom. There died his nephew Frederick, his luckless brother Henry's son, there died at Melfi, fifteen years of age, Conrad's half-brother Henry, the Emperor's and Isabella's son. A report went that both had been poisoned—the boy Henry because he struck a bound falcon to earth and, the King rebuking him, answered him with insolence. Conrad wrote to the Plantagenet : " After giving our grief its time we send to you, to clear away slanders, tidings of the tristful death of our dearest brother Henry, your nephew. Whereas for the so heavy burden of our regiment masculine purpose hardly suffices—for we have had to offer up the most precious part of our heart in lamentation—he has put almost womanish grief upon us. He had already waxed to strength, on his shoulders we could repose our cares, when the bitterness of all-destroying death with swift scythe cut off the flower of his youth and, with the craft of a lurking foe, outwitted the guiding hand of nature ". He trusted (so he wrote) that the tie which the boy had wound about them would not be loosed. But at Vendôme the Legate Albert invested Prince Edmund with Sicily; ragged mercenaries assembled under the standards with the Keys.

Conrad's attorneys defended him before the Pope, the Cardinals and wrathful Brancaleone. He was, they pleaded, King of Rome, lawfully elected; he was not cruel, but held peaceful sway; a manifest lie was the charge that, violating blood-relationship, he had had his nephew or his brother murdered; the Lord had taken Henry from the workhouse of this world into the Father's eternal mansions; he had not the least intention of surrendering to the Pope's judgment; angels of light were easily changed into angels of darkness. On Maundy Thursday, after the sermon in the Lateran, the Holy Father excommunicated King Conrad. In the extravagance of his mercy he accorded Ezzelino da Romano a last respite. For fear of Brancaleone he went to Assisi, on account (so he said) of the summer heat.

King Conrad armed a host of twenty thousand. Manfredi and the barons came to Venosa and Melfi. Diseases carried off hundreds of knights, as heat devours the frost of the north. In the camp at Lavello Conrad sickened also. " Woe is me," he groaned, " why did my mother bear me and my father beget me, since I must suffer so much hardship. The kingdom fades away and sinks into the oblivion of death." He died and the monks hissed it abroad that Manfredi had stifled him under bolsters or had murdered him with diamond splinters in his cup or a poisoned clyster in his guts. Fire destroyed his coffin in the crypt of Messina Cathedral as it stood on the catafalque.

In Germany King Conrad had, by Elisabeth, the widow, a two-year-old son, of the same name as he, Conradin. His testament besought the Holy Father to be guardian to the child.

FROM Anagni Pope Innocent wrote to the inhabitants of Sicily that, sith provision for orphans were a charitable duty, he would preserve for the best-beloved son in Christ, young Conradin, King of Jerusalem and Duke of Swabia, these territories and also his rights in the Kingdom and elsewhere; " *Conradi pueri jure salvo* " they were to insert in their oath of allegiance to the Church. But he wrote to the Plantagenet that he abode by the grant to Prince Edmund. Through Cardinal Deacon Pietro Capoccio he invited the Anti-King William of Holland to Rome at Christmas, for coronation with the Imperial diadem. He sent his kinsman, Cardinal Guilelmo Fiesco, as Legate to Sicily, Alberto Fiesco as Grand Captain there. Pietro Ruffo, the Grand Justiciary, Riccardo de Montenero and Admiral Ansaldo de Mari made their submission. Against the Marquis Berthold, the *bajulus* of the Kingdom, and his brothers, against Manfredi and Frederick of Antioch Innocent fulminated his ban.

When in Capua the Marquis Berthold pressed the Prince of Taranto to take the *bajulate* away from him— Conrad not having dared to put the request to his brother because of the insult to the Lancia—Manfredi objected. He gave in; for Isotta, his uncle Manfred's daughter and Berthold's wife, urged him in his hesitation. The Barons swore that if little Conrad, Corradino, should die childless, the Prince of Taranto should be king. The German Marquis vowed to return with an army and hand out money and jewels. But he did not come. The Legate Pietro Capoccio threatened San Germano. The Lords of Talbangio and Riccardo Filangieri went over to the Pope. Prince Manfredi saw no salvation but in reconciliation with him. He sent Galvano Lancia, who was back in the kingdom, to Innocent. A treaty was concluded. Since before all the world Manfredi had returned into the arms of the Church, the Pope, without imputing to him his father's and brothers' trespasses, would lift the ban from him and, that he might all the more violently be inflamed in gratitude for

CONRADIN: HAWKING

such overflowing benefits, invest him with the County of Andria to boot.   He was to equip fifty men-at-arms for service within the frontiers of the Sicilian Kingdom. Henceforth he was to be Papal Vicar this side the Faro as far as the Abruzzi.   One Sunday in October Manfredi led Innocent's palfrey from Ceperano over the Garigliano bridge.   A golden crucifix floated before the Holy Father.   His girths loosened, and he crashed down.

The Pope resided in San Germano and in Teano. He pardoned Berthold of Hohenburg and nominated him Lord High Seneschal.   Cardinal Fiesco also demanded the oath of vassalage from Manfredi and, as he refused it, the men of the Curia despised him, and many of the barons did not even raise their hats to him.   In a narrow defile the Prince encountered Borello, Lord of Anglone, who was quarrelling with him rancorously about Alesina and l'Onor del Monte San Angelo. Borello's troop was armed, unarmed the Prince.   He secured his helmet, but, in spite of the reviling with which the air buzzed, he urged peace.   Then some of his men came riding into the defile.   Borello fled, wounded in the back by a lance.   The people of Teano believed that he had killed Manfredi and slew him.

Manfredi's men reported to him what had happened. He wanted to inform Innocent through Cervasio de Martino and Goffredo da Cosenza.   Tizio, the Pope's nephew, hurried ahead ; he would answer for Manfredi's guiltlessness.   In Capua the Cardinals and the Papal army were expecting the Holy Father.   Manfredi drew near the gates.   Horsemen and mob poured up to him, with music and cheering.   He went to take his leave of the Cardinals.   But at the bridge over the Volturno, the triumphal arch with the Emperor's statue, the inhabitants welcomed him with singing and the sound of trumpets and pipes and accompanied him to the house in which he was wont to lodge.   Alarmed and hopeful he took his leave as soon as he could and managed to get out of the town.   But he was not two miles from Capua when he heard that his baggage had been seized and that he was being pursued by mounted men. Outside Acerra they passed a wild mountain torrent by a narrow tottering foot-bridge. Manfredi was the last to cross.

In Acerra he sent Goffredo da Cosenza to Berthold of Hohenburg at Arienzo and asked for a meeting. Only hesitating did the Marquis yield to Goffredo's representation that Federigo, dying, had committed his son to him and that if he were faithless he would be ruined with all the Emperor's kin. He said that at break of day Manfredi would find him in the forest near Acerra. But instead of him, a messenger was on the spot; the Pope ordered Manfredi to appear before him in Capua. Galvano counselled his nephew to rapid flight. From Acerra he rode, not to Aversa, but by way of the fort Marigliano. The sons of Federigo's Seneschal Jacopo Capece, the young Neapolitans Marino and Corrado Capece, guided him round the fort of Monteforte by precipitous goatherds' paths.

In the pale moonlit night the ravines appeared even deeper, the torrents roared, the winds howled, birds of prey croaked in the tree tops, and clouds veiled the moon. Leading their horses they reached Marigliano. They declared they were the Marquis Berthold's men. But the gates of the citadel were barred against them. They climbed over the chasm, under the stout wall of the castle. They rested in the fort of Atripalda, where the fair and noble wives of the Capece entertained Federigo's son. In Guarda Lombardia they heard that the Pope's Legate was standing with an army near Ariano. Bisaccia greeted them kindly, Binio with acclamation and flaring candles. As Melfi declared for the Pope, the way to Ascoli alone remained. It was in uproar, the *Podestà* killed. His nephew rode to meet Manfredi and said, as he learned that Ascoli was to be sacked, that Otto of Hohenburg with five hundred foot was near Corneto. Manfredi proceeded to the fort Lavello and to Venosa. His goal was not the church of San Nicola de Aufido, where, as he gave out, he was to meet Frederick of Antioch, but Lucera, the Saracens' town.

On the evening of the first of November he rode out of the gates on Venosa with three squires and a small number of servitors. Night fell and mighty rain. Only by the sound of their voices did they keep from losing themselves in the starless dark. Then Adenolfo, Federigo's chief huntsman, detected a white gleam, the hunting lodge of San Agapito. Here, weary and almost frozen, they lit a fire, great as the danger was. In the gloom they rode on, to before the gate of Lucera. The *Podestà* Giovanni Moro, the brown son of a negress, bred with Boabdil and Otello, Musca and Marzuch in Federigo's harem and Groom of the Chambers still under him, had, betraying the Prince, gone to the Pope with a thousand Saracens. He had entrusted the town to a relative, Marchisio. An Arab servitor of the Prince's called to the watchman : " Behold, your lord, the son of your Emperor, is come. Open the gates to him ". The watchman retorted that Marchisio would not bring the keys, as the Moor had forbidden him. And one said that Manfredi might creep through a hole under the threshold, through which the rain ran off. The Prince dismounted and was about to do so. But the watchman cried : " Why should we suffer that our lord should enter the town in such shameful wise ? Let us break open the gates that he may make his entry as is meet ". They burst open the portals, knelt before Manfredi and kissed the hem of his garment. On their shoulders they carried him into the midst of Lucera. With their fists they forced Marchisio, who was arming himself on hearing the noise, to fall on his knees also. From a window of the Imperial palace Manfredi spoke to the multitude, and all swore him the oath of allegiance. He had horsemen, German mercenaries and an Arab army mad with courage.

Pope Innocent was in Capua. He rewarded Berthold of Hohenburg and his brothers and Giovanni Moro, the heathen who was obedient to the Church. He journeyed to Naples and burst into a passion about Manfredi's victory. He wrote to the King of England that he must come to Sicily with despatch. But Manfredi took Foggia and its citadel also. The Legate Fiesco took to flight, the Papal forces took to flight, Tuscans, Campanians and Crusaders—the horsemen without saddles, without baggage—and many found their graves in the wintry snow of the mountains. Giovanni Moro fled away to the Saracens in Acerenza. They stabbed him and sent the traitor's severed head to Lucera.

Pope Innocent, sick in Peter of Vinea's palace, sighed in the terror of death : " Lord, thou hast chastened me for my unrighteousness ". At his greedy kinsmen he screamed : " Why do you wretches lament ? Do I not leave you rich ? What more do ye want ? " He died on the fourth anniversary of Federigo's extinction. The Cardinals, whom the *Podestà* Tavernieri, Innocent's sister's son, drove into the Conclave, delegated the election, in the name of all, to gorgeous Ottaviano de Ubaldini. He chose the Bishop of Ostia and Velletri, Rinaldo de Conti, Gregory's learned, portly and money-loving nephew, who crowned himself with the tiara by the name of Alexander the Fourth. He excommunicated Manfredi as the murderer of Borello.

WILLIAM of Holland had, at Brunswick, consummated his marriage with Elisabeth, the daughter of Duke Otto. Turning over a light in the delights of the nuptial bed, he set the curtains on fire. The King and Queen fled naked, with them serving women, who were sewing robes of state ; the crown and jewels of gold were burnt up. Conrad of Hochstaden, the Archbishop of Cologne, had the house at Neuss fired in which William was dwelling. Near Coblenz the Archbishop of Treves drowned sundry of his men in the Rhine. In Utrecht church a stone wounded the King in the head. The Queen was captured by the robber-knight Herman of Rittberg near Oderheim ; she had to buy herself free with jewels. William of Holland was at loggerheads with Charles of Anjou about Hainault. Anjou had told him : he would not clear Hainault, and William might offer his friendship to others; he would tempt the water-king to land and vent his spite on him. William challenged him to single combat on the heath near Maastricht. But there was never duel or battle. In the end William of Holland went to war against the free Frisians in the neighbourhood of the Berkemeer. In his heavy armour he got under the ice, the Frisians slew the knight, and, when they knew who he was, held their peace.

The Archbishop of Cologne sent to London Jean d'Avesnes, William's brother-in-law. The German Princes, he declared, were ready to elect Richard of Cornwall, if he compensated them. The Earl of Gloucester and Robert Walerand chaffered in Germany. They promised Archbishop Gerard of Mainz to grease his palm with eight thousand marks. Duke Lewis of Bavaria was young Conradin's foster-father. He had had a feud against the city of Augsburg. Then his consort Mary of Brabant wrote to Sir Rucho of Ottlingen, with whom she often played chess and whom she held dear, while it was his wish to be familiar with her: that he should move the Duke to come with him to Donauwörth and she would then herself grant him what he had so often begged. The folly of a groom gave the letter for Ottlingen to the Duke. He read it, killed the groom and had Mary's head chopped off with a sharp axe, however much Queen Elisabeth complained. He stabbed the noble damsel Eilika of Brennerberg with his knife for playing the bawd. Another he threw from the tower. Then he repented, his hair grew grey, and he made atonement by building the Cistercian monastery in Fürstenfeld. Now, a year later, he solemnly promised to vote for Richard and marry one of Cornwall's daughters or sisters. Twelve thousand marks sterling, eight thousand of them on the day of election, were decided on between him and Jean d'Avesnes, the Bishop of Cambrai, the Provost of Aix, Conrad of Sleyda, Wirich of Dun and Henry of Gymmenik. Eight thousand marks was the Archbishop of Cologne's bribe. For the German crown there was a second competitor, King Alphonsus of Castile. He paid twenty thousand marks apiece to the Duke of Brabant and the Archbishop of Treves. Outside Frankfort Conrad of Hochstaden and Lewis of Bavaria, on their behalf and that of Gerard of Mainz, a prisoner in Brunswick, elected Cornwall; in Frankfort, Treves, Saxony, Brandenburg and Bohemia the Castilian. Richard was crowned at Aix. He made his entry into the city with thirty-two eight-horse wagons, each laden with a barrel of gold as great as a wine-butt of two hogsheads.

In Piacenza Ezzelino da Romano and Uberto Pallavicino had allied themselves against everyone who should call himself Emperor and King without them. Ezzelino leaped against Mantua. The astrologers had prophesied that it was his planetary hour. While he was ravaging the district, the Pope's men, the Crusaders, clambered on to the bridge and dam of Padua. Ansedisio fled. The Crusaders set free them who were gaoled and for eight days emptied merchants' halls and cellars of provisions. The messenger who gasped out the news Ezzelino punished with death. The Paduans who came into his hands he mutilated. He chained Ansedisio with iron. He said he was going to Padua to hew down his enemies like dogs. Then he ended his fraternal feud with Alberico. At Castro Franco they swore constant amity one to the other. Alberico gave up Treviso and three of his sons as hostages. Ezzelino sent to Alphonsus of Castile and offered him the sovereignty in Italy. With Pallavicino and Boso de Doara he was victorious at Torricella; and there were taken prisoners Bishop Philip of Ferrara, the turkey-cock, who had been legate in Germany, the *Podestà* of Mantua, the Bishop of Verona and Everardo, the Dominican, the Apostle of Peace. In triumph Ezzelino made his entry into Brescia. During Lent he invited Bishop Philip to a luxurious banquet, that he might gobble over the smell of the viands, and listened to all he had to say in justification of the plundering of Padua. Many clerics he castrated.

Against the tyrant there made common cause in Cremona Uberto Pallavicino, Boso de Doara, Azzo d'Este and the communes of Cremona, Mantua, Ferrara and Padua. He was purposing to take Milan, with the help of the *Nobili*. The astrologers reported aspects propitious to him. He crossed the Oglio near Palanzuolo. Near Soncino Pallavicino and Boso opposed him; at Marcaria, downstream, stood Azzo d'Este. The tyrant pressed forward against Monza, to seize the crown of Lombardy. The stroke failed. At Cassano on the Adda the allies cut off his retreat and took his baggage. He hurried up, to recapture the Adda bridge. An arrow hit him in the left foot; he had to return to Vilmercato. Martino della Torre came up, the *Podestà* of Milan, the foe of the *Nobili*. But in the morning Ezzelino led his army through an unguarded ford on to the left bank of the Adda. The Brescians turned and went over to the Communes. Ezzelino's army fled to Bergamo or to Brescia, four hundred were taken prisoners. The tyrant was surrounded, but yet he fought. Mazoldo, of the kin of the Lavelongo, smashed down a club on to his helmet. He reeled from his horse, fell, was gagged. They brought him into Boso's slanting tent; he sat there dumb and frightful. They brought him to Soncino. The multitude mocked him. In the night a chapel-bell rang. He called out: "Go and stab dead the priest making such a clamour with the bells". The guards said: "Lord, you are in captivity". "Where was I captured?" asked Ezzelino. The guard: "At Cassano". Ezzelino: "Cassano and Bassano, there is no great difference. That I should die at Bassano was foretold me". In fierce pain he repeated countless times the word Cassano. Minorites and Dominicans came to him, that he should confess his sins and do penance. He said: "I have no sins to confess save that I did not take sufficient revenge upon my enemies, commanded my army badly and let myself be deceived and beguiled. On that account have I come into captivity". He stared before him on to the ground, disdained medicine and food and tore off the linen wet with purulent matter, so that the black-red blood of his wound poured forth. In the morning they found him collapsed, dead.

The Communes, Boso and Azzo besieged Alberico in his rocky castle Zeno, near Bassano. Mesa of Portilia and the German mercenaries surrendered the outworks for gold. Alberico escaped, with his wife Margarita, his six sons, his daughters Amabilie and Griselda and a few faithful henchmen, to a tower, where hunger and thirst plagued them. He said to his children : " The might and wisdom of Ezzelino have been unworthily brought low and, with him, the house of Romano. But unto you may God grant life, victory and revenge. Pray ", he then said to his followers, " the Marquis of Este to be mindful of our former love and that my daughter Adelaide became his son Rinaldo's wife and to guard me against the hatred of embittered foes ". The Communes allowed the garrison to depart unmolested. He himself had a wooden bit put in his mouth by Marco Badoër, the *Podestà* of Treviso. One sat himself upon him and forced him to flounder about on all fours, like a beast. Amidst the sounding of instruments and jeers and yelling he and his family were hauled through the camp. Before his eyes, his sons were executed, dismembered and their limbs thrust into his face. From his wife and daughters they cut away the clothes under their breasts, strapped them to stakes and burned them. Then Alberico was squeezed with pincers, bound to the tail of a steed and dragged to death.

MANFREDI had been victorious over Pietro Ruffo, as he was fleeing to Lipari, over the perjured Cardinal Ottaviano, whom he shut up in Foggia, and Berthold of Hohenburg. He had arrested him and his brothers as conspirators, had condemned them to death on the solemn day at Baroli and commuted the sentence to perpetual incarceration. He made Galvano Lancia

Grand Marshal of the realm, Federigo Lancia Vicar-General of Sicily and Calabria. The report came that young Conradin had died in Germany. Manfredi sent no ambassadors to Bavaria and mourned for him. Barons and Prelates begged him, as the true heir, to take the crown. In Palermo Cathedral Bishop Rinaldo of Girgenti anointed him, the Archbishops of Salerno, Monreale and Taranto crowned him and conducted him to his father's throne. He, Beatrice's widower, married Helena, the daughter of Michael Angelos Dukas, despot of Epirus.

He thanked the city of Siena for her devotion in inviting him to stretch out his hand for the Imperial diadem ; he would be her bulwark and love her before all the cities of Italy. Percival Doria, the Genoese, the commander of his Germans and Saracens, he promoted to be Vicar-General of the March of Ancona, the Duchy of Spoleto and of Romagnola. In the battle of Montaperto the Ghibellines of Florence changed their standards for the white of Manfredi and cried : " Death to the Florentines ". Victory lay with the army of Siena and the captain of Manfredi's horsemen, Count Giordano d'Anglano. The Senator Brancaleone, overthrown by the Romans, had been called in by them once more when the guilds, under the master-baker Matthew de Bealvere, slew the new Senator Emanuel de Madio. He entered upon an alliance with Manfredi, the King of Sicily. Pope Innocent fulminated an excommunication against him and lifted it, for Brancaleone threatened a campaign of annihilation against Anagni. He destroyed one hundred and forty towers belonging to the nobility, the keeps for cowing the peoples. A fever carried him off after he had lain before Corneto. On the Capitol the Romans buried his head in a precious vase atop a marble pillar. To him succeeded his uncle Castellano degli Andalo, an Orsini and an Anibaldi, a Sabello and an Anibaldi again. The Ghibellines in Rome wished to put up Manfredi. Cardinal Johannes de Toleto, the Englishman, worked for the election of Richard of

Cornwall as Senator for life. Then, in Viterbo, Pope Alexander died. James Pantaléon got the tiara, the Patriarch of Jerusalem, who was the son of a cobbler at Troyes in Champagne. He nominated fourteen Cardinals, eight of them Frenchmen like himself.

Pope Urban dismissed in Viterbo the embassy from Manfredi, who had offered to pay thirty thousand ounces of gold for the ceremony of his coronation and ten thousand a year after it had taken place. He wrote to Jago of Aragon, to whom Manfredi had sent his falconer, the *trovatore* Jacopo Mostacci, and who was courting Manfredi's daughter Constance for his son Pedro, that Jago was not to lend his ear to the insinuations of him whose impiety was known to the nations of the earth ; sunk in a pit of evil, he contemned God and man with a front more impudent than the front of a harlot ; he had murdered Borello, disgraced the name of king in arrogating it to himself, were guilty of oppressing priests, cruelty, voluptuousness and heresy ; never would the Curia raise up any scion of Frederick's. Pope Urban wrote against young Conradin, who, to Manfredi's shame, was alive, whom the Florentine Guelphs called to Italy, whose ambassador Bussarus had been fallen upon and assassinated on the way to Florence, while Conrad Kroff of Flüglingen got away. The deeds of the ancestors, Urban wrote, permitted one to infer the corrupt nature of the posterity, a serpent could only bring forth serpents, a bad tree bad fruit only.

A spurious Federigo excited Sicily, the beggar Giovanni de Calcaria. He was about sixty years old, with grizzled auburn hair and the Emperor's nose and chin, and in foul tatters had knocked at every door for maize bread and onion soups. When the women laughed and marvelled at his resemblance to the great Federigo, he invented vague replies ; and then he said that he was he, returning from a pilgrimage that he had undertaken for his soul's health. He withdrew into the wilderness of Monte Ghibello in order that the inquisitive and malcontent might seek him the more. Exiles gathered there, the kith of Pietro Ruffo, killed at Terracina, and Bartolomeo de Mileto. They went with the spurious Federigo into the stronghold of Centorbi, issued letters under the Imperial seal and demanded allegiance of the towns. Riccardo Filangieri, Count of Marsico, the governor of Sicily, cut off their supplies. They got away to Castro Giovanni, received with honours. The Count of Marsico intercepted the spurious Federigo, whom two of his adherents, Guilelmo Malococina and Andrea de Bartholutio, betrayed, and executed him and eleven more. King Manfredi appeared on the island and, for their double treachery, had Guilelmo and Andrea blinded and broken on the wheel. Splendid was his entry into Palermo, which presented him with rich gifts. Enrico de Alba, who possessed lands, precious metals and herds of cattle in Manzara, gave him a hundred mules, broken in by a hundred black slaves.

King Manfredi lived in the Basilicata—in a castle on Lago Pesole, the Palazzo San Gervasio, near pure springs, amidst flourishing woods. He dressed in green, the colour of hope, was a musician and singer and inventive as a *trovatore*. " Paradise has come back to earth ", enthusiasts cried out ; but others declared that it was a garden of the Devil and of sensuality, dedicated to the god of Vanity and to Venus, the naked goddess of love. The King's treasurer was Count Manfred Maletta, full of the lore of hidden treasure and a master of the canzone. The King went staghunting by Lago Pesole. He had a stud, where Apulian horses were crossed with Arab thoroughbreds ; against the quivering foals' necks, as he softly went by of an evening, he would lay his slender head. By the sea, at the foot of Monte Gargalo, he built the town of Manfredonia, from the stones of destroyed Siponto. It possessed a wide haven and the cathedral of San Lorenzo, with a tremendous bell, which pealed and swung under the waves of the Adriatic when the Turks burned Manfredonia to the ground. King Manfredi was familiar with the ten books of Euclid. He completed his father's work on the art of falconry. He sent missives to the Doctors of Philosophy at Paris, who were drawing water from old wells. The Jew Moses of Palermo translated for him Hippocrates's book on the diseases of the horse from Arabic into Latin. And, on days of fever, he interpreted that dialogue touching the Apple that had hovered on the lips of dying Federigo, *De pomo sive de morte Aristotelis* : touching the creation of souls, the transience of material things and of those not subject to the shipwreck of death. But he still drew breath in the flooding golden light of summer in the south.

A S the Church of Rome could not get rid of her troubles through him, Pope Urban broke with Prince Edmund of England. He gave Sicily to another hawk to prey on, bloody Charles of Anjou, who had throttled Boniface de Castellane's rebellion and was lord of Marseilles and Forcalquier and of Piedmont as far as Alba and Asti. In Viterbo his ambassadors swore to a new treaty. Fifty thousand marks of silver he was to pay the Curia when the Kingdom, spite the rebellion of isolated towns and fortresses, were in his hands, two thousand ounces of gold every year at the festival of St. Peter, to present the Pope every three years with a white palfrey, do him solemn homage in person, never suffer himself to be elected Emperor or German King or Lord of Tuscany or Lombardy, never enter into an alliance against the Church. If, within a year, he should not have advanced into Italy with at least a thousand knights and three hundred siege-troops, the treaty would be void. In return the Pope granted the tithe of all church-property in France and Provence, in Lyons, Vienne, Embrun, Tarentaise and Besançon for three years and the ransom of all who should take the Cross against Manfredi and the Saracens of Lucera. Yet again he was minded to excommunicate Manfredi and his followers. On him alone, not on Anjou, devolved the burden of the war.

Since the Pope would hinder the election as well of Manfredi as of Richard of Cornwall, the Conservators of the Roman Republic chose Anjou for their Senator. " Jeremiah saith ", Urban exclaimed, " that all evil cometh from the north. But I see all affliction coming upon us from Sicily." Through his Legate, Cardinal Simon of Santa Cecilia, he accomplished nothing save that Charles should hold his office for five years only. As the tithes came in slowly, the Cardinal told King Lewis, the pious martyr, who, after many privations among the heathen, had returned, to advance the money ; in return he should gain recompense an hundredfold and eternal life. He haggled with Charles of Anjou. If he wanted Gaeta, Capua, Monte Cassino, San Germano and Naples in addition, the tribute would be ten, instead of two, thousand ounces of gold. Charles and Beatrice still hesitating, he intimidated them : the Pope might make a compact with Pedro of Aragon as well. Green in the face, Charles of Anjou assented. King Manfredi invited the Counts and Barons to a court at Naples. The inhabitants of Campania refusing him passage and provisions, he sent Percival Doria to press forward against Rome through the mountains east of Tivoli and the valley of the Teverone. Doria invested the fortress of Colle and crossed the Nera at Arrone ; but there he drowned, as he swam out to a knight reeling in the waves. The Proconsul Pietro de Vico, a Ghibelline, had been driven from Rome. With Count Giordano's German knights he took Sutri ; the town had to swear allegiance to the King. James Cantelmi, Charles of Anjou's deputy, came up with Provençals and Guelphs from Rome. They shut up Pietro in his castle of Vico and retreated, as the report ran that Manfredi was coming and as it was raining and harvest-time at hand. The Ghibellines made themselves lords of Lucca and cast out the Guelphs inimical to the city ; noble Florentine women travailed on the mountain-pastures

19

of San Pelerino, under rocks and bushes. In the March of Ancona Count Giordano caught the Bishop of Verona. Through a Franciscan Urban begged King Manfredi to set him free; if he did so, the Pope would intercede with God to give him renown and His grace. The King returned thanks for the unexpected paternal kindness; and yet the Pope's Holiness had suffered him to be called a son of Satan, had opened his arms to the enemy of his right and set him up as his rival in the Kingdom.

Pope Urban warned Charles of Anjou that for his taking-off Manfredi had sent to France the apostate Cavalcanti and two Assassins of the Lebanon with fifty poisons. By Michaelmas, Charles, in pursuance of his oath, was to be in Italy. The Pope feared that the King would fall upon him in Orvieto. But Manfredi had thoughts of gaining possession of Rome. Pietro de Vico was more impatient than the others. He got friends of his to do open the gate of San Pancrazio and houses that formerly had belonged to him and planned to occupy the Lycaonian Island in the Tiber. Watchmen detected him and shouted, the deputy Cantelmi and the Guelphs under Giovanni Savelli hastened up, they drove Pietro de Vico out of the Piscinula quarter over the Tiber, in which his son was drowned, and he fled with three Ghibellines to Cervetri.

Pope Urban, sick already, left Orvieto. They brought him to Todi and Assisi, into the castle of Diruta, where he lay in the half-slumber of a swoon, and, in a litter, to Perugia. He died, as a comet, that had flamed since September, vanished from the sky. The Cardinals elected, and not till February, the Cardinal of Sabina, the Archbishop of Narbonne, Guido le Gros Fucoldi of St. Gilles in Languedoc, the son of a nobleman of Toulouse and a German mother. He had served King Lewis as privy councillor and, after the death of his wife, had turned Carthusian. In monk's habit he appeared in Perugia. He became Pope as Clement the Fourth.

WHILST yet a Cardinal Pope Clement had written to the Count of Anjou : " The Roman people, renowned of name and proud of spirit, has called you to the governance of the city and desired to behold your countenance. It requires to be treated with great circumspection : for the Romans demand of their Rectors magnificent display, resounding words and terrible deeds, because they maintain the lordship of the world to be theirs. Your deputy Cantelmi and his comrades we praise mightily ; but their small number, the meanness of your disbursement weaken them and your consequence ". Now Charles of Anjou prepared in Provence. The French knights armed themselves under the standard of the fleur-de-lys. The Countess Beatrice pawned her jewels. But, as the Italian merchants' thirteen thousand pounds were insufficient, Cantelmi broke into the almost empty treasury in the Lateran.

King Manfredi advanced against Campania. The Roman Ghibellines under Jacopo Napoleone, an Orsini, and the Germans threatened Rome from Vicovaro. They defeated the Gascon knight Ferrère, who had beguiled the vigilance of Manfredi's fleet, and took him prisoner. The astrologers beheld joyful omens for the King's victory. In the meantime Charles of Anjou had embarked at Marseilles in eighty vessels. Fifty Sicilian vessels sailed against him from Gaeta. Manfredi's admiral blocked the mouth of the Tiber with stones and piles. The tempest scattered Anjou's ships ; with but three he sought shelter in Porto Pisano. Manfredi's fleet had been blown out to sea. Guido Novello, the Count Palatine, who commanded at Pisa on the King's behalf, wanted to cut off the enemy. The Pisans closed the gates against him, until he should concede this or that, and meanwhile Charles of Anjou had time to clear the port again and get away. But yet he was well-nigh wrecked on the Roman coast. He got into a boat and landed near Ostia amid thunder and lightning.

On the rumour of his arrival the Guelph clans issued forth—the Frangipani, Anibaldi, Cenci, Paparoni, Capizucchi, Conti, Colonna, Crescentii, Parentii, Malabranca, de Ponte and Pierleoni. They conducted him to San Paolo Fuori, and he abode in the Benedictine's monastery. The clerics greeted him with Hosannas. But the populace mocked the poor, squint-eyed Count, Carlotto, who knew not how to laugh. On the Saturday before Whitsun he and a thousand dismounted knights entered the city in festal procession. The Guelph *Nobili* gave displays of arms, danced and jousted. Panegyrics were sung in the Senator's praise, but not a penny did the mob get to scramble for, no treasurer threw coins to them. The Capitol was the Senator's residence. He did not take up his lodging there, but, without asking the Pope, in the Lateran. Clement, in Perugia, was indignant at this presumption. He should at his pleasure take up his residence elsewhere, he wrote to Charles of Anjou, and not in Papal buildings nor aver that he had been turned out of them in unbecoming fashion. So Charles of Anjou settled in the Palace of the Quattro Coronati on Monte Celio. Day by day his lack of money worsened. "Can man live by wind?" the Pope complained. "Nowhere are opened the hands of generous givers, and extortion we disdain. The hazard of the enterprize, the consequence of an unhappy issue (if so be) we share with all and each; but we should be afflicted with pangs of conscience and eternal shame to boot, if we were minded to squander the property of the Church and plunge her into piteous poverty." Thrice he wrote to King Lewis, who was wroth with his brother.

In the monastery of Ara Coeli Charles was clothed in the Senatorial insignia and, on the Sunday following, before the altar of the basilica Sancti Salvatoris in the Lateran, invested with the Kingdom of Sicily by the Cardinals Anibaldo of the twelve Apostles, Richard of San Angelo and James of Santa Maria in Cosmedin. The flag of the blessed Peter floated over him. The annual payment to the Curia was reduced to eight thousand marks. From Foggia Manfredi issued a proclamation to the Romans. The Church, he said, wished to hold sway over all kings and countries and to dispose of the Imperial dignity as well. He might assume it for himself, against the will of the Senate, like Julius Cæsar and Frederick Barbarossa ; but he wished to receive it at their hands. He was approaching in force. He wrote this to Guido Novello too : the Count Palatine was to come with the Tuscan army. He himself camped on the fields of Tagliacozzo, threatened Tivoli. But he had to turn back and, at the same time, from Radicofani, Guido Novello as well. Treason began among the Barons in Apulia. In Italy and England the cross was preached against the venom-bloated brood of the Dragon.

Pope Clement despaired nevertheless. " Behold in what confusion ", he wrote to squint-eyed Carlotto, the Church's athlete, " is the whole universe. Thou knowest the reason of our helplessness." He adjured him to become reconciled with his brother : then merchants would lend ten thousand pounds on the security of the church's property in Rome (not counting the Lateran, St. Peter's, St. Gregory's, the Metropolitan churches and the hospitals). Of necessity, Clement wrote to King Lewis, he was a prey to insatiable usury ; by the memory of their mother Blanche he conjured Lewis not to leave his brother in the lurch. If the King were not so inclined, he, the Pope, would offer his back to the scourge and suffer servitude and death for the Lord, if he decreed it. " How wretched ", he complained of shameless Anjou's indigence to Cardinal Simon, " is the life of a prince who in the sweat of his countenance must beg entertainment and clothing for him and his and, in bitterness without end, look upon the hands of his creditor that suck his blood and from whom he gets for a *soldo* what is not worth two *denarii*, and then only with flatteries and unworthy petitions."

The Provençal army marched upon Rome, an army of thirty thousand, two Counts of Vendôme, the High Chancellor Pierre of Nemours, the Constable Gilles le Brun, the Marshall de Mirepoix, Jean de Neelle, the Count of Soissons, Count Courtenay, Guillaume d'Estendard, the Beaumonts, Philip and Guy of Montfort, Robert of Béthune, the son of Gui de Dampierre, Count of Flanders, the Bishops of Narbonne and Auxerre; and with the knights was the Countess Beatrice, who embarked at Genoa. From Soncino on the Oglio Uberto Pallavicino marched against the French with Boso de Doara and armed forces from Cremona, Piacenza, Pavia and Brescia. But Boso gave them notice, so that they got over the river at Pallazolo unhindered. From Mantua the Guelphs pressed forward against Castiglione. Nothing remained for Pallavicino but to retreat to Cremona. The French captured forts, massacred the garrison of Capriolo with women and children. They lay before Brescia, beat Mantuans and Ferrarese at Montechiari and, by way of Mantua, Bologna, Ferrara, Faenza, through Ancona and Spoleto, marched into Rome, where they stole, robbed and plundered.

Charles of Anjou demanded that the Pope should crown him and Beatrice, not in Perugia, but in Rome. On Epiphany Day he was crowned and anointed in St. Peter's by the Cardinal Bishop Rodolfo of Abano, Ancherius Pantaléon, Cardinal Priest of Santa Prasseda, and the Cardinal Deacons Richardus Anibaldi, Godofredus of Alatri and Matthew Orsini. Clement warned him that he would chasten his officials' presumptuousness with the Papal sword. Once again he meditated whether Manfredi might not serve as counterpoise to Anjou and fixed a day for him to prove his innocence. But he did not appear. " Thou must know ", the Pope wrote him, " that the term of grace is over. Everything has its time, but time has not everything. Already the armed hero stands at the door, the axe is already laid to the root of the tree."

KING MANFREDI sent delegates to Charles of Anjou at Rome to treat with him for a peace. "Tell the Sultan of Nocera", the crowned head replied, "that I will send him to Hell or myself to Heaven." King Manfredi summoned to Benevento the Barons, cities and captains. "A fire", he said to them, "that for long smouldered in the distance, has come upon us with the swiftness of lightning." The throne would not be enough for Anjou; he would advance his helpers through the ruin of the Barons. But, after faithless hithering-and-thithering, Pietro de Vico too had joined the Franks. Manfredi fortified Benevento. By way of Capua he hurried to Ceperano and San Germano, between mountains and the *maremme* of the rivulet Rapido.

The army of the French departed from Rome, unpaid, through the dried-up Sacco valley. "God be with you"—thus Cardinal Deacon Ottaviano bade the Church's athlete farewell and blessed him with the sign of the cross. Giordano d'Anglano and the King's brother-in-law, the Count of Caserta, were to defend the defile of Ceperano. It was said afterwards, a servant had reported to Caserta that his wife Violante was Manfredi's incestuous paramour and he had therefore renounced his oath of vassalage. He counselled Giordano to let a portion of the French over the bridge and to attack them when they were cut off. Then he said that there were too many of them and fled. The defile was lost. The French took the impregnable Rocca d'Arce by storm. Their carters fought in undisciplined confusion with the mercenaries; a hundred drivers fell beneath the Frenchmen's swords. The chivalry showed itself, without siege-engines, outside San Germano. Manfredi's mercenaries derided them from the walls and, outside one of the gates, beat grooms who were fetching water from a cold spring. Pietro de Vico assaulted the walls; stones covered him halfway up his body. Then the knight Burkhard and John of Vendôme saw that that gate was unoccupied. They forced it and planted the standard of the fleur-de-lys on its battlements. The Saracens fled, a thousand of them were cut down. The citizens gave up the keys of the town. Venafro surrendered; thirty-two forts did likewise.

Manfredi, with eight thousand knights, abandoned his position near Capua and reached Benevento before the French. In ten days' forced march over the mountains of Alife, Piedemonte and Telesia the enemy, their horses starved or slaughtered in their famine, followed after. They camped in a pine-wood fifteen miles from Benevento and, towards mid-day, stood on the heights of Calaria, beneath them the plain channelled by the Calore and the Sabato. There Manfredi's army glistened, his knights, ten thousand Saracens on foot and eight hundred German men-at-arms, who had just come up. He awaited Conrad of Antioch, Frederick of Antioch's son, from the Abruzzi.

The Constable Gilles le Brun demanded battle. He assembled the magnates of Anjou in front of his tent. They were fighting, he said, in the name of the Saviour. They were to kill the chargers, not the riders, and not with the cut, but with the thrust; then the footmen were to catch them sinking to the ground in their heavy armour and dispatch them. Every knight was to have two footmen at his side or, if there weren't such, ribalds too. The Bishop of Auxerre gave them absolution as they knelt. Manfredi questioned his astrologers; muttering, they foretold him victory. But many Barons crept away during the council of war.

Manfredi ordered his army in three lines of battle. In the first were the German men-at-arms under Galvano Lancia, in the second a thousand Tuscan and Lombard knights under Giordano d'Anglano, in the third himself with fourteen hundred Apulian and Saracen horsemen, between them the Saracen bowmen. The three lines of the French were commanded by Philip of Montfort and the Marshal de Mirepoix, Charles of Anjou and Guy of Montfort, the Constable and Robert of Béthune. A fourth division consisted of the

Florentine Guelphs and Count Guido Guerra, whose flag was borne by Corrado de Montemagno of Pistoja. With wild yells and a hail of arrows the Saracen bowmen overwhelmed the ribalds and laid them low in masses. Philip of Montfort's and Mirepoix's mounted men-at-arms threw themselves upon the Saracens and annihilated them in their violence. But destruction seized upon the *chevaliers* when Giordano galloped against them with the Germans shouting : "*Schwaben, Reiter !*" "Stick the horses," barked Charles of Anjou, "stick them with the point of the sword under the shoulder and in the joints of the armour." The French shouted "Montjoie !" The Germans wavered with their swords and truncheons.

Yet was Manfredi's line of Apulians and Saracens unweakened. He attacked, when a soldier called out to him : "Lord, behold what an heap of your men deserts to the enemy, behold how many are treacherously fleeing yonder". They were Apulian Barons and, among their number, the Count of Acerra. As Manfredi turned round, his helmet, adorned with an eagle of silver, fell into his saddle. He cried : "That is an omen from God". And, to aged Occursio : "Remember that thou wast own sewer to the Emperor, my father, that he commended thee to me before all ; counsel me truly". Occursio answered with humility : "It were too late for that, methinks. Where are your fiddlers and *trovatori*, whom you loved more than knights and grooms, that they may try whether Charles too will dance to their sweet melody ? But your life I will save by my death". He took the silver-eagled helmet and was cut down. With Tibaldo Anibaldi the mellay swallowed up King Manfredi, who wore a painful smile.

The French killed three thousand of the accursed heretics. In the evening Charles of Anjou wrote to the Pope : "I report to your Holiness this victory, which I received from the hand of God, that for so proud a triumph you may give thanks to him, the Almighty, who champions the Church's case with my arm. Be persuaded that, when I have torn up out of Italy the root of all offence, I shall lead the Kingdom back to its old accustomed submission before the Roman Church, to the honour and glorifying of God, to the exaltation of his name, to the peace of the Church, to the happy state of the Kingdom's subjects ". Two days later a Picard rode Manfredi's horse. He had Manfredi's belt. He declared it to be his booty, taken from a dead knight. A naked body was found. The men put it on an ass. "Who'll buy Manfredi?" one of them bawled; but a French Baron punished him severely.

The body had two mortal wounds, in the head and in the breast. "O my Lord, o my King!" captured Giordano d'Anglano cried. Charles of Anjou said that an excommunicated heretic might not lie in Christian earth. They buried him by the bridge over the Calore, in the rose-meadow, under a cairn of stones. But the Bishop of Cosenza, in accordance with the Pope's will, did not rest until the corpse had been plucked forth and huddled away on the frontier of the Abruzzi, in a dark valley on the bank of the Verde.

"Cast down to the ground", Clement jubilated, "are the coursers and towers of Pharaoh, captured or slain the captains of war, broken the horns of the sinful." Galvano Lancia had fled away to his son-in-law Conrad of Antioch, in the Abruzzi. The French sacked Benevento, with its churches and sanctuaries, and murdered. Federigo, the enemy of the Church, had not dealt so, the Pope wrote to Anjou. "Ye have shown nought but avarice, lust and bloodthirstiness. Ye have spared neither spiritual nor temporal goods, neither age nor sex. Crusaders, who should protect churches and monasteries, have taken them by force, plundered them and even done violence upon virgins consecrated to God. Woe upon this unhallowed campaign, this unhallowed prospect!" The King of Sicily appeased him with two candelabra of gold and Federigo's golden Emperor's throne, flooded with pearls, from the treasure-chamber in Manfredonia.

The widow Helena was deserted in Lucera. A citizen of Trani, Manualdo, his wife Amondilla and his friend Amerusio decided her to flee with her three boys and her daughter by ship from Trani to her home in Epirus. Lupone, another friend of his, held a vessel in readiness for her ; because of the adverse wind, he could not put to sea. Manualdo and Amerusio hid the Queen and her children in the castle in which Manfredi had celebrated his wedding with her. Minorites came upon her track, terrified the castellan with the torments of hell and induced him to betray her to horsemen of Charles of Anjou. She died in the dungeon of Parco near Nocera. Beatrice, her daughter, was imprisoned for eighteen years in the Neapolitan island-fortress dell' Uovo. " They may live," Clement wrote to Anjou touching the sons, Enrico, Federigo and Anselmo, " but live as if they had never come into the world, live in order to die in gaol." They lay in bonds ; Enrico went blind.

The King of Sicily had Manfredi's under-treasurer Gezolin of Marra pour all the gold on to a carpet and gloated over it with the Queen. He made his entry into Naples, at the head four hundred French noblemen with plumes and panaches, men of Brabant and sixty grandees with chains of gold about their necks. The Queen sat in a carriage with blue velvet and golden lilies and smiled the smile of mere stupidity.

YOUNG Conradin was four years old at the execution of Mary of Brabant. When he was seven, his mother Elisabeth married Count Meynard of Görz and Tyrol. Then Lewis of Bavaria also married again, the daughter of the Duke of Silesia and Glogau. At ten years of age he held a solemn court in Swabia. Round him stood Bishop Everard of Constance, a Truchsess of Waldburg, who had the sword instead of the stole, the spear instead of the crozier, and Berthold of Falken-stein, Abbot of St. Gall, who organized secular jollifi-cations at Church-festivals and, to the sound of the fiddles, led knights from the banquet to feud or tourney. He taxed the regulars; when he died and mass was said for him, they danced in the streets with their cowls and their lazars' clappers. Young Conradin went to Lake Constance, which had once shimmered before young Frederick, the boy from Apulia. He learned Latin and, from Volkmar of Kemnaten, a vassal of the Lord of Ulten, the craft of knighthood. He knew poets, the cup-bearer Conrad of Limburg, Ulric of Türheim, Canon Ulric of Winterstetten and, in the composition of the *Minnelied*, attained the proficiency of a *Schüler*. But he knew nought of the love of women. Duke Lewis married him to Sophie, Marquis Dietrich of Landsberg's daughter, whom he never saw, and, on that account, took the Castle of Hohenstein as a pledge.

Young Conradin was pale and of fragile beauty, when messengers and refugees came from Rome, Pisa, Siena, Pavia, Verona, from the *Podestà* Lorenzo Tiepolo in Fermo and from Sicily. Slain Manfredi's vassals sought after him, the Lancias, Corrado and Marino Capece and Maletta, and a notary from his court, who had been in Peter of Vinea's chancery, the notary Pietro de Prece. Young Conradin felt fulfilment at hand. Should he die childless, he bequeathed his German and Italian territories to the Dukes of Bavaria. Through all Germany he sent his summons to an expedition across the Alps. He distributed the supreme offices. That of Grand Justiciary he entrusted to Corrado Capece, whom he sent to Pisa, Galvano Lancia was to be his first counsellor, Maletta treasurer in Jerusalem and Sicily. Conrad of Antioch, with Lanciano, he invested with the counties and baronies in the Abruzzi. It were madness, Pope Clement wrote to the Cardinal Priest Simon, to believe but that King Charles, who in one-and-twenty days had robbed brilliant, clever Manfredi of crown and life, would easily withstand this miserable, naked boy. But then, on the Ghibellines stirring in Tuscany, the Pope cursed the great curse: " From the stock of the dragon there hath sprung a poisonous basilisk. Tuscany is already infected with his breath. A knot of serpents, accursed men, enemies to our realm and the vacant realm as well as to our beloved son in Christ, illustrious King Charles, he hath sent out as the ready furtherers of his stratagems to cities, townships, fortresses and nobles. He polisheth up his false tinsel with lies of infamy; these he seeketh by prayers, these by money to lead from the path of truth. This is the giddy child Corradino, grandson to Frederick, sometime Emperor of the Romans, by a righteous judgment reprobated both of God and His vice-gerent. His braggart accomplices are the ungodly men Guido Novello, Corrado Trincio and Corrado Capece and many others, who wish to set up this abominable idol in Tuscany, hire mercenaries openly and in secret, make treaties and enter into conspiracies with those who aforetime have polluted themselves with the like offence." Charles, the sole and lawful King of Sicily, would soon appear in Tuscany himself.

Young Conradin quivered with the affection of a weakling for young Frederick of Baden, the son of Gertrude, who after the death of the Marquis Herman had become the wife of a Russian prince, Romanus. Frederick, the son of King Henry and of Margaret, was dead and Austria in the possession of the Bohemian Ottakar, who, after a barren marriage, put away Margaret, his senior by twenty-four years. Young Frederick of Baden, like Conradin, was landless and dreamed for him of the *Imperium*. He went with him.

Duke Lewis pawned Floss, Parkstein and Schwäbischwörth to Conradin and Ammergau, Schongau, Horingen with the Hibisch to his mother Elisabeth. He saw her for the last time at Hohenschwangau. She had had ill visions. The army assembled by the Lech round Conradin and Meynard and Albert of Görz, whom the Pope hated because of a sacrilege. Albert had surprised Gregory of Montelongo, now Patriarch of Aquileia, in bed in Villanova Castle and dragged him away on a farm-horse to Görz. The news was already flying through Italy that Conradin was at hand. At Cavatono five hundred Veronese knights under Mastino della Scala attacked the forces of Piacenza with the warcry " King Corrado " and put them to flight.

The notary Pietro de Prece composed a manifesto to the princes in the style of Vinea. " By what means ", he asked, " have we ever injured thee, Holy Father, that thou proceedest against us like a step-father so multifariously and unjustly, unless so be thou hold it a grave affront that we yet cumber the earth ? " Not against the Pope were Conradin's hostile emprise, only against Charles, who was inimical to him, did he wish to pit himself in the chess-play of war. He besought the princes to pacify the Pope.

About the Feast of the Nativity of the Virgin he set out for the Tyrol, with Frederick of Baden, Count Maynard, the Cup-bearer Conrad of Limburg, the Marshal Conrad Kroff of Flüglingen, Rudolph of Habsburg and many counts besides. Others advanced from Bregenz by way of the Roman stations Terzen, Quarten and Quinten to the passes in the direction of Chiavenna. Conradin was in Bolzano, three weeks later in Verona. He abode in the Bishop's palace next to the monastery of San Zeno, not far from the eddying Adige. In sombre gown a physician went to him, Federigo's physician Giovanni da Procida. The Ghibellines of Pavia, Padua, Vicenza, Mantua, Ferrara, Bergamo and Brescia did homage to Corradino. Pope Clement excommunicated him, Pisa and Siena.

The delicate young German stayed in Verona for three months. But even if Charles of Anjou gave ground in Tuscany, Conradin remained in perplexity. So great was the lack of money that many had to sell their arms and horses to the smiths and horse-copers. From ten thousand the host melted away to three thousand. The treasurer Maletta fell into disgrace and, for a space, lost his office and his fiefs. Duke Lewis had advanced after him, to return home with a new pledge, the bailiwick of the city of Augsburg and of Füssen monastery and of Schwabeck Castle. Meynard too wanted to go back to the Tyrol. He demanded of Conradin the payment of an old debt. The latter pawned Peiting and said he would redeem it with the first money that God might bestow upon him. He was alone with Frederick of Baden, Mastino della Scala, the still remaining nobles and knights from Germany, Apulia and Tuscany. Through ambassadors he begged Bibar Bondokdar, the Sultan of Egypt, for help. The Sultan negotiated no less busily with Charles of Anjou than with this King of Jerusalem. But Corrado Capece had sailed on a Pisan ship to Tunis and landed in Sicily with Federico, the Prince of Castile who whilom had escaped from the Emperor. " Your King ", he proclaimed, " will come, majestic and strong of arm. The true Lord, King and Heir will come to the people that is his own, to pluck it from the cruel tyranny of foreigners, from the hands of an unlawful King, and to grant it once more the liberties bestowed by his blessed ancestors." At Ociarra the Sicilians raised the eagle of the Hohenstaufens and turned against Folco de Podio's Frenchmen. Girgenti rebelled, Nicosia, Catania and many towns besides. Fire gleamed in Messina. The Senator of Rome, the Infante Enrique of Castile, brother to the Infante Federico, the domineering adventurer, caught the Guelphs as in a net, cast them into the prison on the Capitol and allied himself to the Ghibellines in Tuscany. With the standard of the eagle and armed men Galvani Lancia entered Rome, amid the jubilations of the people. In the Lateran Enrique, the Senator Arrigo, let him dwell, excommunicated as he was. The eagle waved from the walls and towers of the city.

The judge Detesalvo Botto had journeyed to Verona on the day before the Nativity of our Lord. He invited Conradin to Pavia and bound himself to conduct him to Pisa. In January the young German went, across Lake Garda, the Oglio, Boso's Rocca, the Adda, the Lambro, to Pavia. A pigeon fluttered to his mother on the day of his setting forth. The men of Pavia carried a canopy over him. They paid him twelve thousand pounds, and he chose Scala for their *Podestà*. Pisa sent him seventeen thousand ounces of gold. News came of the revolt of the Saracens in Lucera under their Christian captain William of Paris. They poured over Apulia. "Why as King", Pope Clement with scorn upbraided the victor of Benevento, "we yet address thee, since thou seemest to despise the Kingdom, we ourselves do not understand. Headless, given over to Saracens and faithless Christians, it is rent asunder. What thy thieves have left us, the locusts devour. Verily do not think that the Church yet again will take upon herself the toil and outlay. Thou mayest then, content with thy royal title, return to thy County and await thy end or a divine miracle." The squint-eyed victor sought out the Holy Father in Viterbo.

Young Conradin marched from Pavia through the Marquisate of Carreto, reinforced by a thousand men of Pavia and two thousand Ghibelline footmen of the Lanzavecchia. At Vado near Savona lay eleven Pisan ships, too few for the host. So Frederick proceeded by land on through Tuscany. Amid foaming waves Conradin embarked with four hundred picked knights at Vado. But the storms roared, and he was compelled to shelter in Porto Fino, the Genoese port. Ghibellines from Genoa, the Spinola, Doria and Castello, conferred with the young German. Then he continued his voyage.

On Maundy Thursday he held his entry into Pisa, through the toll-gate. He had his quarters in Archbishop Visconti's palace, hard by the white marble cathedral, the baptistery, the leaning *campanile*. Wares were laden on the Lungarno. Life hummed in the workshops and merchants' houses. The Pisans presented the delicate youth with horses, a suit of mail, gay clothes and money. To their messengers to Castelfranco the people there called out that they were passing off someone else for Corradino. For it seemed a fairytale that the daring enterprize of the sea-voyage had succeeded. With honours and revelry Frederick, who had come down over the mountains to Varese and marched along the coast through Motrone, past Jean de Braiselve's French knights, was conducted through the gate of the Lion.

While Charles of Anjou was with him in Viterbo, Pope Clement excommunicated Conradin, Lewis of Bavaria, the Count of Tyrol, Frederick of Baden, Conrad of Antioch, the Prince of the Abruzzi, the Infante Federico, Maletta, the Saracens' captain William of Paris and placed the Ghibelline towns under an interdict. Charles of Anjou gloomily received the cross at his hands. The Count of Anguillara, Bertoldo Rubeo de Orsini and Guelph knights penetrated into Rome almost as far as Hadrian's tomb. In May and June Charles of Anjou besieged Lucera. The Saracens undermined his wooden towers and reduced them to ashes. Then he went to Foggia. But at Whitsun the Pope celebrated high mass in the Dominican church at Viterbo and preached about Corradino. "Be not afraid : this youth, we know, is being led by wicked men unto his death. There is no surer knowledge than this, which is based on the articles of faith." He said : "The boy's greatness vanisheth away as a smoke, he goeth to Apulia as to the shambles ".

Conradin was in Siena, which welcomed him with the *Carroccio*. He walked beneath the baldachino. In the valley of the Arno, at Ponte a Valle, Frederick, Ubertino de Andito, Pallavicino's nephew, Guido Novello and Kroff of Flüglingen defeated Marshal Jean de Braiselve, killed six hundred and took prisoner him and Charles's vicar in Florence, Amiel d'Agoult de Curban. Triumphant they returned to Siena. The Senator Arrigo sent Conradin a poem : "Fair Garden of Sicily, a gardener hath taken thee into his care, which will turn to joys the pains that thou hast suffered ; and he will demand the Emperor's crown of the Pope ". To the Sienese Conradin promised, as soon as he became Emperor, remission of all Imperial taxes and mercantile

20

dues. Thirty Pisan ships under Guido Boccia and Federigo Lancia sailed for the mouth of the Tiber with Marino Capece, Riccardo Filangieri, the Count of Ischia and six thousand men on board.

From Pavia Conradin rode to Rome, by his side Frederick, Conrad of Antioch, the Roman Ghibellines Napoleone Orsini and the Anibaldi, Galvano Lancia and also Pietro de Vico. He avoided Viterbo, merely touching its walls, and proceeded along the Via Cassia. Then he stood at the foot of the Monte Mario, at the Ponte Molle. Triumphal arches rose up from the Ponte San Angelo as far as the Capitol. Flowers and green foliage were spread under the horses' hooves. The Senator Arrigo embraced the young man, the adventurer embraced frailness and beauty. To the sound of cithers and tambourines the women of Rome sang anthems. The young German had reached the Capitol, with the cages of the she-wolf and the eagles, with the Tarpejan rock. The Infante's eyes sparkled.

THE Pisan fleet sailed towards the Apulian coast and anchored on Sicilian ground, off Milazzo. Corrado Capece, Federigo Lancia and Federico were at variance; and so Robert of Lavène could join twenty-two ships of his to the Messinese. He fled when the Pisans, by a feigned flight, had captured the sailing-ships of Messina. The Pisans set them alight and drove them into Messina roads. The harbour-quarter caught fire as well. When the wind veered round, Federigo Lancia had to cross to Calabria. Here Reynold of Ciro commanded the rebels. Brindisi fell away from Anjou, Basilicata, Terra di Bari, Aversa, the County of Caserta; for, with his grandmother Siffridina, young Count Corrado wanted to wipe out the disgrace which his father had brought upon that family by his treachery to Manfredi, the flower of manhood.

Charles of Anjou camped by Lake Fucino and near Scurcola. With ten thousand Germans, Italians and

Spaniards Conradin and Arrigo marched through Tivoli and the Teverone valley. They advanced into Apulia, through the Mura valley and precipitous mountains to the course of the Salto and into the Palentine plain. Charles of Anjou proceeded in battle-array to the heights of Albe. He observed the enemy, but, as his horses were done, he put off the clash till the morning. In the evening light he saw an embassy of well-dressed persons and heard that they were citizens of Aquila with presents for Conradin and the keys of the town. Alarmed for his supplies, he rode by night to Aquila and called to the porter at the gate : " To whose allegiance does the town hold ? " He answered : " To King Charles's ". Then he rode in, and they pledged him their faith. When day began, women and virgins with baskets and also armed men climbed to the French over the mountain slopes.

After sunrise both the hosts were armed. Anjou put eight hundred men in ambush in the valley under Monte Felice, in the cypress-wood round the village of Capella. The first line, Provençals, Lombards and Roman Guelphs, was to advance up to the Salto. The second he entrusted to Marshal Henri de Cousence, who was very like him and who wore the lilies and the King's gilded chain-armour and coronalled casque. Anjou himself hid with Erard de Valéry's men-at-arms in the ambush. He was certain of victory, which Brother Benedetto, a Minorite, had prophesied. " This promise of Brother Benedetto ", he spake, " is worth more to me than if a thousand knights had hastened to my succour. For he has predicted to the Emperor Baldwin in the Eastern Empire much that has really befallen." The Ghibellines' front line, with Spaniards, Lombards and Tuscans, was under Arrigo and the Pisan Count of Donoratico, the second under Conradin, Frederick and Kroff of Flüglingen. In the Hohenstaufen's camp captive Jean de Braiselve's head was smitten off and waved in the air. Then the war-horses, anxiously neighing, clattered against one another.

The Provençals, Lombards and Guelphs under James Cantelmi fled in mountain and forest. The Infante Arrigo smote Marshal de Cousence a deadly blow, and the conspirators dipped their weapons in his blood; the second line of the French fled too. Had the eight hundred now left the defile, their company would not have sufficed for the foemen's swords to feed on. But while mass was being read, Anjou lay in wait. The Ghibellines and the inhabitants of Albe were plundering the Frenchmen's camp, the Germans had undone their plate-armour or were bathing in the molten silver of the Salto. " Now is the time ", cried Erard of Valéry. The eight hundred rolled down on their wearied enemies. Conrad of Antioch, Conradin's treasurer Tommaso of Aquino and Marshal Kroff of Flüglingen were taken prisoners. The banner with the eagle drooped, the Hohenstaufen was carried away by the rout at a water-fall that flowed into the Salto. Charles of Anjou waited, his front turned north-east, for the Infante, who had pursued the Provençals as far as Aquila and, turning back, erroneously believed the battle won for Conradin. He belaboured the boys and foot-soldiers in the French camp. Erard of Valéry, with thirty knights, enticed him away by a feint. The men-at-arms fought man to man. Guy de Montfort had his helmet turned round and, with closed vizor, laid about him like a maniac. Then the Infante too gave up the battle for lost. More than four thousand corpses covered the bloody, groaning valley.

" The tidings of great joy long awaited by all the faithful ", Charles of Anjou wrote to the Pope, " I humbly bring to you, most gracious father, and to the Holy Roman Church, my mother, as it were sweet incense. I pray you, father, eat of the game your son has taken and render the thanks due to the Almighty ". How Conradin had fared, he had not yet discovered; the Senator's horse had been found masterless. Before leaving the battlefield, Anjou already had Tommaso of Aquino and other nobles beheaded. The Roman

Ghibellines he caused to have their feet severed from the trunk, then to be herded together in a house in Albe, which the flames devoured. Potenza and Albe were destroyed, in Corneto one hundred and three of the inhabitants strung to the gallows ; three, whom the King was sending to Melfi, dashed themselves down a precipice. The Saracens of Lucera he punished by starvation or the sword. Guillaume l'Estendard in Sicily tortured the inhabitants of Augusta. Even in cisterns and corn-pits the soldiers ferreted out the defenceless. A hangman executed the Agostans with a broad sword, and when he was tired they brought him a cup full of wine, which he poured down together with blood and sweat. The French set up a pyramid of heads and trunks by the sea. Corrado Capece gave himself up voluntarily to Estendard, who had him hanged on the dreary sea-shore near Catania, after his eyes had been pierced through and through. His brothers met with the same fate in Naples. The Infante Arrigo escaped to San Salvatore near Rieti and told the Abbot that the French had been defeated. But, at the Pope's command, the Abbot surrendered him, by the hand of the knight Sinibaldo Aquilone, to King Charles, after the latter had sworn not to kill him, his princely relative. In vain did scouts search for the physician Giovanni da Procida.

Conradin rested with Frederick, Galvano Lancia, the latter's son Galeotto, the Count of Donoratico, several nobles and five hundred knights in the Castel Vecchio near Tagliacozzo. They fled by way of Vicovaro to Rome. But the Senator's deputy, Guido of Montefeltro, would not give up the Capitol to the boy. After three days they had to get away from the Savelli and Rubeo de Orsini, who routed the old Count of Donoratico out in his hiding-place. The boy did not turn to the coast, but to Saracinesco, Conrad of Antioch's castle, to his wife Beatrice and the wives of Galvano and Galeotto Lancia, Margarita and Gubitosa. But then, even in Saracinesco, he was in danger of Anjou's spies. With his companions and the Romans Napoleone Orsini and Riccardo Anibaldi, he aimed for Sicily. Through Campania they reached Astura and the smooth sea.

They were already in a row-boat, when a fast galley set out after them, one of Giovanni Frangipani's, to whom Astura Castle belonged and who itched with the lust of gold. He stopped the refugees and stood on his defence against Robert de Lavène, who appeared with the Provençal ships, until he himself was assured of the fattest reward. In Genazzano Anjou, the butcher, received the prisoners. They were dragged into a rocky castle of the Colonna, San Pietro near Palestrina. Conrad of Antioch was exchanged against two Guelph hostages in Saracinesco, brothers to the Cardinal of St. Nicholas in Carcere Tulliano, and remained a prisoner of the Church in Viterbo.

Charles of Anjou entered Rome. He had the Lancias' heads struck off in Genazzano, Galeotto's first, before his father's eyes. Then, with the pinioned victims Conradin, Frederick, Arrigo and the Count of Donoratico, he made his entry into Naples, for the supreme deed of vengeance. He convoked a court of four men learned in the laws : Conradin and the rest were to be condemned to death, for that they had taken arms against him, the King, and had sacked and burned monasteries. The Neapolitan Guido de Suzara said : "Not as a robber or instigator to riot did Corradino come, but as claimant of his hereditary rights. To kill him is contrary to law human and divine". All the judges, save the houndish protonotary Robert of Bari, acquitted him. Of his own motion Anjou pronounced for death. Pope Clement wrote to the King that he raised no objection to Conradin's being dealt with according to law.

Conradin sat with the others in the dungeon of the Castel dell' Uovo ; the surf splashed through the gratings. He heard the shrill outcries of a captive girl : it was Beatrice, Manfredi's daughter. He was playing chess with Frederick, when the Constable Jean Britaud de Nangis announced the verdict. Sobbing he embraced his friend, as a man a woman. The Constable sealed their wills. Frederick called himself Duke of Austria, Conradin himself neither Duke of Swabia nor King of Jerusalem. They confessed themselves to a Franciscan and partook of the host. In a chapel near the dungeon psalms were murmured, a muffled requiem sounded. The hangman's mates stumped with the friends to Naples market-place, to the scaffold, whence the deep blue bay, Capri and the fiery peak of Vesuvius were to be seen. Charles of Anjou was watching from a balcony opposite the Church del Carmine, greenish, his lips pressed inwards. Robert de Bari read off the death-sentence. Conradin stripped the jerkin from his body, knelt and prayed. " I forgive thee that thou killest me ", he said to the red hangman, whose very hare-lip was a-grin, and crossed himself three times. He raised his arms to heaven, the axe crunched through the bones of his neck, blood spirted up in a spray. Frederick shrieked with anguish. But he was silenced by the hangman's fist. Silenced were the Count of Donoratico, Kroff of Flüglingen, the Count of Veringen, Frederick of Hürnheim. Charles of Anjou ordered the corpses to be put away in sea-sand, hard by the stony cemetery of the Jews.

Through Pietro de Prece the Ghibellines wrote to Frederick of Thuringia, the son of Margaret, daughter to the Emperor Frederick, and of the Landgrave Albert. The Landgrave lived in adultery with Cunigunde of Eisenberg and made one of his servants swear one night, disguised as the Devil, to strangle Margaret. He went to her and begged for mercy. She fled down the side of the Wartburg on cords. When, before that, she embraced her sons Frederick, Henry and Diezmann, her kiss bit the first so hard that he received the name Frederick of the Bitten Cheek. He now assumed Conradin's titles. From Pavia Enrico de Spernaria, who under Manfredi had become Count of Marsico, travelled to Germany. Frederick the Third sent Frederick of Trifurt as his Vicar-General to Verona. But the Hohenstaufen from Saxony and the Imperial army did not appear. Lucera, Foggia and Manfredonia sank into ruin; a column of red porphyry on Corradino's grave gave place to a tippling-house.

FOR fourteen years the prisoner in the *Podestà's* building at Bologna, King Enzio, had with him in the hall where his wood-and-iron cage hung Conrad of Solimburg, the German Count. This man was coarse and intolerably silly. But only after urgent entreaties was Enzio rid of his company. The fair-haired King sang canzones to himself, the same words countless times—then merely sounds—and often it resembled the crooning of a lunatic.

He had a cordwainer, a tailor, a physician, a notary. By night he had to return to the cage which, at the sixth stroke of the bell, was shut up by a judge of the *Podestà*. One key the judge kept, one the *Podestà* or the guards who perambulated the iron chamber with lances and staves. King Enzio bathed his hands in the moonshine along the wall or crept sleepless from the bundles of straw to the earthen drinking-vessel. By day too several Bolognese kept watch over him. They were allowed to speak to him only when there were many of them, and with the Council's leave. No game of hazard was permitted with the King.

To humiliate him, the guards took his food from him. The Minorite Albertinus of Verona went to them and begged it of them. Then he proposed to them to dice for it: if he won, Enzio was to get his food, a platter full of baked pieces of lamprey, floating in rancid olive-oil. The Minorite won, and the King got his meal. The Bolognese had at first defrayed his expenses. They scolded him for being too extravagant and curtailed his diet. Through his intellect, which still sometimes shone in his apathy, through his wit—the wit was of Federigo's kind—he had won well-wishers in the party of the Lambertazzi. He urged them to vote in the Council against his short commons. They said yea, but refrained. Henceforward only so much was allowed by the municipality as was needed for him and three servants.

He amassed *soldi* and by snoring feigned great weariness. At Carnival-tide, after sixteen years, when his guards preferred to be out of doors in the throng of masks, he bribed the servants, and with a stolen key they let in to him one night Lucia de Viadagoli, whom Pietro Asinello had brought into the hall a few days before, a poor girl from one of the clans in the city. She trimmed his fair beard for him, stroked his fair curls and lay with him. When the morning dawned through the bars, to thawing snow, the guards in their drunken fury tore her away from the King before she was awake. He had said to her: "*Ben ti voglio*", "I wish thee well", and Bentivoglio was the name which she gave to the son she bore him.

The guards shouted in confusion: Corradino had been killed at Scurcola. He asked Pietro Asinello and Raniero Confalonieri of Piacenza to help him escape from his cage. They gave money to the cooper Filippo, who every week brought the prisoner a barrel of wine and demanded back the emptied one. In an empty barrel he carried the King away on his broad shoulders, and none could guess that it was heavier than usual. He had the guards, the gate behind him and was on the way to San Pietro, when a crazy old woman screamed: "King Enzio is in that barrel, no one in Bologna but him has that hair". For one of his golden locks was hanging out through a chink. Filippo and Raniero, who was waiting with horses at the corner of the lane, were punished with death. Pietro Asinello got away, but he lost his possessions.

King Enzio no longer had his hair cut and, as he never moved, became flabby and fat. He fell sick and told the notary Caccianimici what his dispositions were. To Enrico and Ugolino da Donoratico, his grandsons, he bequeathed Sardinia and the Castle of Sassari, moreover Lunigiana, Garfagnana, Versiglia and two places in the Genoese, Varesio and Trebbiano; to Conrad of

313

Antioch the County of Molise; his rights in Jerusalem, Sicily, Arles and the Roman Empire to Alphonsus of Castile and Frederick of Thuringia. He, the pensioner of the municipality, devised to his sister Catarina di Marrano and to his daughters Maddalena and Constanza large legacies in ounces of gold and Bolognese pounds, which he did not possess, and also four hundred gold ounces for his soul's salvation. He chattered and complained that his father, Cæsar Augustus, the lord of the earth, had been willing to pay for him as much silver as would be needed for a ring, capacious as the city-wall. In the night in which he was to die he laughed foolishly, like a child.

He was, as he had wished, buried in San Domenico. The Bolognese felt repentance about him, embalmed the body, in place of the long, dirty, grey woollen cowl gave it scarlet robes, trimmed with fur, a cross of gold, silver and jewels and, into its hand, a golden sceptre. " *Rex erat et comptos pressit diademate crines* " they vaunted in the epitaph.

" IN those days ", so wrote the Monk of Padua, " an unheard-of excitement seized first the inhabitants of Perugia, then the Romans, then the whole of Italy. The fear of the Lord came upon them in such a degree that high and low, greybeards and youths, yea children under five years, naked (but for the covered privates) and casting away all shame, walked two and two in processions along the roads. They hooded their heads after the manner of monks and nuns. With the knots of stout leather thongs they scourged themselves, as if with the eyes of the flesh they beheld the Passion of Christ, so that the blood flowed. They lamented and sighed and poured out streams of tears. They implored God for mercy and the Mother of God for help. As he had forgiven the penitent Ninivites, so he might forgive them, since they confessed their own unrighteousness. Not by day alone, but also by night, hundreds, thousands, yea tens of thousands formed processions, with flaring candles, in the hardest winter. Led by priests with crosses and banners, they proceeded through the towns and made pilgrimages to the altars, before which they threw themselves down in humility. The same happened in villages and townships, hills and dales resounded with their lamentations. Then all songs of joy and love were hushed; only the chanting of the penitent filled town and country. Those sad tones softened the hardest of heart and charmed tears from the most obdurate. The women also took part in these extraordinary penetential exercises; not merely the vulgar from the people, but women of birth, even the tenderest virgins, locked themselves in their chambers for self-flagellation. Whoso lived at enmity then became reconciled, insulters themselves gave the avenging sword to the insulted, usurers and thieves hastened to make restitution of unlawful property. All who had made themselves guilty of a crime, confessed and sincerely bettered themselves. The gaols were opened, the prisoners set free, the banished recalled to their homes. Men did so many good works, that it seemed they were afeared lest Providence might be about to consume them with fire from Heaven or have them swallowed up by an earthquake or send down some other great judgment upon them."

The first of the flagellant preachers was a member of the house of the Oddi in Perugia. The flagellants went to Rome through Tuscany and Lombardy. In Parma the magistrates and burgesses, their banners lowered, joined the procession, bare-foot, amid the blows of the scourges. In Genoa they mocked them that flogged themselves; then the spirit gained power over all the populace. To a whirlwind swelled the cries: "Holy Mary, our Lady, take us sinners in and implore Christ Jesus to spare us". Him who did not scourge himself they considered as worse than the Devil and pointed at him with their fingers. Hermits came from their deserts and fouled themselves naked in muck and snow. The flagellants appeared in France and Germany, in

Hungary, Silesia and Bohemia. Outside churches they threw themselves down in the shape of the cross, so that the porches rattled with their bones. The perjured man cowered on his side and raised three fingers to Heaven, the murderer hammered the ground with his fist, the thief stretched out his hand, opening and shutting it, the adulterer lay on his belly, the toper held his mouth open. The master with the scourge stepped over them all, whoso he had scourged rose up and scourged the others. The flagellants by the Rhine said that the statue of the Mother of God in the minster at Strasburg sweated blood when they approached. Scourging was the true Lord's Supper; for in it their blood was mingled with the blood of Jesus. They carried a dead child about in their midst, in order to wake it to life; it did not wake. Vagabonds and vagrants had authority in their brotherhoods, and as suddenly as they had banded themselves together they fell asunder.

The time saw in the blood-red welkin the Beast that hath two horns like unto the lamb and speaketh like unto a dragon; and in all who had the mark of the Beast and worshipped its image there burned an evil and malignant gland. An angel cut the vines of the earth and cast them into the great wine-press of God's wrath. And the wine-press was trod outside the city, and the blood went from the wine-press up to the bridles of the horses through ten thousand fields of the way. The time saw Anti-Christ and Satan and Gog and Magog. In torn Germany loud-voiced Berthold of Ratisbon preached repentance. As he was preaching six miles away, a ploughman took the oxen out of the yoke and hearkened to the noise in the air. Berthold spoke from a wooden platform under a lime-tree, to the blossoms of which the bees were swarming, and caused the multitude to sit down in the direction in which a little feather blew. "Now, heretic, art anywhere here?" he asked. "Now God Almighty grant there be none before me." In Hungary they saw fiery crowns floating over him. He was the trumpet of the Judgment. In Italy the organs thundered the *Dies irae, dies ille*, the hymn of Thomas of Celano, the hymn of the end of the world.

An Armenian bishop was in England, and a knight of Antioch, who was his interpreter, at Abbot Spigurnel's board told of Cartaphilus. He was the porter in Pontius Pilate's palace who drove the Saviour, bowed down by the cross, from the threshold when he was resting and made mock of him : " Go thy ways, Jesus, and go more speedily. Wherefore lingerest thou ? " And sternly Jesus looked at him and spake : " I go, but thou shalt wait until I return ". Since then Cartaphilus waited for the Son of Man and, as often as he had lived an hundred years, he had to live anew. He wandered about with a long, floating Jew's beard, in an ungirt coat and breeches that were torn to pieces, and torment lay in his red eyes. He sat down nowhere. He had been in Rome under the Emperor Nero and in the Orient under Sultan Saladin. With a black band on his forehead, covered by a blazing crucifix, he had shown himself in Spain, as a ferryman in Holland, at Brunswick, in Vienna and in Poland. And that he showed himself was a sign of the Last Judgment.

KING CHARLES of Anjou had been in Tunis as Crusader with his brother of France. St. Lewis died on a bed of ashes and, dying, cried out : " I see Jerusalem ". The wreckage of the fleet which came to grief at Trapani Anjou stole as jetsam. His insatiable vampires engulphed everything in Sicily. He caused carlines to be struck ; whoso accepted them at a lower rate was branded with coins heated on coals. In Messina money was minted of copper and scant silver, the billons, and the King's officers demanded gold for them. The ploughland was turned into forest. The foreigners would bring a hide, bones or half-rotten flesh into the peasants' cots, accuse them of poaching and undo them. Whosoever the new barons willed they forced to work for them. In the cliffs near Naples lay a horrible cave, threatened by foam and tempest. It was a place of torture and execution.

In the sixteenth year of Anjou's reign Pope Martin, a Frenchman, had been elected in a conclave in Orvieto, from which Charles plucked three Cardinals, while locking the rest up with bread and water. A seal, caught on the coast at Montello, was brought to the Papal court as specimen of an unknown species. It was a monster, like the whale that suckles its young, the sea-monk, the sea-bishop and the sea-dragon. It gave so lamentable and fearful a howl that the people were petrified. For this howl betokened terrible things.

At Easter in Palermo tipstaves of the Justiciary of Val di Mazzara, Jean de St. Rémi, dragged citizens who were praying in the churches from the altars, as debtors of the treasury, and shouted: " Pay, heretics, pay ". On the Tuesday following youths and maidens were tarrying outside the city, on the top of the precipice of Oreto. Beneath pale red agaves and wild fig-trees they set up tables and danced, oppressed. The foreign tip-staves mingled among them and waxed familiar with the girls, pressing their hands and making shameless gestures. The young men, eager to come to blows, raised their voices so high that the myrmidons said to one another: " These heretics must be armed, that they are so insolent ". They searched them and ill-treated them with whips. Then a fair virgin, Fiametta, went past to the Church of the Spirito Santo with her relations and Andrea, to whom she was betrothed. A Frenchman called Drouet stepped forward and felt her bosom. Her senses forsook her. She sank into her betrothed's arms, who, suffocating with fury, screamed: " Death to all these French! " One of his friends disarmed Drouet and was cast to the ground by the myrmidons. The multitude closed their ranks. " Death to the French ", they repeated, pursued the foreigners, over-turned the blood-stained tables and killed two hundred. Brandishing the enemies' swords, they ran to Palermo and, where they found a Frenchman, they struck him down.

DEATH OF ST LEWIS

[*face p.* 318

The multitude hurried through the streets of the city, forced the doors of the houses in which they knew strangers to be, stormed the palace of Jean de St. Rémi, who fled away on horseback through the gathering night. When a suspect appeared, they held a dagger to his throat and commanded him to pronounce the word *ciciri*. If he hissed in doing so, they stabbed him. They butchered the clergy also in the monasteries and children at their mother's breast. They ripped up the wombs of Sicilian women who were pregnant by Frenchmen and hurled their fruit against the rocks. By torchlight the people of Palermo nominated as chiefs of the Republic the knights Roger Mastrangelo, Enrico Barensi, Nicoloso d'Ortoleva and Niccolo di Ebdemonia. They unfurled the banner of the city, the golden eagle, trumpets sounded, and all rejoiced with " Liberty and Happiness ! "

The people of Palermo roamed through the neighbourhood and proceeded to the fortress of Vicari. The archers of Caccamo shot Jean de St. Rémi down from the battlements, overpowered his soldiers and threw their corpses to the carrion-birds. Bonifazio, captain of Corleone, took the French castles round about. The Palermitans sent messengers to the citizens of Messina, still slaves in dust and dirt under King Pharaoh. " God ", they wrote to the city, " says to thee : take up thy bed and walk, for thou art whole. The milk of liberty shalt thou drink ". The people of Messina scoffed at Herbert of Orleans's Frenchmen and Calabrese. Bartolomeo Maniscalpo ran up the cross of Messina in place of the fleurs de lys. In Naples, Charles of Anjou, glaring dumb before him, bit into his stick like a mad dog ; then he proceeded to besiege Messina. With five hundred men on horseback and a thousand on foot, the French fell upon the insurgents at the spring of Aleta, in the reeds of San Gregorio, and defeated them. Baldwin Mussone demanded the death of Anjou's friends, the Risi. They were plucked forth from Mategriffun castle, hewn in pieces and trailed through the streets.

King Pharaoh landed from a ship, adorned with purple, at the abbey of Santa Maria Roccamadore and destroyed the smiling olive-orchards up to the woodland brook Cammari. He penetrated into the suburb of Santa Croce. The Messinese smashed up his wooden watch-tower with stones. Alaimo de Lentini saved the bastion at the hill della Capperina, and after him two women, Dina and Chiarenza. Sickness raged among the French. By Allah the Saracens asseverated before the Messinese, with whom they conversed in the dark, that they had beheld a shape in white veils floating above the walls and warding off the arrows.

King Charles attacked for the last time, with *chats* and storks that had necks, long wooden girders. Panting, bleeding and ragged, his soldiers had to give ground. Then the crooked horns blew the retreat. Anjou lay in his tent like an overpowered bull. King Pedro of Aragon, whose consort was Constance, Manfredi's daughter, had come to Sicily from Africa. He was crowned in the cathedral at Palermo. Behind him stood the conspirators who had counselled him, Roger Loria, Corrado Lancia and gloomy Giovanni da Procida, a man without wife and children—for they were dishonoured or dead—the physician who had stood behind dying Federigo.

A BEARDLESS man, old already, came to Lübeck and said he was the Emperor Frederick that had been driven out. He had blue eyes, which he screwed up against the sun, a thin nose and in stature was rather broad than tall. He spoke of vouchsafing his grace to the city when the Empire was in his hands once more. He rode upon a fine horse, which was lent him, from the Wackenitz to the town hall, to Hinrik Steneke, the mayor, whose ships sailed to Sweden and to Russia and who had often seen the Emperor. The beardless one greeted him majestically and, in the secret room of St. Mary's Church, showed him two charters of which none could know, touching the privileges of the city as an Imperial free town, one with wax seals, the other with a golden seal-case, made out in Italy by the Emperor when the burgesses of Lübeck sent to Frederick before the battle of Bornhövede against Waldemar of Denmark. Hinrik Steneke had no doubts. He honoured the beardless one, and fanfares summoned all citizens to the town hall. But suddenly their guest was there no more, and it was said that he had got into a boat under elder-bushes in front of the salt-warehouses on the Trave and left nothing behind him but a patched doublet.

Then he appeared in the Rhenish lands and said that he had journeyed about on a pilgrimage for thirty years. The cares of empire had lain heavy upon him, and he had wanted to live without them. When he was sick of fever, he had procured a dead man, a scullion of his sewer Occursio, and concealed himself in a room until they had buried the scullion, a red-head from the Palatinate of Hagenau, in his stead. He disclosed all the Emperor's enterprizes and also how he had intended to turn out the parsons, hang his shield on a lime-tree and gain the Holy Land for Christendom once more. The citizens of Cologne marvelled at first. But Archbishop Sifrid and the priests explained to them that the old man was a swindler. So they caught him, shore him and tied him to the pillory over against Saint Gereon's.

He fled away by night into the house of the Austin friars and got into the fortress of Neuss. Here he collected many about him and especially the soldiers who had been with the Emperor at Cortenuova and in Acre. He called them by name and spoke of the renown of their bravery. When he was in an inn-keeper's debt and the man urgently pressed him, he told him to ride, early on the morrow, alone into the country; then he would meet guests from the east: he was to ask them whether they were the Emperor's treasurers. The inn-keeper did so and, so the tale went, met three pitch-black negroes on mules. He conducted them to the beardless one, and the Emperor locked himself into a bower with the blackamoors and the treasure chests they had with them. The blacks were seen no more. They were formed by magic. The gold of the treasure chests the inn-keeper heard chink in his head only. But the Jews gave to the beardless one; for they believed that he would set up again King David's throne in Jerusalem.

When Hagenau and Colmar in Alsace had paid homage to him, the beardless one went to Wetzlar, the free Imperial town. Frankfort, Gelnhausen and Friedberg swore allegiance to him. He sent letters to the Landgraves Frederick and Diezmann of Thuringia, as his grandchildren, and they weened it to be true, rewarding his messengers. He spent two thousand five hundred marks of silver in a year. Then he commanded the German King, Rudolph of Habsburg, to appear before him and receive his fief from him, as Roman Emperor. The Counts of Leiningen and Katzenellnbogen hastened to Rudolph, who was laying siege to Colmar. He advanced with force of arms against Wetzlar and threatened the burgesses to put them under the ban of the realm. They begged him for mercy and handed the imposter over to him. He told his servants that nought would befall him; for Heaven destined him a longer life; he should come to Frankfort and there they would see him again. But a single man remained with him, Dietrich Stal. With him he was brought before King Rudolph and before the court of Archbishop Sifrid of Cologne, Archbishop Eric of Magdeburg, Bishop Volrad of Halberstadt, the Counts of Anhalt, Wernigerode, Blankenburg and Leiningen.

King Rudolph sat amidst the Counts, sober, sulky of face, in a grey felt hat. He questioned the fellow where he had been in the meanwhile. The beardless one spoke smiling of Africa and of Greece, of Romania. The King waxed pale: was this deceit? He enquired after the fellow's age, and he said that he was seventy; but Rudolph reckoned the Emperor Frederick's age as ninety. Yet he hesitated, perplexed by something ghostlike. Then Marshal the Count of Pappenheim loosened the rogue's hip-straps, and they perceived that, to come near to the Emperor's shape, he had stuffed tow under his coat. The King gave a sign to subject him to torture. He wailed that he was Tile Kolup, a clog-maker, and had once served as shield-bearer at Frederick's court. With Dietrich Stal he was roasted against a hill-side by a fire which, fed with dry wood, roared together over the wretches' heads.

A poor woman of Wetzlar searched for the Emperor's bones. She found them not, as though he were not burned, but rapt away and still alive. She crossed herself and spat into the ashes. Then she sat down by the bank, the scorched grass of which smelt of the smoke, and, while the sun drew vapour from the reddened Lahn, gave her puling babe the breast.